A TIME TO LAUGH

A Risible Reader
by Catholic Writers

A TIME TO LAUGH

A Risible Reader by Catholic Writers

COMPILED AND EDITED WITH AN

INTRODUCTION AND COMMENTS BY

· PAUL J. PHELAN ·

EDITORIAL STAFF, NEW YORK SUN

FORMERLY PROFESSOR OF ENGLISH

AT THE UNIVERSITY OF SANTA CLARA

LONGMANS, GREEN AND CO.

NEW YORK · TORONTO · 1949

LONGMANS, GREEN AND CO., INC.
55 FIFTH AVENUE, NEW YORK 3

LONGMANS, GREEN AND CO.
215 VICTORIA STREET, TORONTO 1

A TIME TO LAUGH

First Edition September 1949
Reprinted December 1949

Printed in the United States of America
Vail-Ballou Press, Inc., Binghamton, N. Y.

To My Brothers

TOM AND BOB

"Un frère est un ami donné par la nature."
—Jean Baptiste Legouvé

All things have their season, and in their times all things pass under heaven.

A time to be born, and a time to die. A time to plant, and a time to pluck up that which is planted.

A time to kill, and a time to heal. A time to destroy, and a time to build.

A time to weep, and a time to laugh. . . .

—Ecclesiastes, III, 1–4

NODS AND SMILES

"Nods and becks and wreathéd smiles."

—From "L'Allegro"
by John Milton

This is the orchid department. It's here an anthologist smilingly distributes specimens of the Orchidaceae to those who lent him a helping hand. It's here too that he'd like to distribute specimens of the jimson weed to a few who figuratively stuck out a foot to make progress less smooth. However, "To err is human, to forgive divine," and with a choice like that, which side of the fence would you be on? Let's stick to orchids.

Orchid Number One goes to my mother for her help in keeping my manuscript and correspondence in order. She was a secretary without portfolio — and without salary. Orchid Number Two goes to my brother Bob for careful reading and criticism of the various remarks of mine scattered throughout the book (except this one, which he hasn't seen). Orchid Number Three goes to the typists who did first-rate typing at cut-rate prices. Orchid Number Four goes to Julie Kernan who makes editing a book not merely a venture, but an adventure.

Orchid Number Five goes to you, dear reader, without whom all the toilin' and moilin' wouldn't mean much.

The remainder of the orchids are distributed with a loving flourish among the following authors, agents and publishers of books and magazines who kindly gave permission to reprint the material listed:

The Apostle: Anecdotes from the magazine's humor page, "On the Lighter Side."

ASSOCIATED PRESS: "Valentine Day," by Hal Boyle.

Ave Maria: "A Fog on the Hill," from *Patch and Fan,* by Patrick J. Carroll; anecdote from "Bits Out of Life" column, by Thomas A. Lahey.

THE BOBBS-MERRILL COMPANY: "Multiple Managing Editors," from *Such Interesting People,* by Robert J. Casey.

THE CATHOLIC POETRY SOCIETY BULLETIN: "Lines on a Modern Menace," by Herbert Kenny and "Kin to Mrs. Gurney," by Sister Mary Bertrand.

The Catholic World: "The Farewell Party," by Albert Eisele; "The Grief of St. Mochua," by A. M. Sullivan.

DODD, MEAD AND CO.: "Naughty Girls," from *When the Wind Blows,* by Thomas Butler Feeney.

Duckett's Register: "A Val-iant Effort" and "Saintly Limericks," by Ronald Knox, as recorded by Gordon Albion.

JIMMY DURANTE: "My Deproach to Art," from *Stage Magazine.*

E. P. DUTTON AND CO.: "Flight," from *Golden Apples of the Sun,* by Rosemary Obermeyer; "Jottings from a Psycho-Analyst's Note-Book," from *Essays in Satire,* by Ronald Knox; "A Personal Matter," and "Lambs' Tails with Potatoes," from *Welcome to All This,* by D. B. Wyndham Lewis.

E. P. DUTTON AND CO. and *Yank,* Army weekly: "How to Get Lost in a Jungle," by Joseph McCarthy; "The Package APO," by James O'Neill; and "Hot Jeep," by Tom Shehan, from *The Best from Yank,* a volume of selections from *Yank,* Army weekly, published by Dutton.

HELEN PARRY EDEN: "The Duplicity of Monsignor Scalabrin," from *Whistles of Silver,* by Helen Parry Eden, published by the Bruce Publishing Company.

CYRIL B. EGAN: "The Object of My Affections," which appeared in the *Saturday Evening Post;* and "Ode to a Fishcake."

NORBERT A. ENGELS: "Crossword Puzzles," by Norbert A. Engels, which appeared in the *St. Joseph Magazine.*

FABER AND FABER, LTD.: "The Death of Polybius Jubb," from *Adamastor,* by Roy Campbell.

FAMOUS ARTISTS CORPORATION, agents: "Mr. Brunton Views Ireland," from the play, *Where Stars Walk,* by Micheal MacLiammoir.

SAMUEL FRENCH: "Justice Holmes Greets Washington," from the play, *The Magnificent Yankee,* by Emmet Lavery; the play is based in part on Francis Biddle's biography, *Mr. Justice Holmes,* and was originally produced by Arthur Hopkins.

OLIVER ST. JOHN GOGARTY: "Mr. Pirrie, Pyrophile," from *Mourning Became Mrs. Spendlove,* by Oliver St. John Gogarty; "To an Old Tenor," from *Poetry Magazine,* Chicago.

HARPER AND BROTHERS: "Cookbooks," from *Kitchen Fugue,* by Sheila Kaye-Smith.

Harper's Bazaar: "First Confession," by Frank O'Connor.

The New York Herald-Tribune: "Victory Spelled Backwards," by Red Smith, from his column, "Views of Sport."

HOUGHTON MIFFLIN CO.: "The Unwilling Missionary," from *Vespers in Vienna,* and "The Clergy and the Cinema," from *The World, the Flesh, and Father Smith,* both by Bruce Marshall.

LIGUORIAN PAMPHLET OFFICE: "In Faint Praise of Altar Boys," by J. J. Galvin.

LITTLE, BROWN AND CO.: "The Happier Hunting Ground," from *The Loved One,* by Evelyn Waugh.

Liturgical Arts Magazine: "Artistic . . . but Very Plain," by Doran Hurley.

LONGMANS, GREEN AND CO.: "Tidbits," from *Maura Laverty's Cookbook,* by Maura Laverty.

COMPTON MACKENZIE, LTD.: "The Pigeon Officer," from *Keep the Home Guard Turning,* by Compton Mackenzie, published by Chatto and Windus.

FRANCIS MACMANUS: "The Professor," from *Pedlar's Pack,* by Francis MacManus, published by the Talbot Press, Dublin.

THE MACMILLAN COMPANY: "The Spaeman," from *The Big Tree of Bunlahy,* by Padraic Colum; "Chung Cheng-liu," from *The American Sporting Scene,* by John Kieran.

DECLAN X. MCMULLEN CO.: "Truth Is a Fixed Star," from *After Black Coffee,* by Robert I. Gannon.

JOHN P. MULGREW: "And Life Goes On," excerpts from the column in *The Witness,* Dubuque, by John P. Mulgrew, and from his *Yearbook of Jazbo of Old Dubuque.*

DOUGLAS ORGAN, publisher: "And Seeing, They Understood," from *Marjorie and Me,* by Bernard Basset.

PAULIST PRESS: "Ain't Psychology Grand," from *This Our Day,* by James M. Gillis.

A. D. PETERS, agent: "Geraldine Brazier, W.O.O.F.," from *Captain Foulenough and Company,* by J. B. Morton, published by the Macmillan Company, London; "Mr. Milk Goes to Russia," from *Morton's Folly,* by J. B. Morton, published by Doubleday, Doran and Co.; "The Happier Hunting Ground," from *The Loved One,* by Evelyn Waugh; "Cookbooks," from *Kitchen Fugue,* by Sheila Kaye-Smith, published by Harper and Brothers.

H. I. PHILLIPS: "G.I. Blueprint for Peace," from *Private Purkey's Private Peace,* by H. I. Phillips, published by Harper and Brothers; "The Better Mousetrap," and "Saint Nick Visits the Salesgirl," from the syndicated column, "The Sun Dial," by H. I. Phillips, appearing in *The New York Sun* and elsewhere.

PRENTICE-HALL, INC.: "An Armful of Cabbage," from *How to Be Poor*, by Frank Fay.

PRITCHETT AND BRANDT, agents: "The Angel Arrives," from *Career Angel*, by Gerard Murray.

G. P. PUTNAM's SONS: "Epistle to St. Paul," from *By Post to the Apostles*, by Helen Walker Homan.

MARTIN QUIGLEY, JR.: "Mark of the Gaels," from *Great Gaels — Ireland at Peace and in War*, by Martin Quigley, Jr.

THE SALVATORIAN FATHERS, Publishing Dept.: "Isolationist," from *Sing Joyfully*, by Mary Fabyan Windeatt.

Scholastic Magazine: "Sixteen," by Maureen Daly.

SHEED AND WARD, INC.: "Jokes," from *Convent Boarding School*, by Virginia Kenny; "The Ungrateful Bricklayer," from *Twelve Tales of the Life and Adventures of St. Imaginus*, by Frances Maguire; "The Common Cold," from *Rime, Gentlemen, Please*, by Robert Farren.

The New York Sun: "Advice to Font Parents," and "Gorg Bernad (U No) Has a Spel," by Paul J. Phelan.

The Brooklyn Tablet: "A Kelly Spurns His Name," by Doyle Hennessy.

THE VIKING PRESS: "The Confessional," from *A Purse of Coppers*, by Sean O'Faolain.

EDWARD T. WALLACE: "Storytellers," from *Barington*, by Edward T. Wallace, published by Simon and Schuster.

MAURICE WALSH: "Thomasheen James and Thirty Pieces of Copper," from *Thomasheen James*, published by F. A. Stokes Co., copyright 1936, by Maurice Walsh.

DOUGLAS WOODRUFF: "Military Moments," and "Just Jests," from *More Talking at Random*, by Douglas Woodruff, published by Burns, Oates and Washbourne, Ltd.

The New York World Telegram: "My Day," from the column by Westbrook Pegler, which formerly appeared in *The World Telegram*, and now appears in *The New York Journal-American* and is syndicated by King Features.

INTRODUCTION

It's unreasonable to demand a reason for an anthology of humor. The essence of a humorous collection is seasoning not reasoning. So those who are more inclined to the philo-comic than the philo-sophic may walk right on through the anteroom of this introduction to the main ballroom where festivities are in full swing. You can always drop back anytime you wish, and I'll still be here.

Now, if the gentleman who remains will make himself comfortable, and put aside his copy of Plato's *Dialogues* for a moment or so, I'll try to explain the convictions lying behind a book of humor by Catholic authors.

No, thank you, I don't smoke; but, here, I always carry matches for friends. You like smoking? That's a pleasant word "like." It conjures up a picture of enjoyment and contentment you can't get too many copies of in this world today. As the poet said, "Every joy is gain, and gain is gain, however small."

That brings me to the first reason for my book, if you don't mind my swinging the conversation around that way. Robert Gibbings, in his volume *How Lovely Is the Lee,* tells of a visit to the remains of an ancient monastery on High Island, off the coast of Galway. There he discovered a wonderful collection of seventh-century illuminated manuscripts, all done in that wonderful script by those wonderful Irish monks. At the end of one of the texts, Mr. Gibbings found a personal note, written in a neat small hand by a monk whose labor of love was completed. It said: "Good-by little book. These are things which I liked so much that I could not help copying them."

My learning and my labors don't approach those of the venerable monk; nevertheless, I would like to send this book out into the world with the monk's very words. For here you will find "things which I liked so much that I could not help copying them." It is my hope that this volume will give others the pleasure it has given me.

Not that the joys of an anthologist are unmitigated. Tom Boggs, the poet, said that he read his way through fifty thousand poems to gather sixty-eight. I'm sure that every anthologist, at times, feels like paraphrasing the old hymn to read, "Nobody knows the rubble I've seen." But the collector is always buoyed up by the purpose which led him to his task in the first place. It's very much like the fun of looking for rare pipes. Or roses. Or gems.

In my case, there were several other reasons above and beyond the joy gotten from collecting. Yes, I am about to get real philosophic, I suppose. For a long time I've had a twofold conviction: 1) That in this modern era, when a number of people slyly try to divorce religion from vital human activity, it would be a good thing to show how close the connection is between religion and that very vital human need — humor; 2) That a very good way to emphasize the connection between religion and humor would be to put the spotlight on modern Catholic humorists, members of a brotherhood with a grand tradition going back to Alexander Pope, John Dryden and Geoffrey Chaucer.

There are many persons attempting to spread the slander that religion is a dessicated mummy, a curious museum piece. And if they had their way they would picture this mummy as wrapped in depressing, morbid, gloomy black. History proves them liars. Not that there haven't been holy men with long faces. But the heart and soul of the Christian tradition has been the spirit of cheerfulness. Our Savior picked the simple gaiety of the wedding at Cana for the occasion of his first public miracle; and the hagiographies are full of cheerful saints, even as the histories are full of despairing sinners.

Search the Scriptures and what do you find? The Bible tells us that there is "a time to laugh." It tells us that one of the rewards of the good man is that he may often be merry, because he has found favor before God.

Don't misunderstand me in this matter of religion and humor. Religion, in Catholic eyes, is of course, finally, a matter of faith and grace. That's why, fortunately for some of us, God won't require an ear-to-ear grin as an admission fee to heaven. But I don't see how you can get away from the possibility that one of the natural paths to faith and grace may well be up the pleasant hilly slopes of hilarity.

Take wit and satire, for example. If you don't mind my throwing metaphors around a bit, I'd like to think of them as the advance guard of the army of Truth in the war against evil in men's minds. In their most effective forms wit and satire shatter the enemy fortresses of falsehood, hypocrisy and sham, with all the devastating force of an atom bomb. In another way they resemble flame throwers that swiftly consume flimsy pride. The milder forms resemble top sergeants, very useful in keeping stupid or careless members of the faithful in line.

Humor, on the other hand, is not destructive in intent or effect. It is constructive. It is linked with peace, not warfare. It is akin to the tools of reconstruction, not to the weapons of force. In its more modest forms humor is an analgesic, a soothing, restful balm. In its highest forms it is the "milk of Paradise," and for ennobling man is brother to poetry, superior to philosophy. After all, philosophy is "a torch of smoky pine that lights the pathway but one step ahead." But quick flashes of humor frequently act radar-like to spot mankind's ultimate goal, Eternal Truth and Goodness, and to lead us there unerringly.

Do you remember what Carlyle wrote? "How much lies in laughter; the cipher key wherewith we decipher the whole man." This couldn't be so if humor were not linked in some way with our deepest emotions and feelings. Where does a man get his philosophy of "the importance of not being earnest"?

The real humorist's spirit of playfulness and his ability not to take things too seriously come from a deep intuitive sense which enables him to see life in its deeper relationships. Like the poet, the humorist goes beyond the confused cacophony of this world and catches the strains of the Universal Harmony. The humorist looks out, not from an ivory tower, but from a convivial banquet hall. Yet he is not so blinded by the man-made lights within that he cannot see outside "that Light whose smile kindles the universe." The humorist senses the sustaining Love which unites all forms of being, and all men with each other. When the poet senses these things he sings. When the humorist has the vision he laughs. But both are paying obeisance to Truth and Goodness. And both feel compelled to rally men around them and lead them, Pied-Piper fashion, in the direction of the Light and the Love.

The Christian, the Catholic humorist, is, I think, the luckiest in the world. His humor may not be the best in quality, but the reasons for his humor are the best. He is not still stumbling manfully, with purely natural aids, up the slopes of hilarity toward grace and faith. He is at the summit. His humorous outlook has a supernatural vista.

Does all this help even a little to convey to you the conviction that humor is connected with man's natural or supernatural religious outlook? Humor and religion, hilarity and holiness have something in common. If a man knows certainly where he is going, he can really enjoy himself better on the way; and the more certain he is the better he can enjoy himself. That's what I've been trying to point out.

Well, as I was saying way back when you lit your first smoke, I have felt all these things about religion and humor rather strongly for a long time. I hope you won't mind if I intrude a little personal history here. The idea of spotlighting modern Catholic humorists first came to me while I was a graduate student of English literature, and a college teacher of rhetoric and poetry. I mention this to prove that graduate study has some compensations other than the constant threat of being smothered to death by the dust on terrifying tomes in the secluded jungles of library stacks, and to prove that teaching poetry to freshmen has other rewards besides nerves that jangled worse than their most puerile jingle.

Teaching and studying in this way inevitably bring you face to face with persons such as Chaucer, Dryden and Pope. I immediately liked their faces, and enjoyed their company. I looked on them as the Big Three of the Catholic tradition of wit and humor. In my travels I also met people like Robert Henryson, William Dunbar, John Skelton and Alexander Barclay. They were people off the beaten path. I don't suppose their names are familiar to many, outside of "English majors." But they impressed on me the golden thread of wit and humor which down through the centuries binds together and brightens the Catholic tradition in literature.

What puzzled me, however, was that though Catholic scholars paid due homage to the Big Three and, in lesser degree, to the others in the Catholic tradition of humor, modern Catholic humorists didn't seem to rate a single bit of professional pointing-at-with-pride. Not so much as a pinky was extended in their direction. "Is it the rust we value and not the gold?" I asked myself.

It was at this point that I formulated my second conviction: that a very good way to emphasize the close bond between incense and nonsense was to call attention to modern Catholic humorists who are striving — some mightily and others admittedly mite-ly but all striving — to make use of their talent τὸ ἀλλὰ βελτιόν, "for the Greater Good."

The result of these cultural cogitations was my book *With a Merry Heart*, which appeared in 1943 and which was the first collection ever made of examples from the lighter side of modern English and American Catholic culture.

In that volume I emphasized the older generation, Hilaire Belloc, G. K. Chesterton, Maurice Egan, Elizabeth Jordan, Agnes Repplier, Canon Sheehan, James Jeffrey Roche, Father Tabb, Austin O'Malley, Maurice Baring, Finley Peter Dunne, Arnold Lunn, Catholic literary stalwarts of the early decades of the twentieth century.

The present collection deals with the "younger generation." Encouraged by the interest aroused by *With a Merry Heart*, I've explored further in the field of Catholic humor. I've brought together new authors, and new material by established authors, to bring the report on my journeyings up to date. In this book I've been concerned solely with "contemporary," that is, living authors, though it's true that some of the writers in the Church militant may have become members of the Church triumphant before you meet them here.

That's about all I have to say. I hope I haven't bored you or turned this anteroom into an "anti-room." But then you could have gone ahead with the others (there were others, weren't there?). Just one more point, as long as you've stayed this long. You know, as you sit here in my company, the halo of smoke from your cigarette is strictly non-sectarian looking. I can't tell whether you're a Catholic or a Methodist. If you are not a Catholic, I hope that you will enjoy this family picture; and I feel that most of the authors you probably have not met before. I think you will find that "Catholic humor" is as catholic as any other sort.

PAUL J. PHELAN

CONTENTS

7. THE IRISH — HERE AND ON THE OULD SOD

8. HEADLINES AND DEADLINES

9. ACROSS THE FOOTLIGHTS

10. FREUD AND PHOBIAS

1. THE YOUNG FRY

1. THE YOUNG FRY

"Come in," he said, "and play awhile with me;
I am the little child you used to be."

— From "The Child in the Garden"
by Henry Van Dyke

Arranging selections in a book of humor is a lot like eating spaghetti. If you concentrate on the matter too long and seriously, winding in and out and trying to decide what to pick up first and what last, you take all the fun out of it. In readable matters, as in edible ones, it's better just to plunge in and follow your natural instincts. That is what has been done, more or less, in setting up this book. The various compartments may not be watertight. There may be some seepage from one to the other. But I hope that the arrangement will at least afford groups of related topics for conversational or cogitational purposes.

Who comes first, chronologically or in any other way, in every village, town, hamlet and city in our fair country? I didn't quite hear your answer, with all the gleeful shouting, for here they come — the young fry — rushing pell-mell to the front pages of the book.

Some years ago "the barefoot boy with cheek of tan" symbolized youth. Nowadays the style trend is toward the barefoot boy (or girl) with tongue in cheek of tan, or vermilion.

Compare Hal Boyle's seventh-grade (in the academic sense) love affair with the idyllic, bucolic *mésalliance* told of so glowingly by John Greenleaf Whittier in his poem "Schooldays." In each story a boy is in love with a girl. Whittier's girl had "tangled golden curls." Boyle's had "hair like a maple tree in autumn," presumably before the leaves began falling very heavily. Whittier's girl, you will

3

remember, went "above" her boy friend by winning a spelling bee. Boyle's girl didn't have to go above him. She was up there already, three inches taller.

Notice, if you please, the reaction of these two young maidens of different generations. John Greenleaf's miss tells him:

> "I'm sorry that I spelt the word:
> I hate to go above you,
> Because," — the brown eyes lower fell —
> "Because, you see, I love you!"

But what did Hal Boyle's modern miss do to make him feel better? She turned up her nose and stuck out her tongue. I'm not preaching about the cynicism of modern grammar school graders. But, as Jimmy Durante says, those are the conditions which prevail.

Henry Wadsworth Longfellow tells us that "the thoughts of youth are long, long thoughts." Fortunately, however, the long, long thoughts are seldom deep, deep thoughts. Their average measurement is from the top of a vanilla soda to the bottom. So it is that Hal Boyle will eventually forget his "false Beatrice." Similarly, Maureen Daly, whose forgetful young man in the story "Sixteen" is a "false Romeo," will not be eternally disconnected from love's sweet message because of the telephone call which never came. The whimsical, imaginative writing of these two makes me feel that their luck wasn't so good as Whittier's but that their style will do very well.

Frank O'Connor's little masterpiece "First Confession" is another classic example of the imaginative, whimsical approach to childhood. As his story so well exemplifies, what makes children especially appealing in literature is the fact that their "tremendous" problems, looked at in the bright noonday of adult experience, throw such little shadows that we're forced to laugh. A critic has said that O'Connor is at his best when he "launches his wild, irreverent attacks on puritanism with a shillelagh in one hand, a glass of porter in the other, and his eyes alight with a compassionate smile." I like O'Connor's compassionate smile very much. But I like his impish grin even more.

The same spirit of inspired impishness, with an added spice of gypsy background, is found in Rosemary Obermeyer's book *Golden*

Apples of the Sun. The selection I've reprinted shows the attempts of Rhona, orphan gypsy girl, to run away from St. Joseph's Boarding School for Girls. I hope modern psychiatrists will note the skill and tact with which Sister Paul of the Cross unties the knots manufactured with such loving care by this problem child.

Another presentation of the problem child is that made by Father Thomas B. Feeney, who points out that some plain ornery children are fast becoming plane-ornery children, and jet-propelled at that. Father Feeney, by the way, has appeared jet-propelled himself, in his rise to a poetic fame rivaling that of his brother Leonard. Cyril Egan, who ought to know after teaching for years, rounds out our psychiatric studies with some advice on how to teach teen-agers Latin. It has something to do with the fact that emphasis on love as an actuality will lead to interest in love as a verb, in any language.

I can't help thinking that this section may be frightening to prospective newlyweds. A vision of schoolgirls who make faces, stick out tongues, have unhappy love affairs, or write "Rules for Me" which include "Beware the nun that holds the big rosary around her waist so that it doesn't jingle," is not conducive to making matrimony popular. And I'm not even mentioning the little tyke who makes elaborate plans to kill his grandmother. Timid souls, therefore, are advised to read only Virginia Kenny's picture of boarding school life. Here you will find more conventional children whose greatest fault is torturing the English language. As uncle to four nieces and five nephews I can vouch for the authenticity of Miss Kenny's juvenile jokes. In fact, more times than I care to recall, I have been made to look very dull by not having at my finger tips the right answer to such queries as 1) What is the only kind of dress you can't wear? An address. 2) How do sailors wash their clothes? They throw them overboard and they're washed ashore. 3) Which travels faster, heat or cold? Heat, because you can catch cold. 4) Why did they build an iron fence around the cemetery? Because the people were dying to get in. . . . You see what I mean?

HAL BOYLE

Valentine Day

I hate Valentine Day. I was in grammar school — young, happy, in the prime of life, and doing well in arithmetic. I had conceived for a fellow-traveler in the seventh grade a grand passion that made the Caesar-and-Cleopatra affair seem low-grade burlesque.

This small-fry queen had everything. Her hair was like a maple tree in autumn. Her nose had the grandeur of a profile on an old Greek coin. Her eyes were those of a kitten. Her voice was soft water falling on old moss. And when she wore bloomers playing basketball, I saw with a sigh of happiness there were no knobs on her knees. Knobs — why, there wasn't a freckle. What a woman!

There was only one thing wrong with this romance. She was three inches taller than I. To me it was no towering difference. At that period, I liked them tall and stately. I didn't mind if I took her to a movie matinee and the street car conductor made me pay an adult fare for her while letting stumpy me ride for half fare. What is money to a man in love?

But this discrepancy in altitude galled her. She lacked that high disdain of crowd opinion that marks true greatness. It annoyed her when the rude ruffians in the class jeered at us as we walked home together.

But my overgrown Juliet couldn't stand the laughs. She gave me the heave-ho, and switched to the tallest guy in school. He sat in the next row. I had to pass their love notes back and forth. Mine she never answered.

I tried to grow taller by walking on tiptoe. I hung by my arms from the gym bars so long my hands still stretch to my knees. I gained a half-inch. I tried to read up on something I'd heard of called adolescence. But the librarian wouldn't let me get at the books on the top shelf. She just told me I'd start to grow when my voice changed. And me — still singing alto!

Finally I decided I'd have to buy her love back — the oldest delusion since Eden. I peddled the *Kansas City Star* on street corners for a month until I had piled up $3.50 over the cost of living. I plunked it all down for a big cedar box full of chocolates tied with a huge red satin bow.

When I slapped my present down on the classroom table on Valentine's Day it was the biggest event in the history of the seventh grade. I kept my eyes on the floor, hoping only my chest wouldn't burst and spill my heart on the desk. I sneaked a glance over and saw my false Beatrice with a red face tearing up the valentine I had put into the box. She didn't know she was tearing me to pieces, too.

When I dared to look up again, class was over and my lost love and her tall boy friend were walking out eating my candy. As they reached the door she turned and made a face at me. Yes, and she stuck out her tongue. Through all these years I remember only that it looked heart-shaped.

I sat all alone at my desk. My teacher — that wonderful woman — came over and whispered:

"Don't mind too much, Harold. She will never forget your present."

Well, neither have I. I hope she grew so tall she keeps bumping her head on doorways the rest of her life. Now you know why I hate Valentine Day.

MAUREEN DALY

Sixteen [*]

Now don't get me wrong. I mean, I want you to understand from the beginning that I'm not really so dumb. I know what a girl should do and what she shouldn't. I get around. I read. I listen

[*] This story originally appeared in *Scholastic Magazine*, is copyrighted by the editors, 1938, 1945, and is reprinted with their permission.

to the radio. And I have two older sisters. So you see, I know what the score is. I know it's smart to wear tweedish skirts and shaggy sweaters with the sleeves pushed up and pearls and ankle socks and saddle shoes that look as if they've seen the world. And I know that your hair should be long, almost to your shoulders, and sleek as a wet seal, just a little fluffed on the ends, and you should wear a campus hat or a dink or else a peasant hankie if you've that sort of face. Properly, a peasant hankie should make you think of edelweiss, mist and sunny mountains, yodeling and Swiss cheese. You know, that kind of peasant. Now, me, I never wear a hankie. It makes my face seem wide and Slavic and I look like a picture always in one of those magazine articles that run — "And Stalin says the future of Russia lies in its women. In its women who have tilled its soil, raised its children — " Well, anyway. I'm not exactly too small-town either. I read Winchell's column. You get to know what New York boy is that way about some pineapple princess on the West Coast and what Paradise pretty is currently the prettiest and why someone, eventually, will play Scarlett O'Hara. It gives you that cosmopolitan feeling. And I know that anyone who orders a strawberry sundae in a drugstore instead of a lemon coke would probably be dumb enough to wear colored ankle socks with high-heeled pumps or use Evening in Paris with a tweed suit. But I'm sort of drifting. This isn't what I wanted to tell you. I just wanted to give you the general idea of how I'm not so dumb. It's important that you understand that.

You see, it was funny how I met him. It was a winter night like any other winter night. And I didn't have my Latin done either. But the way the moon tinseled the twigs and silver-plated the snow drifts, I just couldn't stay inside. The skating rink isn't far from our house — you can make it in five minutes if the sidewalks aren't slippery, so I went skating. I remember it took me a long time to get ready that night because I had to darn my skating socks first. I don't know why they always wear out so fast — just in the toes too. Maybe it's because I have metal protectors on the toes of my skates. That probably *is* why. And then I brushed my hair — hard, so hard it clung to my hand and stood up around my head in a hazy halo.

My skates were hanging by the back door all nice and shiny for I'd just gotten them for Christmas and they smelled so queer — just like fresh smoked ham. My dog walked with me as far as the corner. She's a red Chow, very polite and well-mannered, and she kept pretending it was me she liked when all the time I knew it was the ham smell. She panted along beside me and her hot breath made a frosty little balloon balancing on the end of her nose. My skates thumped me good-naturedly on my back as I walked and the night was breathlessly quiet and the stars winked down like a million flirting eyes. It was all so lovely.

It was all so lovely I ran most of the way and it was lucky the sidewalks had ashes on them or I'd have slipped surely. The ashes crunched like cracker-jack and I could feel their cindery shape through the thinness of my shoes. I always wear old shoes when I go skating.

I had to cut across someone's back garden to get to the rink and last summer's grass stuck through the thin ice, brown and discouraged. Not many people came through this way and the crusted snow broke through the little hollows between corn stubbles frozen hard in the ground. I was out of breath when I got to the shanty — out of breath with running and with the loveliness of the night. Shanties are always such friendly places. The floor all hacked to wet splinters from skate runners and the wooden wall frescoed with symbols of dead romance. There was a smell of singed wool as someone got too near the glowing isinglass grid of the iron stove. Girls burst through the door laughing with snow on their hair and tripped over shoes scattered on the floor. A pimply-faced boy grabbed the hat from the grizzled head of an eighth-grade blonde and stuffed it into an empty galosh to prove his love and then hastily bent to examine his skate strap with innocent unconcern.

It didn't take me long to get my own skates on and I stuck my shoes under the bench — far back where they wouldn't get knocked around and would be easy to find when I wanted to go home. I walked out on my toes and the shiny runners of my new skates dug deep into the sodden floor.

It was snowing a little outside — quick, eager little Luxlike flakes that melted as soon as they touched your hand. I don't know where the snow came from for there were stars out. Or maybe the stars were in my eyes and I just kept seeing them every time I looked up into the darkness. I waited a moment. You know, to start to skate at a crowded rink is like jumping on a moving merry-go-round. The skaters go skimming round in a colored blur like gaudy painted horses and the shrill musical jabber re-echoes in the night from a hundred human calliopes. Once in, I went all right. At least after I found out exactly where that rough ice was. It was "round, round, jump the rut, round, round, round, jump the rut, round, round — "

And then he came. All of a sudden his arm was around my waist so warm and tight and he said very casually, "Mind if I skate with you?" and then he took my other hand. That's all there was to it. Just that and then we were skating. It wasn't that I'd never skated with a boy before. Don't be silly. I told you before I get around. But this was different. He was a smoothie! He was a big shot up at school and he went to all the big dances and he was the best dancer in town except Harold Wright who didn't count because he'd been to college in New York for two years! Don't you see? This was different.

At first I can't remember what we talked about, I can't even remember if we talked at all. We just skated and skated and laughed every time we came to that rough spot and pretty soon we were laughing all the time at nothing at all. It was all so lovely.

Then we sat on the big snow bank at the edge of the rink and just watched. It was cold at first even with my skating pants on, sitting on that hard heap of snow but pretty soon I got warm all over. He threw a handful of snow at me and it fell in a little white shower on my hair and he leaned over to brush it off. I held my breath. The night stood still.

The moon hung just over the warming shanty like a big quarter slice of muskmelon and the smoke from the pipe chimney floated up in a sooty fog. One by one the houses around the rink twinked out their lights and somebody's hound wailed a mornful apology to a star as he curled up for the night. It was all so lovely.

Then he sat up straight and said, "We'd better start home." Not "Shall I take you home?" or "Do you live far?" but "We'd better start home." See, that's how I know he wanted to take me

MAUREEN DALY 11

home. Not because he *had* to but because he wanted to. He went to
the shanty to get my shoes. "Black ones," I told him. "Same size
as Garbo's." And he laughed again. He was still smiling when he
came back and took off my skates and tied the wet skate strings in
a soggy knot and put them over his shoulder. Then he held out his
hand and I slid off the snow bank and brushed off the seat of my
pants and we were ready.

It was snowing harder now. Big, quiet flakes that clung to twiggy
bushes and snuggled in little drifts against the tree trunks. The
night was an etching in black and white. It was all so lovely I was
sorry I lived only a few blocks away. He talked softly as we walked
as if every little word were a secret. "Did I like Wayne King, and
did I plan to go to college next year and had I a cousin who lived
in Appleton and knew his brother?" A very respectable Emily Post
sort of conversation and then finally — "How nice I looked with
snow in my hair and had I ever seen the moon so — close?" For the
moon was following us as we walked and ducking playfully behind
a chimney every time I turned to look at it. And then we were
home.

The porch light was on. My mother always puts the porch light
on when I go away at night. And we stood there a moment by the
front steps and the snow turned pinkish in the glow of the colored
light and a few feathery flakes settled on his hair. Then he took
my skates and put them over my shoulder and said, "Good night
now. I'll call you." "I'll call you," he said.

I went inside and in a moment he was gone. I watched him from
my window as he went down the street. He was whistling softly
and I waited until the sound faded away so I couldn't tell if it was he
or my heart whistling out there in the night. And then he was gone,
completely gone.

I shivered. Somehow the darkness seemed changed. The stars
were little hard chips of light far up in the sky and the moon stared
down with a sullen yellow glare. The air was tense with sudden cold,
and a gust of wind swirled his prints into white oblivion. Everything
was quiet.

But he'd said, "I'll call you." That's what he said, "I'll call you."
I couldn't sleep all night.

And that was last Thursday. Tonight is Tuesday. Tonight is Tuesday and my homework's done, and I darned some stockings that didn't really need it, and I worked a crossword puzzle, and I listened to the radio and now I'm just sitting. I'm just sitting because I can't think of anything, anything but snowflakes and ice skates and yellow moons and Thursday night. The telephone is sitting on the corner table with its old black face turned to the wall so I can't see its leer. I don't even jump when it rings any more. My heart still prays but my mind just laughs. Outside the night is still, so still I think I'll go crazy and the white snow's all dirtied and smoked into grayness and the wind is blowing the arc light so it throws weird, waving shadows from the trees onto the lawn — like thin, starved arms begging for I don't know what. And so I'm just sitting here and I'm not feeling anything. I'm not even sad because all of a sudden I know. All of a sudden I know. I can sit here now forever and laugh and laugh and laugh while the tears run salty in the corners of my mouth. For all of a sudden I know, I know what the stars knew all the time — he'll never, never call — never.

CYRIL B. EGAN

The Object of My Affections

Amo, Amas, Amat —
I love, you love, he loves — *What?*

The adolescents yawn and yearn
To live and love, and not to learn.

Drearily chanting their drowsy matins,
Objectless lovers are lousy Latins.

The verb is active, the subject willing;
But what's the object of all this drilling?

Surely affection, even in grammar,
Calls for direction, drama, and glamour.

Give youth a break, a run for his money,
A star for his car, a Hollywood honey.

Hark to the Goons as gaily they render
Accusative case in the Feminine Gender:
    Hurray — Hurrah-bo —
    Amo, Amabo
    Greta Garbo!

———————

THOMAS B. FEENEY

Naughty Girls

THE EIGHTEEN NINETIES
Because her mother punished her
For being bold and proud,
Elaine ran up into her room
And whistled right out loud.

THE NINETEEN TWENTIES
Because her mother told her twice
To mind her etiquette,
Marie put on a boy's attire
And smoked a cigarette.

THE NINETEEN FIFTIES

Because her mother frowned at her,
Clarice went raging mad,
She stole a jet-propulsion plane
And flew to Leningrad.

VIRGINIA ARVILLE KENNY

Jokes

On rainy nights, sometimes, we have a meeting of the grammar school girls. If we are going to have a meeting, it is announced at the evening meal, and we all clap our hands. Then we all go to the school hall, and Sister Mary Frances has charge. These meetings are so much fun that we wish it would rain or snow so that we can have them often. They are so good that some of the Sisters and some of the high school girls come just to listen.

The point of each meeting like this is that it helps toward self-expression, poise, and confidence. Each grammar school girl who comes to the meeting must walk up onto the stage and tell the audience a joke. When all the jokes are told, the girls vote on what three jokes were the best. Then the three winners come up and Sister Mary Frances gives each one a prize, a box of candy or a pretty handkerchief or a tube of toothpaste or something like that. You're supposed to vote not only on the joke itself, but also on the way it was told, on the posture and diction and clearness of the girl who tells the joke.

The jokes are supposed to be short and quick, so that every girl will have a chance. We tell jokes like, "What did the boy dove say to the girl dove?" and the answer is, "He said, 'I'm *coo-coo* about you.'" And another one is, "Why did the little boy cut the worm in two?" and the answer is, "Because the worm looked so lonesome." And another is, "Use the word 'science' in a sentence," and the answer is, "Science is those things which say 'No Smoking!' " And another is, "What did the mother say to her little boy about Euripides?" and the answer is, "She said, 'Euripides new trousers and I kill you.' "

The best fun of all is when the tots from the lower grades get up to tell their jokes. They are always funnier than the jokes they tell. And sometimes they say the joke and don't understand it themselves. And Sister Mary Frances has all of us trained not to say out the answer when we know it. If we know the answer, we are supposed to act as if we didn't and let the little girl have the joy of telling it herself. For instance, if a little girl asks, "How did the little boy know that his hand hurt?" we're supposed to keep quiet and not shout out, "Because he put his hand on the window-glass and felt the pane." Or if a little girl asks, "Did you hear the story about the bed?" we're trained to let *her* answer, "I just made it up," and laugh and clap when she does. With the very little girls it's funnier when we know the answer because sometimes they give the wrong answer and we scream. One of them asked, "Why is the statue of Christopher Columbus honest?" and instead of answering, "Because it's on the Square," she said, "Because it's on the corner." And one of them asked, "How many cows give milk?" and instead of saying, "Every udder one," she said, "Every one with an udder." And sometimes they don't put the question the right way. Instead of saying, "What did the lady say when they asked her if she had red stockings?" so that the answer could be, "She said she didn't have much time for reading," one little girl said, "What did the lady say when they asked her if she had *ever* red stockings?" When we all roared out loud at the question, the little girl got all mixed up. And when we were quiet again, she said, "The lady said that she didn't have time for red stockings," and that made us all laugh until we nearly fell onto the floor.

And one night one of the little girls in the second grade got up onto the stage to tell her joke. She put her hands behind her and smiled down on us, and got us laughing before she even began. Then when we were all quiet again, she asked in a loud clear voice,

"What did the bumble-bee say when he stung the bull on the behind?"

That's as far as she got. Sister Mary Frances turned scarlet, took the little girl by the hand, and led her down from the stage. There were a few more jokes, but we hardly heard them because we all got the giggles. Finally Sister Mary Frances couldn't bite her lip any longer, and she got the giggles. So in a shower of giggles and laughter, we voted on the three best jokes of the evening. We were all so silly that we couldn't pick out the winners, and Sister decided to put it off until the next meeting. We kept up the giggles even after we were all in bed, and the Mother of the Dormitory had to speak to us or we would have stayed awake all night. It was one of the best times I ever remember.

For weeks, after that, we kept asking and asking the little girl to tell us the answer. But no matter what we did we couldn't get her to tell us. We asked everybody we met, but nobody had the answer. Whatever the little bumble-bee did say is still a secret, and we never found out what it was.

ROSEMARY OBERMEYER

Flight *

One day in the second year I was in that school, the prefect sent for me specially. A nun told me to follow her, and she led me into a little parlor, very private, where Sister Paul-of-the-Cross was sitting with a letter spread out on her black lap.

"Sit down, Rhona," she said. "Thank you, Sister Clare."

I sat down on the arm of a chair, and stared at Sister Paul-of-the-Cross. She was hard, but I liked her a little.

* From *Golden Apples of the Sun* by Rosemary Obermeyer, published by E. P. Dutton & Co., Inc.

"This chair, dear."

When she said "dear" I knew something was wrong.

"Rhona," she said, tapping the letter very slowly, "I have a message from Mr. St. Peter. Your foster-mother is dead."

She looked down at me very kindly through her thick glasses, expecting me to burst out crying. I was sorry Mrs. St. Peter had died, but she wasn't my real mother; so I didn't do anything, just sat and waited.

"Perhaps you wonder what will happen to you in the future. That is only natural. Well, I have some good news concerning that. Mrs. St. Peter has provided for you in her will. Do you understand? There will be money enough for you to finish your education here at St. Joseph's."

"Couldn't I take the money, and go away?"

The prefect's glasses seemed to grow thicker and her eyes smaller. "How can you suggest such a thing? No, my child, Mrs. St. Peter has entrusted you to me, and it is our duty to bring you up an educated Christian girl."

As soon as I could, I got away from that parlor. I thought: There is nothing any more to keep me here except the iron fence and Sister Paul-of-the-Cross. Right away I felt freer and more alive.

I began to get the hang of how to slip into the woods next the convent. A rich man owned it, a Mr. Hepburn. No one dared put a foot in it except himself and his friends, but sometimes they did, so he hired a guard to make the rounds and fire rock-salt on the chals and tramps, and had signs all around that a blind man could see — "NO HUNTING OR TRESPASSING ALLOWED." The convent fence next his property was a tall iron one with spikes at top and bottom. But in places the ground sagged a little; so that any thin wriggly *chavo* could get under it if he tried. Sister Agatha, the botany teacher, was always making us collect leaves and flowers; that was the only study I ever liked in that place. I used to get the hardest-to-find plants, so that she praised me. She even showed the notebook to Sister Paul-of-the-Cross, who called me in one day.

"Sister Agatha tells me you have the best notebook in the school."

"Thank you, Sister."

"Where did you find the wild orchid?"

The ground was getting slippery, but I did the best I could. "I don't remember just where," I said. "There may be some behind the nuns' convent."

"You haven't found them anywhere else, have you?"

She looked at me so shrewd and so deep with her winter's smile, even her thick glasses let it shine through. You couldn't fool her if you tried a hundred years.

"Yes, Sister," I said.

"Thank you for telling me the truth," she said. But when I started to bound out of the room, she called me back. "There is something I should like to have you read to me." She handed me a crumpled piece of paper fished out of the waste-paper basket. "Begin!" she commanded.

I began to read.

"The title," she cut in.

"Rules for me," I read, wishing I could swallow the paper.

"I. Beware the nun that holds the big rosary around her waist so it doesn't jingle.

"II. It is easier to climb under a fence than over it.

"III. Do not eat too much. A fat one cannot climb under a good fence.

"IV. At the table, hide your food under your dress, you may need it later.

"V. For the botany notebook, get your flowers from the wood. That is the hard way, but the best.

"VI. It is best to walk sneaky so you can hear the guard coming.

"VII. If you are caught, show your notebook and cry because you were made to get a flower that grows nowhere else.

"VIII. If any nun hears about your going under the fence, lie out of it; but if Sister Paul-of-the-Cross catches you, tell the truth."

When I had finished, Sister Paul-of-the-Cross sat looking sternly at me across her desk, but I could see that she was smothering down a smile. She made the sign of the Cross with the silver part of her rosary as though asking for help.

"You have written your own commandments," she said finally, "now you shall write the commandments of God one hundred times." And not a word about the wood!

A couple of days later I was back in her office again, and this time the talk was all about the wood. I stood in front of her, scratched and dirty, one sleeve of my uniform torn clean off.

"You were found hiding in Mr. Hepburn's wood," said Sister Paul-of-the-Cross, cold and sharp. "Why did you do this? Tell me the whole truth!"

"I — I wanted to run away. I hid there so's I could sneak out after dark."

A smile crept thin around her mouth. "Do you know that the whole school was ordered to pray that you would be found? And you were found, God found you."

"No, He didn't!" I said. "Look at my sleeve, Hepburn's dog tracked me down!"

For a month I wasn't allowed out except when a nun took me for exercise. Back and forth, back and forth, we paced like in a cage. Generally she chose the paved walk next the wood to remind me I was on the right side of the fence. I used to squint at that wood and think, "Curse you for a bad wood! I loved you, so thick and friendly, but you were not the way out. I will have to find another way!"

When the month of punishment was over and I was free an hour every day, I kept my eyes open for a change of clothes. I found a cap in the woods. A little later I made a deal for some torn overalls. It happened this way. Behind the school was a convent house where some old nuns lived, waiting to die; and they used to feed poor people who came every morning to the gates. When no one was looking, I talked with a woman. I told her about a place behind an urn where I'd hide one of my uniforms if she would leave her son's work clothes.

Then one day in June, the whole school went to the Children-of-Mary picnic. That was the one day of the year when the back gates were opened to let us walk on ground that didn't belong to the convent. It was free ground, springier, wilder even, with no holiness in it. It even smelled better.

We walked across a field, jumping and skipping around the horse pulling the car packed neatly with bags of food, and watching Sister Paul-of-the-Cross standing up like a gladiator. I wanted to lope ahead of everybody, but I didn't dare. I could feel the boy's

overalls hitched up under my uniform, and running might bring
them down.

A little farther on, Sister Agatha was waiting on a grassy slope to
welcome us and set the limits to our wanderings. . . . And there
was a little stream curling at the foot of the slope with some thick
bushes hiding it.

When we had eaten, and the nuns had counted us, and everyone
stretched out on the slope feeling lazy, I just strolled into the alders
and cut off my hair with some little scissors, ripped off my dress,
shoes and stockings, and let down the overall legs, and smiled and
patted myself all over, for I was just lined with stolen bread. I
slouched the cap on my head, the visor down low. I looked into the
stream and thought, you look like a little convent girl — like a
potato you do! I buried my school clothes and sneaked through the
brush.

Doing that was light as fluff, as easy as pie. Even the nuns had
gone over on the side of gluttony (one of the seven deadly sins),
and the girls had stuffed themselves so much they just lay on the
hillside and sank into a snake-sleep and dreamed about supper.

Every step I took made me feel lighter and prouder of myself.
But I felt frightened, too, kind of dizzy in the head. The world
seemed big again, strange, more alive, and beautiful. I nearly cried.

I struck west into the sun, following a little road to make better
time. I walked all that night, lying low the next day. I ate most of
the bread to keep the butter from melting inside my clothes, and
when it was gone I started on the dried apricots. If I met anyone, it
was just farmers and dogs. I kept out of the way of boys, much as I
could, but I think I fooled everybody. Things were going so well, I
might have known something would happen.

Daytime I hid under bridges, any place I could crawl into. I
lived on some raisins and a few bird's eggs I found. When four days
had gone by, I felt safe, because even the color of the earth had
changed; it was black and loamy now, and the crops were turning
more to corn. Without asking questions I found out I was about
fifty miles from the convent and no one I ever met turned around to
look at me.

Then one afternoon about sunset, when I was walking down a

dusty road, my mind full of nothing but how to get a mouthful of water, I heard a buggy coming behind me. Well, I knew that clopping was no farmer's horse! I didn't take time to look around, I just dived through some elderberry bushes, sailed over a saggy barbed-wire fence, and found myself in a hayfield. There was a short red-faced man pitching hay there, but his back was towards me. I dived into a stack and wormed in just as the buggy drove in on a cart road I hadn't noticed. I made a little hole in the hay and saw Mother Agnes and Sister Paul-of-the-Cross get down and come towards me, too, because the man was pitching hay on the stack I was lying in.

"Lord, they've had the whole school praying again!" went through my head. "I'll be found and dragged back! There must be something to this praying business, or they'd never have trailed me here. Oh, St. Anthony, cover me, hide me!"

Mother Agnes began the talking. "Good day, sir," she said. "Have you seen a child run into your field?"

"What's that?" said the old man turning around, and pretty gruff, I thought, for talking to nuns. "What's the trouble, now?"

"One of the boarders has run away from St. Joseph's Convent School," explained Sister Paul-of-the-Cross.

"And where might she have run to, now?" he said, flumping a fork of hay on top of me, so that I trembled.

"She might be in this stack," said Sister Paul-of-the-Cross, neat as a button.

"She might be," said the man, and to show them, he thrust the pitchfork down into the stack several times — and into my leg! I bit my tongue to keep from crying out. He must have felt the twitch of me. He paused a bit, and then drew the fork slowly out.

"There's blood on it!" breathed Mother Agnes, her voice trailing off into a spider web.

"So there is!" said the man. "Trace of blood on one of the tines. Must be a rat."

I was watching Mother Agnes's shoes, and they went backwards a few steps, her toes curling in them. "Sacred Heart of Jesus," she whispered. "Pray for us!" But Sister Paul-of-the-Cross's shoes stayed there, firm as two boulders in a field.

"I didn't hear anything," said Sister Paul-of-the-Cross. "Rats squeak, don't they?"

"Maybe this one ain't hurt bad, I gave it just a nick," said the old man.

"What is your name?"

"Mr. O'Callaghan. And what might yours be?"

"Sister Paul-of-the-Cross. You are a Catholic?"

"Did you ever hear of an O'Callaghan that wasn't?"

Sister Paul-of-the-Cross gave a little dry laugh.

"But are you a good Catholic! That is what I want to know. Would you bring up a child in the way of the Church?"

"By all the saints in Heaven!" snorted the old man, "do I look like a damned heathen? Any child of mine goes to church, and with me leading it by the hand, too."

Sister Paul-of-the-Cross must have beckoned to Mr. O'Callaghan, for the two of them went off a little ways. I could hear the prefect mumble low and earnestly with the old man. In a little while they came back. Then Mother Agnes said hurriedly, "I don't think she is here, Sister. Shall we be going?"

"Good-bye, Mr. O'Callaghan," Sister Paul-of-the-Cross said. "Forgive us for troubling you. The one we are searching for is not here, after all. . . . A child would have screamed. Yes, yes, an ordinary child! God keep you and help you with — with any burden He may send you."

There must have been a frost-smile on her face when she said that. She was a high-up, respected nun, but she had told a lie, and carried it off as well as any Romany. I admired her so much, I nearly forgot the pain in my leg.

———————

FRANK O'CONNOR

First Confession

It was a Saturday afternoon in early spring. A small boy whose
face looked as though it had been but newly scrubbed was being
led by the hand by his sister through a crowded street. The little
boy showed a marked reluctance to proceed; he affected to be very
interested in the shop-windows. Equally, his sister seemed to pay
no attention to them. She tried to hurry him; he resisted. When she
dragged him he began to bawl. The hatred with which she viewed
him was almost diabolical, but when she spoke her words and tone
were full of passionate sympathy.

"Ah, sha, God help us!" she intoned into his ear in a whine of
commiseration.

"Leave me go!" he said, digging his heels into the pavement. "I
don't want to go. I want to go home."

"But, sure, you can't go home, Jackie. You'll have to go. The
parish priest will be up to the house with a stick."

"I don't care. I won't go."

"Oh, Sacred Heart, isn't it a terrible pity you weren't a good
boy? Oh, Jackie, me heart bleeds for you! I don't know what they'll
do to you at all, Jackie, me poor child. And all the trouble you caused
your poor old Nanny, and the way you wouldn't eat in the same
room with her, and the time you kicked her on the shins, and the
time you went for me with the bread knife under the table. I don't
know will he ever listen to you at all, Jackie. I think meself he
might send you to the Bishop. Oh, Jackie, how will you think of
all your sins?"

Half stupefied with terror, Jackie allowed himself to be led
through the sunny streets to the very gates of the church. It was an
old one with two grim iron gates and a long, low, shapeless stone
front. At the gates he stuck, but it was already too late. She dragged

him behind her across the yard, and the commiserating whine with which she had tried to madden him gave place to a yelp of triumph.

"Now you're caught! And I hope he'll give you the pinitintial psalms! That'll cure you, you suppurating little caffler!"

Jackie gave himself up for lost. Within the old church there was no stained glass; it was cold and dark and desolate, and in the silence, the trees in the yard knocked hollowly at the tall windows. He allowed himself to be led through the vaulted silence, the intense and magical silence which seemed to have frozen within the ancient walls, buttressing them and shouldering the high wooden roof. In the street outside, yet seeming a million miles away, a ballad singer was drawling a ballad.

Nora sat in front of him beside the confession box. There were a few old women before her, and later a thin, sad-looking man with long hair came and sat beside Jackie. In the intense silence of the church that seemed to grow deeper from the plaintive moaning of the ballad singer, he could hear the buzz-buzz of a woman's voice in the box, and then the husky ba-ba-ba of the priest's. Lastly the soft thud of something that signalled the end of the confession, and out came the woman, head lowered, hands joined, looking neither to right nor left, and tiptoed up to the altar to say her penance.

It seemed only a matter of seconds till Nora rose and with a whispered injunction disappeared from his sight. He was all alone. Alone and next to be heard and the fear of damnation in his soul. He looked at the sad-faced man. He was gazing at the roof, his hands joined in prayer. A woman in a red blouse and black shawl had taken her place below him. She uncovered her head, fluffed her hair out roughly with her hand, brushed it sharply back, then, bowing, caught it in a knot and pinned it on her neck. Nora emerged. Jackie rose and looked at her with a hatred which was inappropriate to the occasion and the place. Her hands were joined on her stomach, her eyes modestly lowered, and her face had an expression of the most rapt and tender recollection. With death in his heart he crept into the compartment she left open and drew the door shut behind him.

He was in pitch darkness. He could see no priest or anything else. And anything he had heard of confession got all muddled up in his mind. He knelt to the right-hand wall and said: "Bless me,

Father, for I have sinned. This is my first confession." Nothing happened. He repeated it louder. Still it gave no answer. He turned to the opposite wall, genuflected first, then again went on his knees and repeated the charm. This time he was certain he would receive a reply, but none came. He repeated the process with the remaining wall without effect. He had the feeling of someone with an unfamiliar machine, of pressing buttons at random. And finally the thought struck him that God knew. God knew about the bad confession he intended to make and had made him deaf and blind so that he could neither hear nor see the priest.

Then as his eyes grew accustomed to the blackness, he perceived something he had not noticed previously: a sort of a shelf at about the height of his head. The purpose of this eluded him for a moment. Then he understood. It was for kneeling on.

He had always prided himself upon his powers of climbing, but this took it out of him. There was no foothold. He slipped twice before he succeeded in getting his knee on it, and the strain of drawing the rest of his body up was almost more than he was capable of. However, he did at last get his two knees on it, there was just room for those, but his legs hung down uncomfortably and the edge of the shelf bruised his shins. He joined his hands and pressed the last remaining button. "Bless me, Father, for I have sinned. This is my first confession."

At the same moment the slide was pushed back and a dim light streamed into the little box. There was an uncomfortable silence, and then an alarmed voice asked, "Who's there?" Jackie found it almost impossible to speak into the grille which was on a level with his knees, but he got a firm grip of the molding above it, bent his head down and sideways, and as though he were hanging by his feet like a monkey found himself looking almost upside down at the priest. But the priest was looking sideways at him, and Jackie, whose knees were being tortured by this new position, felt it was a queer way to hear confessions.

" 'Tis me, Father," he piped, and then, running all his words together in excitement, he rattled off, "Bless me, Father, for I have sinned. This is my first confession."

"What?" exclaimed a deep and angry voice, and the sombre

soutaned figure stood bolt upright, disappearing almost entirely from Jackie's view. "What does this mean? What are you doing there? Who are you?" And with the shock Jackie felt his hands lose their grip and his legs their balance. He discovered himself tumbling into space, and, falling, he knocked his head against the door, which shot open and permitted him to thump right into the centre of the aisle. Straight on this came a small, dark-haired priest with a biretta well forward on his head. At the same time Nora came skeltering madly down the church.

"Lord God!" she cried. "The snivelling little caffler! I knew he'd do it! I knew he'd disgrace me!"

Jackie received a clout over the ear which reminded him that for some strange reason he had not yet begun to cry and that people might possibly think he wasn't hurt at all. Nora slapped him again.

"What's this? What's this?" cried the priest. "Don't attempt to beat the child, you little vixen!"

"I can't do me pinance with him," cried Nora shrilly, cocking a shocked eye on the priest. "He have me driven mad. Stop your crying, you dirty scut! Stop it now or I'll make you cur at the other side of your ugly puss!"

"Run away out of this, you little Jade!" growled the priest. He suddenly began to laugh, took out a pocket handkerchief, and wiped Jackie's nose. "You're not hurt, sure you're not. Show us the ould head. . . . Ah, 'tis nothing. 'Twill be better before you're twice married. . . . So you were coming to confession?"

"I was, Father."

"A big fellow like you should have terrible sins. Is it your first?"

" 'Tis, Father."

"Oh, my, worse and worse! Here, sit down there and wait till I get rid of these ould ones and we'll have a long chat. Never mind that sister of yours."

With a feeling of importance that glowed through his tears Jackie waited. Nora stuck out her tongue at him, but he didn't even bother to reply. A great feeling of relief was welling up in him. The sense of oppression that had been weighing him down for a week, the knowledge that he was about to make a bad confession, disappeared. Bad confession, indeed! He had made friends, made friends with the priest, and the priest expected, even demanded, terrible sins.

Oh, women! It was all women and girls and their silly talk. They had no real knowledge of the world!

And when the time came for him to make his confession he did not beat about the bush. He may have clenched his hands and lowered his eyes, but wouldn't anyone?

"Father," he said huskily, "I made it up to kill me grandmother."

There was a moment's pause. Jackie did not dare to look up, but he could feel the priest's eyes on him. The priest's voice also seemed a trifle husky.

"Your grandmother?" he asked, but he didn't after all sound very angry.

"Yes, Father."

"And why did you want to kill her?"

"Oh, God, Father, she's a horrible woman!"

"Is she now?"

"She is, Father."

"What way is she horrible?"

Jackie paused to think. It was hard to explain.

"She takes snuff, Father."

"Oh, my!"

"And she goes round in her bare feet, Father."

"Tut-tut-tut!"

"She's a horrible woman, Father," said Jackie with sudden earnestness. "She takes porter. And she ates the potatoes off the table with her hands. And me mother do be out working most days, and since that one came 'tis she gives us our dinner and I can't ate the dinner." He found himself sniffling. "And she gives pinnies to Nora and she doesn't give no pinnies to me because she knows I can't stand her. And me father sides with her, Father, and he hates me, and me heart is broken and wan night in bed I made it up the way I'd kill her."

Jackie began to sob again, rubbing his nose with his sleeve, as he remembered his wrongs.

"And what way were you going to kill her?" asked the priest smoothly.

"With a hatchet, Father."

"When she was in bed?"

"No, Father."

"How, so?"

"When she ates the potatoes and drinks the porter she falls asleep, Father."

"And you'd hit her then?"

"Yes, Father."

"Wouldn't a knife be better?"

" 'Twould, Father, only I'd be afraid of the blood."

"Oh, of course. I never thought of the blood."

"I'd be afraid of that, Father. I near hit Nora with the bread knife one time she came after me under the table, only I was afraid."

"You're a terrible child," said the priest with awe.

"I am, Father," said Jackie noncommittally, sniffling back his tears.

"And what would you do with the body?"

"How, Father?"

"Wouldn't someone see her and tell?"

"I was going to cut her up with a knife and take away the pieces and bury them. I could get an orange box for three pence and make a cart to take them away."

"My, my," said the priest. "You had it all well planned."

"Ah, I tried that," said Jackie with mounting confidence. "I borrowed a cart and practised it by meself one night after dark."

"And you weren't afraid?"

"Ah, no," said Jackie half-heartedly. "Only a bit."

"You have terrible courage," said the priest. "There's a lot of people I want to get rid of, but I'm not like you. I'd never have the courage. And hanging is an awful death."

"Is it?" asked Jackie, responding to the brightness of a new theme.

"Oh, an awful blooming death!"

"Did you ever see a fellow hanged?"

"Dozens of them, and they all died roaring."

"Jay!" said Jackie.

"They do be swinging out of them for hours and the poor fellows lepping and roaring, like bells in a belfry, and then they put lime on them to burn them up. Of course, they pretend they're dead but sure, they don't be dead at all."

"Jay!" said Jackie again.

"So if I were you I'd take my time and think about it. In my opinion 'tisn't worth it, not even to get rid of a grandmother. I asked dozens of fellows like you that killed their grandmothers about it, and they all said, 'No, 'twasn't worth it.' . . ."

Nora was waiting in the yard. The sunlight struck down on her across the high wall and its brightness made his eyes dazzle. "Well?" she asked. "What did he give you?"

"Three Hail Marys."

"You mustn't have told him anything."

"I told him everything," said Jackie confidently.

"What did you tell him?"

"Things you don't know."

"Bah! he gave you three Hail Marys because you were a cry baby!"

Jackie didn't mind. He felt the world was very good. He began to whistle as well as the hindrance in his jaw permitted.

"What are you sucking?"

"Bull's eyes."

"Was it he gave them to you?"

" 'Twas."

"Almighty God!" said Nora. "Some people have all the luck. I might as well be a sinner like you. There's no use in being good."

PAUL J. PHELAN

Advice to Font Parents *

Everybody goes daffy over baby's first tooth, baby's first word and baby's first step. But not everybody seems so happy about baby's

* This article was written at the special request of Mabel Greene, *New York Sun* fashion editor, for a "Mothers-to-be" section in 1946. Statistics had shown the birth rate that post-war year was the highest in U.S. history.

first name. Well, anyway, it's said that seventy-five per cent of the people in the country wish that their "given" names had never been given.

Next time you meet a fellow named D. John Jones, ask him about that "D." If you're a dear friend, and can duck quickly, he may soften up and confide that the "D" stands for Derwillinger. The real story behind many a lost weekend has never been told.

A lot of this moniker misery could be done away with. Parents should become cognomen conscious. When fond parents become font parents they should be ready for their baptism of fire. Some day a little tyke, about to be christened Oswaldo, will look the priest right in the eye and blurt out: "Quit your kidding!" To forestall such a *Dies Irae* in the baptistry is my purpose here.

Are we Americans jellyfish? It's true that babies are arriving about one every three minutes in a city like New York and that distraught parents have a mere forty-eight hours to put a name on a birth certificate. But a London mother, with all her troubles, took time to give her daughter not one puny little name but twenty-six, beginning with Amelia and ending with Zenus.

Sometimes naming a baby is admittedly tough. When number 14 came along the Bowens of Iowa called him "Finis." When number 15 came they were stuck. Finally they called him "Postscript."

The place where the baby is born will frequently suggest a name. A baby born in a lifeboat was named after the boat, Vigna. A boy born in a midwestern flood was called Noah. Of course Westchester Hospital Smith might not sound too well. Naming babies after a city or town helps. Years ago in England, Philadelphia was a popular name for girls. In our own country we have Sioux City Sue. But, again, think twice before winding up with Low Point Junction O'Reilly.

An intelligent squint at the surname will give ideas. Your last name is Vine? How about Wistaria Vine, or Clinging Vine. And if you are of the California glamour set, Hollywood-and Vine. The last name is Green? How about Vera Green? Then, of course, Candy Barr and Lucky Starr. And if you have a colorful last name why not a colorful first name. Thus, Rinso White or Reckitts Blue. A man in Australia once thought his daughter was not glamorous enough, and called her Poore Pickens.

Our Puritan ancestors, swell people though they were, were very somber and gave names like Humility Bradford, Hate-Evil Scott, Elected Mitchell and Kill-Sin Williams. Down South Africa way, in Nyasaland, the young native couples like to pick European names. One tribe for a long while used publishers' catalogues as source books. Their chieftain is named Oxford University Press. And speaking of book learning, in Louisiana Mr. and Mrs. Stanley Bardwell called one son Duke and the other Loyola, after favorite universities. One day some parents will better them by coming up with a Kansas State Teachers Graduate School Class of 1915 Cum Laude McCorkle.

Current events will often provide the spark for a name. A Texas man named Ford called his latest son V-8. A Bronx man, in the 1930's, named his daughter Norma Depression Jacobson. Another man was said to have called his son Prosperity, figuring he'd never get lonesome because his son would always be just around the corner.

A Brooklyn man named Doe gave his son the name John, which was, naturally, entirely legal. During the war, a sergeant called his baby Points, a young lady out west was named Invasia Renfrow and a California girl got the title Dee Day Edwards.

It's good to give names that are not too difficult to spell. A former Manhattan baker got writer's cramp every time he wrote his name: Leiansszuieusszesses Willihiminizzileizzii Hurrizzissteizzii. His co-workers called him Leo Ward.

A Southern boy who was inducted into the Army said that he couldn't remember his name. Before the hurriedly summoned psychiatrist arrived, the youngster explained that his name was so lengthy he had to carry it written on a card. The card said: "Daniel Wisdom May I Know Faith and Spirit Chose John's Divine Communion Field Moses Meekness and Joshua Zeal Wins the Day and Conquer All Murphy." His buddies were glad when they could soon call him "Sarge."

Another thing to remember is initials. No one wants his son to be an H.O.G. or his daughter an S.A.P. Of course with girls it's difficult because a girl, by marriage, may leave a G.A.P. in one family to become a G.A.G. in another.

Psychologists say that certain names call up certain pictures. Rightly or wrongly, people picture Richard as handsome but a sissy; Edward as friendly; Joan as young and good-looking; Adrian as artistic; Thomas as conservative; and Harry, of course, as a person who wears glasses and plays the piano.

Here's a confidential tip. All parents want their babies to be one in a million. Then why do they give them names like Mary, which is one in twenty-four, or Elizabeth, which is one in twenty-seven. There are 6,000,000 Marys in the United States, according to one source, and 4,000,000 Johns; and James, George, Charles and William account for 20,000,000. Which seems to prove, by the way, that every Tom, Dick and Harry isn't named Tom, Dick or Harry.

Everybody knows that naming a baby takes more diplomacy than running a meeting of the United Nations Security Council. In naming a baby there are Uncle Wilbur, and Aunt Kate, and Cousin Aldawillda and sister Authelia, and mommy's mom and pop, and daddy's mom and pop, and mommy's grandmom and grandpop, and daddy's grandmom and grandpop, and the best man, and the maid of honor, and the flower girls, and the ushers, and the waiters at the reception, and the taxi driver, and the train conductor who was so nice on the honeymoon.

One solution for the whole business might be to give all babies numbers. In this way we would have baby No. 1 of family group 637,856, U.S.A. Another solution would be that of Mr. and Mrs. Joseph Cody of San Pedro, California. They're permitting their baby to pick his own name when he grows up. But this makes it tough on baby, who, in addition to those named above, will have two added starters to argue with, mother and dad.

Out of the Mouths . . .

(These anecdotes are from the humor page of *The Apostle* magazine, which has the best such page of any Catholic magazine which has come to my attention. Thomas Lahey's yarn is from his column "Bits Out of Life" in *Ave Maria* magazine.)

And there's the street urchin who remarked to his little companion, seated beside him on the curb: "Gee, I'll bet in heaven they think I'm dead. I haven't said my prayers for a week!"

Little Mary (saying her night prayers): "Dear Lord, I know I'm a bad girl, and I do wish you would help me to be better, and if at first you don't succeed, try, try again."

Pastor: "So, Johnny, I hear that God has sent you two more little brothers."

Johnny: "Yes, and He knows where the money's coming from. I heard Daddy say so."

The story is told of the little girl who, when she was asked by her mother to repeat the text of her pastor's sermon, replied: "Our pastor's text was, 'Don't get scared, you'll get your quilt.'" It was only when an elder sister had been questioned that the text was identified as: "Fear not; the Comforter will come." — Thomas Lahey.

As everyone knows, Dominican priests celebrate Holy Mass according to the rite of their Order, which varies slightly from the accustomed rite we see in our churches.

One such Dominican priest was celebrating Mass in a city parish, where he was visiting. At the beginning of the Mass, he turned and whispered to the altar boy, "Bring me the water and wine."

The altar boy, with long experience at serving Mass in the accustomed way, was only momentarily startled by the untimely request.

With an air of great understanding, he leaned over and whispered consolingly to the priest, "Don't you worry, Father, I'll tell you when it's time."

2. GUNS AND GUFFAWS

2. GUNS AND GUFFAWS

*"Theirs was the glee of martial breast
And laughter theirs at little jest."*

— From "Marmion"
by Sir Walter Scott

War is inhuman. But it has its human side. Even in a push button war somebody might push the wrong button. The G.I.'s guns may change, but his guffaws will always be of the same general issue. In this section you'll find a special "detail" of military mirth-makers, American and British, of the vintage of World War II. The American serviceman's humor is best described as ham on wry, with plenty of mustard. It gains its objective by a frontal assault, and doesn't bother to wait until it sees the whites of their eyes. It talks out of the side of its mouth the way Joe McCarthy does when he explains that being lost in a jungle isn't so bad: "You will be glad to learn that you have much less chance of catching poison ivy in the average jungle than you have around Lake Winnepesaukee, New Hampshire." James O'Neill savagely tears apart APO packages and strews the contents over the landscape, filling in the gaps between the ruins with raucous remarks like the one describing hard candies from home as "dextrose blockbusters." Tom Shehan gives a hard-boiled account of a hard-boiled guy whose methods, like the American soldier's humor, weren't very subtle.

Messrs. McCarthy, O'Neill and Shehan, by the way, were staff members of the Army weekly *Yank*. However, being on *Yank* didn't mean you were a "pencil-pusher." *Yank* reporters were officially newspapermen but when they went overseas they carried a field pack and a Garand. If their plane was attacked they dropped

37

their pencils and grabbed machine guns. These writers got their humor straight off a mud-soiled cuff, right out of the side of a heat-parched mouth. Mr. McCarthy, for example, was the managing editor of *Yank* for two and one half years, and was given the Legion of Merit Award for his successful efforts. But he knew what it was to lug 75 mm. pack howitzers onto a beach during an invasion.

This trio's sketches help reveal the composite "humorous" American soldier of World War II. He is a fellow who never reads anything except beer bottle labels and the *Daily Racing Form*. He's a cynical goldbricker who'll hide in the eaves of a tent to escape work, even though that's more work than the work. He is always being needled, literally and figuratively. He hates KP, MP, stingy supply sergeants and prepared goody-goody packages from the home front. He likes week-end passes. He also likes "one Lana Turner and one case of Scotch," or better yet "one Scotch and one case of Jane Russells."

The American serviceman also has his serious moments. H. I. Phillips writes cleverly of how the soldiers want to make sure that the statesmen's postwar aims hit the bull's-eye as accurately as the soldiers did during the conflict. Private Purkey, that fugitive from a gasoline filling station and the first comic soldier of World War II, waged a terrific war, and when peace came quickly reconverted and started waging a terrific peace. He didn't want the war aims to be endangered by "leaks in noble hopes, confusion in objectives, back-sliding and signs of a heavy frost on high ideals."

Some of our English cousins are also lined up in uniform in this section. Their humor is not as earthy as the Americans'. J. B. Morton's story of the "belle of the Southern Command" skillfully combines subtle irony with the broad strokes of a mad, hilarious melodrama. A note of subdued sarcasm is evident in Compton Mackenzie's picture of the home front. He shows what a flutter the hunt for a suitable pigeon officer gives the Home Guard commander on the island of Little Todday which was in about as much danger of invasion from Hitler as Jackson Hole, Wyoming. Mr. Mackenzie, in that mild way the English have, gives home-front goings-on the bird. Bruce Marshall's Colonel Nicobar is with the British Army of Occupation in Austria. The occupation army was sort of like the Home Guard abroad, old chap. That may help to explain how the colonel, not a religious man, suddenly found himself an unwilling airborne missionary and aide to a determined Austrian nun. She made him fly her to Rome to get the Pope to get the hierarchy to get down to earth in speaking the truths of Christianity. Mr. Marshall's is high-flying hilarity.

JOSEPH McCARTHY

How To Get Lost in a Jungle *

Everybody in the Army seems to be writing handy pocket guides these days telling you How to Keep from Getting Lost in a Jungle. These books are all right but a lot of my friends are not reading them. In the first place, my friends never read anything, anyway, except beer bottle labels and the *Daily Racing Form*. In the second place, my friends are all goldbrickers and they don't want handy pocket guides that tell them how to keep from getting lost. All they want is to get lost, as soon as possible.

"The thicker the jungle the better," one of them remarked the other day, squeezing himself into the barrel of his M1 when the first sergeant approached to select a detail.

So my friends have requested, through channels, that I write a piece about How to Get Lost in a Jungle. They couldn't have picked a better man.

I happen to be an expert on getting lost. I spent most of the Carolina Maneuvers in 1941 at the top of the center pole in my pyramidal tent, where nobody could find me when there was a truck to be unloaded. As a matter of fact, I would have beaten Ship-

---

* Reprinted from the work, *The Best from Yank,* the Army weekly, copyright 1945, by Franklin S. Forsberg. By permission of E. P. Dutton & Co., Inc., publishers.

wreck Kelly's old record one week but a certain corporal, who shall be nameless, set the tent on fire and smoked me out.

I also happen to be an expert on jungles. I spent most of my summers as a youngster in a jungle near the Gillette razor blade factory in South Boston, Mass.

The first thing to remember if you want to get lost in a jungle is not to lose your head. There are a lot of head hunters in the jungles. If you put your head down somewhere for a minute while you are washing your feet or pressing your pants, a head hunter is liable to pick it up and walk off with it.

And don't be afraid of a jungle. A lot of soldiers get nervous when they find themselves in a jungle and notice that it has no traffic lights or sewers. But the jungle is really your friend. It provides heaps and heaps of food which can be found in the form of animals and plants. It also provides malaria mosquitoes, leeches, snakes, crocodiles and nettles but there is no need to go into that now. However, you will be glad to learn that you have much less chance of catching poison ivy in the average jungle than you have around Lake Winnepesaukee, New Hampshire. Here is another bit of good news about jungles: it hardly ever snows there, so the chances are you won't be liable to slip on an icy sidewalk and hurt yourself.

I see that the T-5 down there in the fifth row with the Good Conduct ribbon and the whistle has a question. Would you mind speaking a little louder, bully? You say you want to know what kinds of food in the jungle are safe to eat?

Well, my fine chowhound, my advice to you is to make the acquaintanceship of some young monkey about your own age who knows the neighborhood. Just watch what he eats. Then follow his example and you'll make out okay. But be careful about the kind of monkey he is before you start associating with him. Be sure he doesn't drink too much or run around with loose women. Many a careless GI in the jungle has been led to rack and ruin by hanging out with the wrong type of monkey.

Now let me see, where was I?

Oh, yes. The best way to get lost in a jungle is to get rid of your compass. I wouldn't recommend this, however, because the supply sergeant may get nasty and swear out a statement of charges to be deducted from your next month's pay. Pawning the compass wouldn't do either. You might get grabbed for hocking government property and sent to Leavenworth to cool off for a few years. But then again, if you want to look at the bright side of it, Leavenworth is an excellent place to get lost in, too. Even better than a jungle because it has no malaria mosquitoes.

I find the best way to get lost is to ask directions from an MP. Simply go where he tells you to go and, in no time at all, you won't have the slightest idea of where you are.

But be careful about crossing state lines. Even though we are at war, don't forget that they are still able to get you for violations of the Mann Act.

That covers about everything except malaria mosquitoes and the natives. The best remedy for mosquitoes is to burn punks. This is getting rather difficult to do now because most of the punks in the Army have either gone to OCS or have been released under the 38-year-old law.

There is no need to try to cover the natives. They have been walking around without clothes all their lives so you can't expect them to do anything different.

In closing, I suggest that you bring this page with you next time you feel like getting lost in a jungle. It might come in handy to light a fire with.

COMPTON MACKENZIE

The Pigeon-Officer

Captain Paul Waggett was preoccupied with the little problems of organization and equipment and correspondence that during the Second World War kept company commanders of the Home Guard in a condition of patriotic deediness, and the red, white, and blue of their morale from browning off.

There was the question of the pigeon-officer, for instance. It began with one of those light-hearted little enquiries on tissue paper sent round to all company commanders of the 8th Inverness-shire Battalion, Homeguard:

> Please recommend a suitable pigeon-officer for the company under your command.
>
> C. B. Grant
> Capt. and Adj.

Captain Waggett smiled sadly. He was on the point of replying that there was no suitable pigeon-officer on either Great or Little Todday when on Saturday May 31st a priority telegram was received at Snorvig:

> Reference my F. A. 562/233 of May 27 Please hasten your reply because sub-stratum of command are pressing for an answer.
>
> Hog
> Fort Augustus

Captain Waggett went to the telephone. "Put me through to Mr. Beaton at Bobanish, please . . . hullo, is that you, Mr. Beaton? . . . yes, Captain Waggett speaking . . . I had very nice letters from the Brigadier and the Colonel to say how much they had enjoyed their stay here . . . yes, very pleased, I think . . . but what I rang up for was to ask if you knew anything about pigeons . . . you don't? . . . you wouldn't care to make yourself responsible for a pigeon-cot at Bobanish? . . . no, it's a military matter. I expect it means Hitler is on the move again . . . you feel you have enough to look after without making yourself responsible for pigeons . . . quite . . . yes, I sympathize, Mr. Beaton . . . you don't think Mrs. Beaton would undertake the responsibility? . . . yes, of course, fowls do take up a lot of time and she has such splendid eggs . . . no, we've been finding it rather difficult this year to get as many as we should like . . . oh, that's extremely kind of Mrs. Beaton. Mrs. Waggett will be delighted . . . perhaps you'd give them to Donald Ian when the lorry . . . three dozen? . . . Oh, I'll call for them myself with the car . . . thank you very much. . . . No, I quite understand about the pigeons."

He rang off.

"Is Mrs. Beaton going to let us have some eggs?" Mrs. Waggett asked brightly.

"Three dozen, but she won't undertake these pigeons. I think I'll try the banker."

He picked up the receiver again. "Put me on to Mr. Thomson at the Bank, please . . . Hullo, this is Captain Waggett. I wonder if by any chance you like pigeons, Mr. Thomson? . . . no, no, no, not to eat. Western Sub-Stratum Command want a pigeon-officer for the Toddays. If you understood the job I think I could obtain commissioned rank for you . . . I see, you'd rather remain an N.C.O. . . . no, I'm afraid I don't exactly know what we're going to do with the pigeons when they do arrive . . . I take it they're intended for messages if our communications are cut . . . no, perhaps they won't be much use . . . I was going to suggest that to Fort Augustus. But I've had an urgent telegram from them and I must try to find somebody."

"Wouldn't Mr. Thomson do anything to help, Paul?" Mrs. Waggett asked when her husband rang off.

"I think it's Mrs. Thomson," he said darkly.

Mrs. Waggett sighed. "Strange how disobliging people can be. I should have thought, knowing how much you have to do, Mr. Thomson would have welcomed an opportunity to help. Without any children and without any fowls I should have thought Mrs. Thomson would have rushed at the idea of looking after pigeons."

"I suppose it's those cats of hers," he said.

"I think people who keep three great cats at a time like this deserve to be invaded. What would Mrs. Thomson do if she had three evacuees battening on her like poor Gladys?"

"Don't work yourself up old lady. I'll try Norman Macleod." He picked up the receiver again. "Watasett schoolhouse please.

Oh, is that you, Catriona? Is your brother about? . . . he's gone fishing? . . . Fishing where? . . . well, of course strictly speaking he ought to get permission from me whatever he's fishing for in Loch Sleeport . . . I was going to ask him if he knew anything about pigeons . . . oh, he shot two yesterday, did he? . . . no, I daresay, he didn't suppose I would object . . . yes, I know they're destructive . . . but it's the principle of the thing, Catriona. I do want people to understand that I pay rent to the Department of Agriculture for all the shooting and fishing in both islands and if your brother starts shooting pigeons without asking my permission somebody else will be shooting grouse . . . no, I'm sure he wouldn't dream of shooting grouse . . . well, I was going to ask him if he would like to gain a pip . . . pip . . . no, no, p-i-p — pip . . . become a second lieutenant . . . no, of course I understand you don't know what he'd like . . . but it would be a question of keeping pigeons . . . it's a Home Guard business . . . yes, very well, I'll ring again when he comes in."

Waggett hung up the receiver.

"She's an awfully stupid girl, Catriona Macleod. I couldn't make her understand what a pip was. She thought I was talking about a pipe. But I shan't recommend Norman Macleod to be a pigeon-officer. With his communistic ideas he'll just make it an excuse to start poaching again. Catriona said he was out for lythe, but I don't trust him. If he caught a sea-trout he'd eat it in a flash. I did hope that making him a sergeant in the Home Guard would cure him of poaching, but I'm afraid he can't be trusted. It's very discouraging."

"All these communists are alike, Paul," said his wife.

"I'm afraid you're right old lady," he sighed, with a pessimistic shake of the head. "Well, there's only George Campbell left. He's not really fit for commissioned rank, but I suppose I ought to give him the chance."

Captain Waggett picked up the receiver once more. "Put me through to Carrybou schoolhouse, please . . . hullo . . . oh, is that you, Mrs. Campbell . . . is George in? . . . it's Captain Waggett speaking . . . he's working in the garden? . . . would it be too much trouble to ask him to come and speak with me? . . . well, it's about his taking on the responsibility for the pigeons we

have to keep for the Home Guard . . . oh, I beg your pardon
. . . oh, yes, certainly the pigeons would have to be fed . . . on
Sunday? . . . Of course, like every other day . . . well, so far
as feeding pigeons is concerned, Mrs. Campbell, Sunday *is* like
every day. You feed your fowls on Sunday, don't you? . . . Well,
I really can't indulge in a theological argument over the telephone,
Mrs. Campbell . . . if you object to your son's being made pigeon-
officer we'll say no more about it . . . yes, yes, . . . but I don't
want to listen to grumbles about the Home Guard. You ought to
feel very glad that George hasn't been called up."

Captain Waggett cut off abruptly.

"That woman is quite impossible, Dolly. Quite impossible. Well,
if the Germans ever do come to Great Todday I hope they'll come
on Sunday, that's all I've got to say. I don't know what to do about
this pigeon-officer. Do you think Doctor Maclaren would take it
on?"

"Oh, Paul, it would only end in more trouble between you and
him. I don't think that's a practical suggestion. I don't really."

"Well, shall I ask Alec Mackinnon?"

Mrs. Waggett shook her head. "He's so resentful of you, Paul.
If you gave him this pigeon business to do they'd become his pigeons
at once, and you'd never have any say in them."

"If the chicks were here," said their father, "I'd offer to take on
the pigeons myself. I suppose you . . ."

"Oh, please, Paul," his wife begged. "You know I'll do anything
I can, but I don't think I *can* undertake pigeons."

"Very well," he said in a resigned voice. "I'll have to wire Fort
Augustus that I can't recommend anybody here as a pigeon-officer."

And this telegram had no sooner been sent off than a telegram
arrived from Fort Augustus to cancel their previous telegram because Western Sub-Stratum Command had decided that owing to
the need for conserving shipping space no pigeons could be sent to
the islands.

"All that trouble for nothing," Waggett commented sadly.
"However, we *must* remember there's a war on."

BRUCE MARSHALL

The Unwilling Missionary

With its blue leather upholstery and streamline scarlet chassis, the general's car had plenty of sex-appeal, but luckily it had speed as well, for the colonel required it if he was going to get back to the convent, pack, and arrive out at the airfield at Schwechat in time for the departure of the aeroplane.

When he arrived at the convent, he found that his batman, as usual, had gone up to barracks on some probably frivolous errand, but Schwester Kasimira heard him come in and volunteered to help him with his packing. He was standing with his overcoat open helping her to bundle things into his suitcase when Reverend Mother Auxilia, passing along the corridor, heard their excited voices and came in to enquire what was happening.

"The Herr Oberst is going to Rome," Schwester Kasimira explained, as she squeezed the toothpaste up from the bottom of the colonel's tube and screwed the top on properly. "Is it not wonderful? Perhaps he will have time to see the Holy Father. Perhaps even God will give him a great grace and he will be converted, although I have been hearing that Rome is not a very good place for being converted in, which is hard to understand, since Almighty God willed that the Head of His Church should live there."

"Is this true, Herr Oberst?" Reverend Mother Auxilia asked.

"Unfortunately, yes, Reverend Mother," the colonel said, trying to straighten out a leg of his pyjamas which had become entangled inside the other. "A beastly conference. General's orders. And I don't know how long I'll be away. Plane leaves Schwechat at eleven hundred hours which doesn't give a chap much time. Sometimes I wish these highly paid officers would be a little more considerate. Can't even take my batman with me. I don't suppose I'd be allowed to, anyway, but even if I were I couldn't because as usual the little shocker's nowhere to be found. Oh, I know he's got an immortal soul, Reverend Mother, but at this moment I'd appreciate the fact a little more if I had the power to call down punishment on it."

"In that case, Herr Oberst, I shall be your batboy," Reverend Mother Auxilia said.

"Decent of you, Reverend Mother," the colonel said. "I'm sure you'd do a much better job of work than that cigarette-sucking scum McCosh."

"I mean, Herr Oberst, that I am coming with you to Rome," Reverend Mother said.

"Eh?" the colonel said.

"I mean, Herr Oberst, that I am coming with you on that aeroplane to Rome," Reverend Mother Auxilia said.

"Look here, Reverend Mother, that's quite impossible," the colonel said. "You don't understand. The authorities would never hear of it."

"I am going to see His Holiness the Pope," Reverend Mother Auxilia said. "In 1585 our Holy Founder flew to Rome to see Pope Sixtus the Fifth; in 1946 I am going to fly to Rome to see Pope Pius the Twelfth."

"Look here, Reverend Mother, a joke's a joke, I know, but you don't seem to understand that I've to get a move on," the colonel said.

"What you do not seem to be understanding, Herr Oberst, is that I am not joking," Reverend Mother said and walked out of the room.

She didn't appear to be either, for when he got downstairs the colonel found her sitting in the back of the general's car, with a small black travelling bag on her knee.

"You see, I have not kept you waiting, Herr Oberst," she said.

The colonel was in a quandary. He could not very well ask the driver to eject her from the car nor could he eject her himself. It was also unlikely that the nuns, who were her spiritual subordinates, would be willing to help him. And it was already half-past ten, which did not give him too much time if he were to reach the aerodrome by eleven. And Reverend Mother was a big bulky woman and she looked very much as if she were determined to go on sitting there.

"Look here, Reverend Mother, for the last time," he said.

"I quite agree, Herr Oberst: for the last time," Reverend Mother Auxilia said.

"Please to be taking Reverend Mother with you, Herr Oberst," Schwester Kasimira began to plead. *"Bitte schon,* Herr Oberst, *bitte schon."*

"It seems that I shall have to be taking her to the aerodrome anyway, and even for that I shall probably get into trouble," the colonel said, tossing his suitcase in beside the driver and himself getting in beside the Reverend Mother Auxilia. "If this is your idea of spiritual whoopee, Reverend Mother, I am afraid it is not mine."

"Gute reise, gute reise," Schwester Kasimira said, waving her hand as the car drove off.

This time the colonel did not shout *"Verfluchte Schweinbunde!"* at the tramcar-drivers, although they blocked his way several times, because he was too angry with Reverend Mother Auxilia to bother about tramcars. He sat there, huddled in his overcoat, wondering what he would do with her on his arrival at the aerodrome and whether it would be quite in form for him to send her back home again in the general's car.

"I am understanding that you are very angry with me, Herr Oberst, but perhaps you will not be so angry when I shall have explained," Reverend Mother began as they shot across the Schwarzenbergplatz and turned up the Rennweg. "You have been complaining since a long time that the cardinals and bishops of the Church have not spoken out the true things of the Christian religion in words that the common and sorrowing people of the earth could understand. You have said even that was one of the reasons that you were not being a Christian. And the Russian colonel has been saying the same things and the brother of Schwester Kasimira also has been saying the same things, so that I have been forced to believe you. That is what I am going to be saying to the Pope when I am reminding His Holiness of the visit that our Holy Founder, Saint Walburga of Graz, paid to his predecessor in 1585. I am going to be asking His Holiness to be saying one clear very much all out thing which will make simple the gospel of Christ to those who are needing so badly to accept His teaching and to become good."

"Reverend Mother, I know, I know," the colonel said. "I appreciate all you say, but what you're asking me to do is quite impossible."

"Please to be reflecting a little, Herr Oberst," Reverend Mother Auxilia went on. "Please to be thinking of all the unhappy people in the war, please to be thinking of all the men like yourself and like Colonel Piniev and like the brother of Schwester Kasimira, who are wanting to see the light, but who are not seeing it, because the Pope and his cardinals and bishops have not been holding Christ's lamp at the right angle, so that communists and Russians and Chinese and South Americans and even Japanians and everybody else shall understand and so there shall be no more unkindness and hurt and fire and wandering families on the earth. Please to be reflecting a little, Herr Oberst."

The colonel allowed himself to be tempted for a moment. After all, big things always came from small beginnings. Hitler and Mussolini had been small bad beginnings. Why shouldn't Reverend Mother Auxilia be a small good beginning? Why shouldn't she, like Saint Francis and Saint Ignatius Loyola and Saint Theresa of Avila, and perhaps like her Holy Founder, Saint Walburga of Graz, before her, shake up the sloth of the Universal Church, which, when all was said and done, could provide the only alternative to communism and the atom bomb. Civilisation was threatened as never before in history. Only one thing could save it: the conscious pursuit of goodness by at least a majority of the world's inhabitants. And if the Pope were really to put the skids under his bishops, priests, and deacons . . . He pulled himself up quickly. The thing wasn't within his terms of reference, as Brigadier Catlock would say.

"Reverend Mother, please believe that I would do all in my power to help you in such a mission, but that it is strictly outside my competence to get you a seat on that plane to Rome," he said. "Hang it all, the brigadier had to arrange my own passage."

"Herr Oberst, Almighty God will get me on the aeroplane," Reverend Mother Auxilia said.

There was no answer to that one, the colonel decided, as they entered the Russian Zone and swung out under the wooden arch-way onto the highroad. As they overtook lorries packed with Russian soldiers standing up like pencils in a box, he longed for a discipline to come to the world, so that men might know that the more they pursued their own ends, the less they would attain them. The dis-senting manufacturers in England in the early nineteenth century had not, in the first instances at any rate, amassed wealth because they sought it; they had amassed wealth because their religion had made them industrious. He was still thinking about the dissenting manufacturers in the early nineteenth century when the car rode through the ruins of Schwechat to a standstill in front of the aero-drome, where an aircraftsman was walking about with his hat on and with a cigarette dangling from his lips. His unsoldierlike ap-pearance made the colonel so angry that his eyes were poaching up to a recriminatory size long before the young pilot officer ap-proached.

"Here's your ticket, sir," the officer said. "Aircraft's ready. We were just ticking over till you came." He motioned in the direction of an aeroplane, standing about fifty yards away.

"Who is that woozy scalawag over there?" the colonel thundered, brandishing his stick at the untidy aircraftsman. "Look here, young man, I know the R.A.F.'s done a fine job of work and that we shouldn't have won the war without you, but can't you get that chap to understand that he's scarcely contributing to the prestige of the Empire by wandering around looking like a scruffy organ-grinder. For one thing, we're in an ex-enemy country, inhabited by people who've been used to the discipline of the German army, and for another, this is the Russian Zone and it's scarcely a good advertise-ment to the Soviets."

"I know, sir, but my wrong doesn't make your right," the officer said.

"What in the name of Thor and Woden do you mean?" the colonel asked.

"I mean that you've no right to bring unauthorized Austrian civilians on to the airfield," the officer said.

"I beg your pardon," the colonel said.

"That nun in there has no right to be here," the officer said.

"Not only has that nun, as you so rudely term her, a perfect right to be here, but she is also flying with me to Rome," the colonel said, letting his temper swing right out of him. "Look here, young man, do you know who you're talking to?"

A change came over the officer's expression as he looked at the colonel's shoulder straps.

"I beg your pardon, sir, I'm sure," he said. "You see, I hadn't realized and I distinctly understood Brigadier Catlock to say . . . But, of course, it's all right for the lady to go to Rome, if you say that you're willing to take the responsibility."

"Of course I'll take the responsibility," the colonel said.

"And of course you'll have to make things right at the other end," the officer said.

"Of course, I'll make things right at the other end," the colonel said.

"Herr Oberst, I was always telling you that Almighty God would be getting me on the aeroplane," Reverend Mother Auxilia said to the colonel as he stood aside for her to climb up the steps.

Far below them stretched the academic sea, friendly, like a pale blue quilt. Colonel Nicobar and Reverend Mother Auxilia sat side by side in the Dakota, sandwiched in between two layers of Unrra. The colonel was beginning to be sorry that his outburst of temper had led him into the indiscretion of intruding Reverend Mother Auxilia into Italy. He was also beginning to be uncertain as to how he was going to be able to manage her exit from the airfield at Rome and to doubt how far his rashness would contribute to the conversion of the world.

"Ten thousand feet," he said to Reverend Mother Auxilia so that she would not see how disturbed he was.

"Our Holy Founder, Saint Walburga of Graz, flew at twenty thousand feet and she didn't touch down at Udine," Reverend Mother Auxilia said.

The colonel gave it up after that, thankful that it was difficult to talk in an aeroplane, although the Unrra witches behind seemed to be doing their best, yapping away through their big tusky teeth when they weren't too busy guzzling.

"Have a biccy, general," one of the Unrra witches said, leaning over and holding out a paper bag.

"I am sorry, young woman, but I never eat biscuits," the colonel shouted above the roar of the propeller.

"A piece of choccy, then, general?" the Unrra witch persisted.

"I am sorry, young woman, but I never eat chocolate, and what is more I am not a general," the colonel said.

"What does he say, Mildred?" the second Unrra witch said.

"He says that he doesn't like choccy and that he's not a general," the first Unrra witch said.

"*Jawohl,* General, *assolutamente generale,* cross my swords and hope to die," the second Unrra witch said. "Not like choccy? Would you, then, a leetle feesh like?"

"Salmon paste sandwiches," the first Unrra witch explained.

"I wouldn't eat a salmon paste sandwich if I were alone with one on a desert island," the colonel said, and then, looking down at his shoulder straps, saw the dreadful thing that had happened: he was wearing the general's overcoat, which he must, in his hurry to depart, have taken from the peg outside the brigadier's office in mistake for his own. Dismally he understood why the pilot officer at the airfield had not raised more objections when he had insisted on taking Reverend Mother Auxilia with him on the aeroplane. More dismally he knew that nobody would ever believe that he hadn't taken the general's overcoat on purpose. Brigadier Catlock wouldn't believe it. The general himself wouldn't believe it. There'd be no end of a stink. Probably there'd be a court-martial. He'd be lucky if he got off with being reduced to lieutenant-colonel again. He might even be dismissed from the service. There seemed to be no limit to the number of links in the chain of possible catastrophes.

When he had become sufficiently accustomed to his dismay to be able to communicate it to another, he attempted to tell Reverend Mother Auxilia what had happened.

"Reverend Mother, I've been and gone and done it," he said.

"Of course you have, Herr Oberst, but I am still thinking that it was a little Almighty God too," Reverend Mother Auxilia said.

"I mean I have taken the general's overcoat by mistake," the colonel said.

"And is that so very important?" Reverend Mother Auxilia asked. "Surely the general will be able to wear your overcoat until you have returned to Vienna. You must both be the same largeness of man, otherwise it would not have been possible for you to have taken his overcoat by mistake."

"The general's not staying in Vienna," the colonel said. "He's one of those War Box wallahs that swan around putting their fingers in other people's pies. Besides, it's not the overcoat that matters; it's the badges of rank," he tried to explain, pointing to the crossed swords and the crown and the star on his shoulder. "It's like a canon wearing a mitre, if you understand what I mean."

"According to the Ambrosian rite canons are allowed to wear mitres when a bishop is pontificating," Reverend Mother Auxilia said.

"My dear Reverend Mother, this is not the Ambrosian rite, but the British Army," the colonel said. "Don't you understand that I've done a terrible thing? I've laid myself open to the charge of having attempted to pass myself off as a general when I am only a colonel. That's why that silly young pip-squeak allowed me to take you on this aeroplane: because he thought I was a general."

"Herr Oberst, are you wanting to know what I am thinking?" Reverend Mother Auxilia asked. "I am thinking that it wasn't you that took that overcoat by mistake; it was our Holy Founder, Saint Walburga of Graz."

"I'd like to see Brigadier Catlock wearing that one," the colonel said. "Or a court-martial."

"Herr Oberst, I can see that you are not a great believer in the supernatural order," Reverend Mother Auxilia said. "I am repeating, therefore, that it is my opinion that it was our Holy Founder, Saint Walburga of Graz, who inspired you to take your general's overcoat. She was doing so in order that I might fly to Rome, as she has already done in 1585, in order to tell the Holy Father that he must be giving counsel to the nations of the world in a clear and understandable language. Therefore, you will be having no need to worry. Saint Walburga of Graz, who inspired you to take your general's overcoat, will also be inspiring your general to understand why you have been taking his overcoat and even to rejoice that you have taken his overcoat, for so noble and so worthy a purpose. And in any case I shall speak to the Holy Father about it, in order that he may explain to all the people of the earth about your general's overcoat at the same time as he will be explaining to them about leading a good and Christian life."

"But Reverend Mother — " the colonel began.

"Please, Herr Oberst, to be allowing me to be thinking about the important message which I shall soon be delivering to the Holy Father," Reverend Mother said.

Spiralling down over the roofs of Rome, the colonel looked at his watch.

"Just a little over three hours," he said to Reverend Mother Auxilia.

"In 1585, our Holy Founder, Saint Walburga of Graz, did it in under two," Reverend Mother Auxilia said.

———

J. B. MORTON

Geraldine Brazier, W.O.O.F.

"Geraldine Brazier, belle of the Southern Command!" Colonel Fritter's voice trembled with emotion as he gave the toast, and every officer in the mess of the 14th Loyal North West Huntingdonshire Fusiliers knew that he referred to the loveliest W.O.O.F. in the British Army. Yet there was one man who braved the displeasure of his commanding officer and the sneers of his fellows. For Captain Roy Batter-Pudden sat in taciturn silence as the toast was drunk, and heard himself called a prig. And as the port-type circulated more freely and tongues were loosed, the more silent became the Captain.

Geraldine Brazier, the loveliest W.O.O.F. in the British Army, was always doing odd jobs in the camp of the Loyal North West

Huntingdonshire Fusiliers. The officers and the men trusted her implicitly, and her mere presence made them happier. Nobody had any hesitation in talking to her about military matters, since she was so obviously heart and soul in her work. To see the Colonel raise his hat to her on the parade ground was to realize that respect was mingled with admiration. And the adjutant boasted openly that none of his clerks or orderlies knew as much about his private papers as this efficient, serious-minded girl, who turned a blind eye to all attempts at flirtation. It was left to surly Captain Batter-Pudden to mutter that Geraldine was getting to know too much, and was too deeply in the Colonel's confidence. But Batter-Pudden's black looks only earned him the epithet "Curmudgeon."

Often when some important general arrived at Cuddlingham to inspect the battalion the Colonel would say, half in jest, "Oh, sir, you really ought to see our prize W.O.O.F." And the general, stroking his moustache, and wacking his leg with a riding switch, would reply, "Ha! Yes! I've heard of her. Deuced pretty poppet, they tell me." And then Geraldine, simpering somewhat, would be led forward and introduced. And all ranks would cheer to the echo when the general complimented her on her looks. Yet she remained her sweet, innocent, simple self. One day, for instance, the Colonel surprised her reading a strictly private memorandum from the head-quarters of his command. "Naughty, naughty," he said, taking it from her. "I couldn't understand a word of it," said Geraldine. "What does it mean?" "Not for little beauties," replied the Colonel, mightily relieved.

No higher compliment could have been paid to Geraldine Brazier than when the Colonel said one day in the mess, "I really believe she knows where all my confidential documents are better than myself." A murmur of approbation greeted this avowal. But Captain Roy Batter-Pudden was heard to say, "Do we know anything of her antecedents, sir?" The Colonel gaped awkwardly for a moment. Then he said, "Isn't it enough for us that her Commandant, Mrs. Cluckaway, recommended her highly?" It was evidently enough for all of them, except the sombre Batter-Pudden. At this very moment the beautiful W.O.O.F. was making notes from a confidential memorandum that had just arrived. She worked late, and as Batter-

Pudden took his way to his quarters he was surprised to see a light coming from under the door of the Colonel's office.

When Captain Batter-Pudden saw the light under the door of the Colonel's office, and noted that the time was 11:53 P.M. he said to himself, "How odd! How very odd! Who can be working in there at this hour?" Hoping to surprise some diligent, conscientious brother-officer, he approached the door stealthily, on tiptoe. He said to himself, "I will fling the door open and cry 'Boo!' and then laugh at his discomfiture." For Batter-Pudden was a simple-minded man, and fond of elementary jokes.

Creeping up, he laid his hand on the door-handle silently, twisted as though to the manner born, flung it wide and shouted breezily, "Boo!" For answer, the loveliest girl he had ever seen turned swiftly to face him, and he found himself challenged by the gentian-blue eyes of W.O.O.F. Geraldine Brazier.

For a long moment Batter-Pudden and the girl faced each other in silence. The Captain's thoughts raced through his head like bags in a hurricane. He remembered his suspicions of this superb creature, and as he gazed at her he found it hard to believe that she was not as innocent as a prawn. Her arched eyebrows expressed surprise at the intrusion, until the Captain began to feel like some dull clod who has blundered into the boudoir of a delicately nurtured peeress. He moistened his dry lips and shifted on his feet. A slow smile irradiated Geraldine's face. She made no attempt to conceal the papers she was holding. Finally, with a gasp, Batter-Pudden said, "You!" "Yes," was the reply, "only little me, Captain." Staggering under the impact of her beauty, the soldier felt more and more foolish, like a little boy caught stealing marmalade. "You!" he repeated, as she turned her enormous eyes full on him again.

"What are you doing here?" asked Captain Batter-Pudden, greatly daring. "Looking through these papers," was the reply, delivered in a voice so melodious that the Captain's face assumed the famous Covent Garden gape. Spite of himself he knew that he was on the brink of falling in love with this radiant creature. Yet he knew where his duty lay. Setting his teeth until his jaw ached, he said sternly, "Pr-pr-private papers — my dear." A blush like the sunset on Helvellyn mantled her cheeks. "You mustn't call me your dear," she said in a small voice, lowering her eyes and veiling them with lashes that seemed to the Captain's fevered imagination as long as his arm. "Tck, tck," he replied, "I meant nothing by it." "That is what you men always say," replied the W.O.O.F. "This situation must be cleared up," said the Captain. And at that moment his trained ear caught a stealthy step outside in the corridor.

As that stealthy step approached there burst upon Captain Batter-Pudden the difficulty of the situation. Here he was alone at midnight in the Colonel's office with a renowned beauty. Geraldine Brazier appeared to be quite unmoved. "Don't you realize — ?" began the Captain. Duty and chivalry warred in his brain. Was he to denounce the girl, was he to protect her, by saying that it was he who had been looking at the papers? How explain her presence? After a hard struggle, duty won. The door opened, and the Captain stood stiff as a ramrod. It was the Colonel. "You!" cried the Colonel. "You, sir!" exclaimed the Captain, and Geraldine, not knowing to whom the Colonel's cry was addressed, murmured innocently, "You!" Embarrassment hung like a pall on the Colonel's face. He grinned foolishly. "I just looked in, my dear," he said. "You mustn't call me your dear," said Geraldine, smiling at the Captain.

The Colonel's eye fell on the litter of secret documents scattered about the table, and his face changed. "I was just passing the time," said Geraldine. "I hope you have not read these," said the Colonel. The Captain smiled sardonically. "Of course if you don't trust me," said Geraldine sulkily. The Colonel weakened but Batter-Pudden interposed. "I ask myself, sir," he said, "why should a W.O.O.F. come to your office at midnight to study secret documents?" Duty and chivalry fought for mastery of the Colonel. Chivalry won. "I'm sure," he said, "this little lady acted with the best intentions." At that moment a stealthy step was heard outside in the corridor. "Hide me, hide me!" cried Geraldine in a whisper. Colonel and Captain calmed her panic and awaited events. Slowly the handle of the door was turning.

The door opened and revealed the bland face of Major Horse-ferry. "Ha!" he said heartily, as he observed the others. The Colonel and the Captain smiled uneasily. "Quite a party," said the Major, "eh, little lady?" Geraldine was about to answer when yet another stealthy step was heard outside. And so the long night wore on. One stealthy step succeeded another, until there were twelve officers in the Colonel's office. And then Captain Batter-Pudden, addressing them all, said firmly, "Colonel, gentlemen, brother officers, I accuse W.O.O.F. Geraldine Brazier of breaking in here to look at secret documents." There was a gasp of amazement, and the Colonel cried, "Oh, I say, look here, I mean, what." But Geraldine said calmly, "I can explain everything." "Fire away, my dear," said the Colonel.

"Gentlemen," said Geraldine, "I will refrain from pointing out that I might ask how many officers happen to have crept quietly into this room. What was their business, apart from forcing upon me their unwelcome attentions? But no. I will confine myself to the explanation of my own actions. Gentlemen, I was discovered here looking through various documents. I had intended to memorize a few unimportant details. Why? Because I have — (and here she lowered her voice and her eyes) — an old mother, lonely, and impoverished. She is so proud when she knows her daughter enjoys the confidence of the Army. She thinks I am even consulted by the War Office, and I let her think it, for she has not long to live. But to make her last days happy I have to be able to quote documents of seeming importance. Gentlemen, it is a kind deception, and one that I feel sure you will condone. And — " At this point yet another of those damnable stealthy steps was heard outside.

An exclamation, perfectly timed, burst from the twelve officers in the Colonel's office, as the door opened slowly to admit a frail old lady, leaning on a large umbrella. From beneath a mop of hair protruded a kindly face, with blue spectacles twinkling above a fat nose. "And who the devil may you be, madam?" asked the Colonel, bowing courteously. But before the dear old newcomer could answer W.O.O.F. Geraldine's cry of "Mater! What are you doing here?" sent a thrill through the assemblage. Sardonic, sinister, sombre Captain Roy Batter-Pudden said crabbedly, "Yes, what, indeed, are you doing here — mater?" The old lady seemed to be overwhelmed. Her lips trembled, and when Geraldine approached and stroked that dear face and muttered, "There, there, dearest mater," Colonel Fritter clandestinely wiped his bloodshot eyes with his sleeve. Then silence fell, as the dear old lady began to whisper to her daughter.

Those hardened soldiers who had faced carnage and destruction with steely eyes, were softened by the sight of mother and daughter. They recalled their own mothers — all of them except Batter-Pudden, whose suspicions never slept. As for Colonel Fritter, as if to give the lie to those who say that soldiers are cruel, he sobbed as strong men sob, until the medals on his chest rattled like hail on the tin roof of a railway shed in mid-November. Still clinging to her enormous mother, Geraldine said, "Gentlemen, my friends. My old sick mater has come to tell me that she does not want me to get any more documents for her. She says that my motives might be misunderstood. Ah, gentlemen, there is no sacrifice she would not make for me." Too moved to speak, they gulped foolishly. All except Batter-Pudden, who had seen mater's spurs beneath her long dress!

"Why does your mother wear spurs?" asked Batter-Pudden casually. For a moment the girl changed color, and fear came into her eyes. "Perhaps she came here on horseback," suggested Colonel Fritter.

"Naturally," said Geraldine, "why else should she wear spurs?"

"How else could she have come?" added the Colonel fatuously.

"Is her sight bad?" asked Batter-Pudden.

Geraldine sighed. "Alas!" she said, "she is almost blind. Hence those blue glasses."

"And yet she wants documents to read?"

"I read them to her," said Geraldine.

"My dear daughter, she is so much an angel to me," said mater, speaking for the first time, in a deep, musical voice.

"Where is the horse?" asked Batter-Pudden.

"It goes home of its own accord," replied Geraldine.

"And your mother can see to ride on a moonless night?"

"Only just. It is a great strain for her," said Geraldine quickly.

"Gentlemen," said Batter-Pudden, in an ominously soft voice, "here is the position. A very old lady, half blind and feeble, rides here on horseback on a moonless night to tell her daughter that she doesn't want any more confidential documents read to her. What was her daughter doing here at midnight?"

"What are any of us doing here at midnight?" asked a gallant subaltern.

"He's got you there, Batter-Pudden," said the Colonel, whose sympathies in this matter were obvious.

"Of course," said Geraldine, with a pretty pout, "if you gentlemen don't trust me — "

"There, there, my dear," said Colonel Fritter, "we all trust and admire you."

A chorus of approval came from the assembled officers. "I wonder," said Batter-Pudden, in a dangerously calm drawl, "I wonder why your dear old mother has a pair of men's braces hanging below her skirt."

Captain Batter-Pudden's words sent all eyes to Geraldine's dear old mater, who, after a guilty start, said calmly, "These braces which I wear and which have slipped down, are a family heirloom. They were worn by my grandfather." So saying the old dame made shift to tuck them in under her skirt, but as she did so a package fell to the floor. Geraldine, whose dainty foot would not have covered a grain of rice, tried to hide it by stepping on it. But Batter-Pudden was before her. He picked it up and handed it to the Colonel. "A German surely." Then, as though realizing what this meant, he turned to Geraldine. At that moment, with a cry (in a deep bass voice) of *"Heil,* Hitler!" the old "lady" leaped to the window, smashed it, and dived through!

"That was not your mother," said Colonel Fritter haughtily to Geraldine Brazier, as Captain Batter-Pudden and several officers dashed in pursuit of Ludwig von Rumpelglutz. But the girl was no whit abashed. *"Nein,"* she said savagely, "and I his daughter am not." "I must ask you for your name," said the Colonel icily. "Dorothea Stuttgarten," replied the pseudo-W.O.O.F. "You know what this means," said the Colonel. "The firing squad."

With a last attempt to melt this iron soldier, the girl softly stroked his sleeve. But the Colonel flicked her hand off as though it had been a bug. "This is no time for dalliance," he barked. "I place you under arrest and charge you with espionage. It grieves me to be harsh with one so beautiful, but war is war." Only the sobs of the girl broke the silence.

. . . . Dawn was breaking over the Tower of London when Colonel Fritter and Captain Batter-Pudden stopped their staff car at the entrance to the Bloody Tower to give the password of the day, which happened to be "Scunthrope." From the car descended two blindfolded prisoners — Dorothea Stuttgarten, more beautiful than ever in her anger and mortification, and Ludwig von Rumpelglutz, minus the wig and braces but still wearing the telltale spurs. Colonel Fritter handed a piece of paper and a pencil to the Orderly Officer, who signed for the prisoners. He then bowed low to the girl, holding her hand rather longer than was necessary, while Batter-Pudden turned away from the cold fury of her eyes. A crowd of onlookers murmured sympathetically, and when Rumpelglutz spat at a woman who offered him a carton of 2,000 cigarettes, there were cries of pity. Then the cell doors clanged on the prisoners.

Bang, bang, bang! A volley rang out, two bodies sagged and fell. Two enemies of England paid the last dread penalty. Far away in the officers' mess of the Loyal North West Huntingdonshire Fusiliers, Colonel Fritter complimented Captain Roy Batter-Pudden on having done his duty. But the Colonel did not say that he treasured in his pocket book a fragrant handkerchief once dropped by the false W.O.O.F. And the Captain did not say that he could not breathe her name without a catch in his throat. Conversation in the mess that night was desultory. Next day a new W.O.O.F. was sent to take the place of "Geraldine" (as they still affectionately called her). The newcomer was so ugly that the Colonel said heartily, "Spy or no spy I preferred that other poor gal."

"Hear, hear!" murmured the officers, sighing heavily.

———————

JAMES O'NEILL

The Package APO *

Somewhere in the Persian Gulf. — Now that the Army Postal
Service has restored the soldier's privilege of getting packages from
home, we would like to commend the APS for putting in the clause
which says the soldier must ask for a package to get it.

This requirement that soldiers must ask for packages is not, as
some believe, an effort to limit the number of packages. It springs
from the demands of soldiers that they be protected against the
parcel post system. Reports might show that the first AEF in Ireland
as long as a year ago was actually sabotaging incoming box-laden
boats by purposely not claiming title to the merchandise at time
of delivery.

This practice spread until thousands of boxes lay purposely un-
claimed on wharves all over the combatant world, and the Army
Postal Service probably conducted an investigation to discover why.
The APS no doubt discovered the reason: no soldier would claim a
package because (a) he knew what was in it, (b) he had enough of
what was in it or (c) even his worst enemy and first sergeant had
had enough of what was in it.

From now on we get an even break with the people who make
up packages. We get to tell them what to put in.

Up to this time there have been only four variations of the box-
sending theme.

Let us discuss them, now that they are a thing of the past:

TYPE A — THE GOODIE BOX

Invariably consisted of one of two items — candy, or home-
made cookies. There were two choices open to the unfortunate

* Reprinted from the work, *The Best from Yank,* the Army weekly, copyright 1945,
by Franklin S. Forsberg. By permission of E. P. Dutton & Co., Inc., publishers.

recipient of home-made cookies. He could, if still in love and his sweetheart sent them, try to eat the cookies. This lovelorn type cabled home the next day for a new upper plate and a stomach pump. If the guy wasn't in love or just didn't give a damn, he took the sensible course of donating love's handiwork to the Engineers for road markers or dummy land mines.

Type B — Gooey-Yum-Yum Kandy Kit

En route the kit was placed by considerate stevedores between the engine-room boilers and a shipment of Grant tanks. When the soldier received it, he could use the mashed-up goo for pasting French postcards or Yank pin-ups on his barracks' wall. Or, if he had a little goat's blood in him, he might start right in eating Gooey-Yum-Yum's wrappings, partitions, string, APO number and all.

Suppose the sender was the thoughtful type and sent hard candy that stayed hard. Tell me who in hell is going to sacrifice his native-likker-weakened molars on a job a couple of Grant tanks couldn't do? The ingenious AAF is said to be using these dextrose block-busters over Berlin, the only practical use so far discovered.

Type C — The Knit-One-and-Purl-One Box

The sort of box that caused the recent high female death rate by accidental self-stabbing. It contained the Knitted Glove or the Knitted Pullover Sweater. Already enough has been said on this gruesome subject in newspaper editorials, syndicated columns, joke books, and returned packages marked "Wrong Address."

Type D — The Odds-and-Ends Box

This always fell into one of the following divisions:

1. The Sewing Kit. This was the 1,442d one the helpless GI received. Despite all the Boy Scout and Sewing Kit Concession propaganda, the average GI doesn't know how to sew. Even if he did, Whistler's Mother couldn't darn the craters he plows through a sock. Upon receipt of the sewing kit, the soldier carefully took out the needles to pin up that picture of Jane Russell and threw the rest away.

2. The Compact Shaving Kit. This monster was delivered by a detail of 10 and, when opened, resembled a surgeon's operating room, complete with X-ray equipment. It so scared the dogface he refused to shave with anything for a month.

3. The Cigarette Lighter. It didn't work, but there was plenty of fluid at the PX. It did work, but there was not a drop of fluid at the PX. Or no PX.

4. The Photograph. Usually sent by that much-maligned creature, the Girl Back Home, who, unless she was straight out of Vogue, included an original little note, "Put this in the mess hall to scare the rats away." It could do the job very well. If the girl was a looker, she had had the picture taken with one of the boys back home "just to make you feel a teeny-weeny bit jealous." The guy looked like Cary Grant and was either sporting a pair of oak leaves or clutching a $1,000 war-industry check in one hand.

5. The Canned Tidbit. Usually tied in a maze of fancy ribbon, this was something the dogface hopefully ripped open with anxious hands only to discover a can of Spam. (Last week the mess sergeant was clubbed to death with empty cans that had contained this ersatz chicken.)

Now that us soldiers overseas are allowed to select the contents of our packages from home, here are four types of gift boxes we would like to receive:

> A — One Lana Turner and one case of Scotch.
> B — One Dinah Shore and one case of Scotch.
> C — One Rita Hayworth and one case of Scotch.
> D — One Scotch and one case of Jane Russells.

H. I. PHILLIPS

GI Blueprint for Peace

The blueprint as drawn up by Pfc. Purkey with assists from many quarters, and with more horse sense on it than realized, was as follows:

To the Peacemakers:

This is a Blueprint for Peace which me and some of my buddies made up out of our own heads on account of we think if we have not views on a peace who has?

Me and the boys know there is so many blueprints in circulation that they are as much in demand as longer commercials on radio programs but we got a conviction the world is in a more dangerous spot right now than it was at any time when the fighting was going on and that a GI has got such a big stake in what comes next he would be a heel if he did not have guts enough to speak up and make a few suggestions straight from the horse's mouth.

We even go so far as to think a GI should have a place at the peace table, but if there is not no chance of that (on account of he talks too straight) he should anyhow have the right to do a little kibitzing on the side lines.

The GI is plenty worried.

He is afraid the war aims is in danger from low visibility, leaks in noble hopes, confusion in objectives, back-sliding, and signs of a heavy frost on high ideals.

A GI gets the creeps at the thought of a old style peace made from the 1919 pattern and enforced no better than No Smoking signs in subways and nothing gives him the heebie-jeebies like the chance another peace will turn out to be just a rest period in a slaughter house.

We got the idea the soldiers, sailors, Marines, airmen, engineers, ground crews, medics, Wacs, Waves, and everybody else in the war was never so scared of anything at the front as they are scared that the job they have tried to do will have to be done over.

We think the hundreds of thousands of men and women that died in this global fracas was the type that never went back on a pledge, ran out on a duty, or scuttled a mission, and that they would settle for nothing less from the peacemakers.

We got a notion that straight talk is the need of the hour and that what we have been through makes us specialists in it.

The GI is plenty stuck by the peace problems and he don't pretend to have a deep grasp of all the facts or know all the answers but he would be dumb if he did not realize that he has got too much at stake to trust to luck, old routines, and past performances.

Me and my buddies has done a lot of talking with others and found they all think the same way which is that the job of making a bright new world is not going to get nowhere without the following specifications:

1. The abolition of baloney, bunk, goose grease, applesauce, and what is commonly called "the old malarkey" from all deliberations.

2. No double talk. (This means positively.)

3. Night and day illumination of the goal posts. (And no dimming of the lights to secretly move the posts.)

4. Strict adherence to the postwar goals as expressed by our leaders when men was dying for them. (And no stalling!)

5. No support of plans so snafu and dizzy they commit the world to another blind date with destiny.

6. A realization of the fact this world cannot exist half man and half rat. (Even a five percent rat quota is too high.)

7. A global study of rat control in the clear understanding that rats can't be fought by resolutions or amendments.

8. The same courage by peacemakers that was expected of men in the fighting planes, mountain passes, jungles, trenches, and foxholes, and on all the oceans of the world.

9. Down the drain with every impulse to pussyfoot, hedge, dodge, straddle, or pull a fast one.

10. The blitzing of any disposition to gamble the future of the

world on a policy of expediency. No walking in our prewar sleep
. . . and no sleeping on our post-war walks.

11. The creation of some organization to safeguard the peace
by armed co-operation against international cut-throats. You can't
keep out of no free-for-all brawl by pulling down the shades and
humming "Hearts and Flowers."

12. The constant realization that such a organization must come
in on a backbone and a wallop and not on a paper wing and a prayer.
One more Geneva rabbit rhumba will make the alert signal the
main dependence of civilized man.

13. An approach to all problems in the spirit of King David and
never in the spirit of Mickey Mouse.

14. The creation of a League of Nations that never mistakes a
double chin for muscle and don't think a back-bone is something
to be shown only by strip-teasers.

15. A pledge by the four great powers to cement relations (but
never confuse cement with bubble gum) and to stay in the line-up
to the finish no matter who comes to bat.

16. A recommendation that the slogan of the next league for
the maintenance of peace be, "Always beat a gangster to the draw!"

17. No determination to force the American, British, or Russian
way of life on anybody else. (A way of life is not no nightshirt or
no derby hat. A realization of the fact that any people's way of life
looks screwy to the other fellow, regardless of the fact it may have
more gadgets, subways, escalators, and crooners.)

18. There has got to be a league to keep the peace and the league
had better be led at first by the four or five big powers with the
guts, the weapons, and the disposition to do it. No big armies of
occupation is necessary. It can be done by combined superdooper
air power.

19. The peacemakers has got to realize that the Germans is
troublemakers by instinct, nature, choice, and profession, and there
is not no use trying to sit down and talk things over with them.
(Can you talk sense to Garguantua and Toto?)

20. We must not let no war lord escape on the ground he didn't
get the right vitamins.

21. The Krauts has shown they is pushovers for any leader or

group with train-shed voices, wild eyes, weird ideas, big feet, funny faces, and cockeyed programs. Nothing that has been tried before can cure them.

22. There should be a understanding that while the builders of the bright new world must admit a duty to improve the lot of peoples in many parts of the globe, one way of life can never be merged with no other through a shotgun wedding or the distribution of money through a leaky hose.

23. We all got to keep our noses clean together or we will all go to the cleaner's separately. The big question before the peace commissions is whether we get a happier world out of this war or just a slap-happier one.

24. Closer attention has got to be paid to the microphone as an instrument of troublemaking, war, and disaster, and there should be an international test for radio orators with a message. Also a thumbs-down sign on freedom of the air waves for noisy dimwits and professional disturbers.

25. All peacemakers should keep pasted in their hats the idea that if we ever have another war the question will not be "What'll we do now?" but "What hit us?" And they got to realize, through things like the V-1, V-2, and V-3 bombs, that another global fracas will be a combination of Dante's *Inferno* and *The Last Days of Pompeii,* with a gooseflesh radio scenario by Orson Welles chucked in for extra creeps.

Note: The above was got up with the help and approval of a lot of service men and women of all sexes. Even the suggestions of Corporal Herman Feinstein and Pfc. Matt Hollis didn't do no harm. A rough draft of the general idea was passed around and got hundreds of signatures including those of two Congressmen, a dozen famous entertainers, and a lieutenant colonel. The lieutenant colonel was the only one who didn't read it and maybe thought it was another requisition for atabrine.

If I had of had more time I could of got the whole Army, Navy, Air Force, Marines, merchant seamen, and even some generals and admirals.

If even as much as one suggestion in the blueprint helps in any way in making a lasting peace it will be O.K. And anyhow my kid can never look me in the face and say I didn't try.

Yours truly,
Oscar Purkey, Pfc.

P.S. The greatest danger to the peace is scrapping among ourselfs. England has got to understand that to get along with Russia and Uncle Sam she has got to regard "God Save the King" as taking in a few more people than him. Uncle Sam has got to understand that from the Russian and British angle he can't always be regarded as the answer man on a global "What's Your Problem?" program. And the Russians has got to realize that while Russia may be the bear that walks like a man he ain't the bear that walks like three men.

If we can be as good friends in making peace as we was making war all will come out swell.

THOMAS SHEHAN

Hot Jeep *

His name doesn't make much difference, because nobody called him anything except Hot Jeep. What's more, he's too good a guy to have land in Leavenworth just because I want to tell his story.

Braidwood McManus, our battery clerk, was responsible for his monicker. Some of the boys from the ack-ack outfit down the road were over one night, and they asked what this character did in our battery. Braidwood, who has a knack for names that fit, told them that he had charge of the "Hot Jeep Department." So they called him Hot Jeep, and it stuck.

* Reprinted from the work, *The Best from Yank*, the Army weekly, copyright 1945, by Franklin S. Forsberg. By permission of E. P. Dutton & Co., Inc., publishers.

That was back when we first landed in Africa. Everything was confused: police supervision hadn't been organized too well, and it was a rare occasion when an outfit had the same number of vehicles at reveille that it had at retreat. Not that they were stolen. Nothing of Uncle Sam's is ever stolen; somebody else just uses it. When our outfit found itself with fewer vehicles than was called for in the table of basic allowances, Hot Jeep would go out and pick up enough to make up the deficit, with maybe one or two extras thrown in.

This was known as "moonlight requisitioning." Hot Jeep became so proficient at it, particularly at picking up the vehicle from which he derived his name, that he was not bothered much even by the padlocks and chains the MPs ordered as required equipment for every vehicle.

At one time Hot Jeep had been Dutch Schultz's chauffeur, but he got mad when we introduced him to visitors as a gangster. "The only rap I ever had against me," he would scream, "was when I voted three times in Waterbury at two bucks a pop. I would'na been caught then only I forgot how to spell McGillicuddy, the name I was votin' under."

Hot Jeep was a technical sergeant and maybe he deserved the rating. The top kick always gave us that old business about the T/O when any of the rest of us asked about ratings. But Hot Jeep's work did not go unnoticed; we took inventory after we got to Italy and found we had 105 vehicles whereas our TBA called for only 25.

"The Old Man made me a tech the time I sneaked behind the Jerry lines at Gafsa and got him a Volkswagon," Hot Jeep would explain when anybody asked him about his five stripes.

More than commercial reward, Hot Jeep craved appreciation. It must have been the ham in him because he would talk as long as the boys would sit around and listen to his stories of how he "requisitioned" this or that item the battery had needed.

He got so good that the CO even loaned him out to his friends. All they had to do was let the Old Man know that red tape had them down and he would tell them to let Hot Jeep know what they wanted.

Hot Jeep probably reached his peak on a trip to Oran. It was a little out of his line, but he put it across. We hadn't had any PX rations for a month when the CO got word that a boat had docked at Oran with all kinds of supplies such as razor blades, candy, cigarettes and the like.

Hot Jeep was ordered to go to Oran with a weapons carrier and pick up our rations before the word got around to the other outfits and the stampede started. He asked to have another vehicle and another driver sent along with him, and the CO, probably guessing what he had in mind, told Sgt. Hardfeet, a dumb guy with no imagination whatsoever, to take a vehicle and follow Hot Jeep's instructions.

As we were able to reconstruct the story afterward, our friend Hot Jeep had Sgt. Hardfeet fill out the requisition slips for our outfit's PX supplies. Then when the major in charge turned to Hot Jeep and asked what he could do for him, Hot Jeep replied that he wanted to draw supplies for the Two-O-Sixth Field Artillery at Maison Carree, Col. Wilson in command. The major signed the requisition slips, and Hot Jeep drew the rations at the same dump where Hardfeet drew his.

They had been back from Oran for an hour or two and were sitting around with the boys when Sgt. Hardfeet said: "Hey, ain't you gonna take those rations over to the Two-O-Sixth?"

"Ya blockhead," said Hot Jeep, the rage of an unappreciated artist written on his face, "there ain't no Two-O-Sixth!"

DOUGLAS WOODRUFF

Military Moments

NATIONAL PARACHUTING

On internal evidence, I think the following descriptions of how the nations behave as parachutists were made up by a Frenchman:

"The Germans. One pilot, fourteen parachutists. The pilot pulls the lever, the bottom drops out of the plane, the parachutists are dropped.

"The English. One pilot, one parachutist. The pilot says 'Are you ready, Bill?' Bill says 'Are you sure this jumping has been passed by the House of Commons?' 'Yes, quite sure. Go ahead if you're ready.' 'And by the House of Lords?' 'Yes, by the Lords as well.' Whereupon Bill jumps.

"The Italians. One pilot, fourteen men, one parachutist. The fourteen men are to throw the parachutist out.

"The French. One pilot, fourteen parachutists. When the pilot gives the word to jump, it is discovered that the parachutes have been left behind. The plane lands and they adjourn to a café to hold an enquiry into whose fault this is. It is dark before the enquiry is finished.

"The Spaniards. One pilot, one parachutist. The pilot cries 'Now! Jump for Spain!' The parachutist refuses; his patriotism is being exploited by people he does not approve of. The pilot says, 'Then jump for the love of God.' The parachutist refuses again; he no longer believes in God. The pilot cries 'You are afraid to jump! I believe you are a coward.' The parachutist cries 'You believe I am a coward! I will show you!' He takes off his parachute, and jumps."

Being an Englishman, I find little verisimilitude in the English part, but the Italians are the most entitled to complain.

The Rising Generation

A letter tells me of a small son to whom his mother was teaching the creed. When she came to "suffered under Pontius Pilate," he interrupted to ask, "was he a bomber pilot or a fighter pilot?"

Promotion

A French definition of promotion is "being called a fool by an ever-increasing number of subordinates. . . ." There was painted up in the Maginot Line this table:

"Lieutenants are friends,
Captains are comrades,

Majors are colleagues,
Colonels are competitors,
Generals are adversaries,
Marshals are enemies."

3. CASSOCK AND BIRETTA

3. CASSOCK AND BIRETTA

"Dear old Father O'Flynn, his umbrella under his arm, shrinking and downtrodden . . . humbly taking his orders from everybody in the parish."

— From *Truth Is a Fixed Star*
by Robert I. Gannon

How do you like your clergymen — roasted on a spit, or frozen on a pedestal? In a good deal of literature the man of the cloth has been cut to a pattern too good or too bad to be the real thing.

Goldsmith's long-suffering vicar of Wakefield surpassed any clergyman most of us have ever met, in the size and radiance of his halo. I remember too how Chaucer's theological student failed to impress me. He was like a statue made of Carrara marble, a beautiful and precious soul, but colorless and lifeless. His insatiable appetite for books gave me a tome-ic ache.

At least more interesting are portraits of clerics born of sarcasm and satire and christened with vinegar. But these portraits are too broad to stay long with the truth. Chaucer's friar is a gay rogue, a great one with the bar maids and rich widows. However, he makes you think he's the reflection from a Coney Island fun-mirror. Similarly Robert Browning splashes on gaudy and naughty colors to highlight Fra Lippo Lippi, the frustrated monk who rebelled at instructions on his painting and went out to paint the town red.

Early American writers, in the tradition of irreverence for things religious which was contemporary with the Puritan emphasis on the rugged virtues, gave us characters like "well-fed Dominie Double-Chin, who had long dozed over his sermons in the pulpit and his beer in his parlor," or George Washington Harris's Parson Bullen, "an old pious tub of soap grease."

Modern writers have tried to get more verisimilitude into their portrayals of clergyman. An excellent portrait of the human emotions of a priest, overwhelmed momentarily by a feeling of paternal love for his brother's son, is found in De Maupassant's story, "The Christening." Even more expert are portrayals like those in A. J. Cronin's *The Keys of the Kingdom* and Willa Cather's *Shadows on the Rock* and *Death Comes to the Archbishop* where we can admire the priests' piety and yet have concern for their personal problems.

Curiously enough, it was the detective story, I think, which helped most to get the clergy out of their literary rut. G. K. Chesterton brought onto the scene a roly-poly priest, Father Brown by name, with a face "as round and dull as a Norfolk dumpling." This polite, urbane, little priest-detective, who made the arch-criminal Flambeau look about as clever as the puny proponent of a shell game at a county fair, turned the scales in favor of the clergy in the modern fiction world. Father Brown has had strong allies in Owen Francis Dudley's Anselm Thornton, "the Masterful Monk," and Bruce Marshall's Father Malachy, of the miracle of the same name. In this section are several portraits typical of the "new look" in fictional clergymen, with the emphasis, of course, on the lighter side. Bruce Marshall's Father Smith and his co-clerics, Monsignor O'Duffy and Father Bonnyboat, are "one of us." The Monsignor thundered from the pulpit against the movies when they first came in, calling them a "new-fangled toboggan slide down to the depths of the nethermost pit." But he was broadminded enough to view the cinema, human enough to enjoy a slapstick comedy and bighearted enough to make amends by buying tickets for the entire membership of the St. Vincent De Paul Society.

And I'm sure that one of the most delightful clergymen I've ever met is Monsignor Scalabrin. If Robert Browning had met this clever Monsignor he would have made him the subject of an Italianate sketch, wherein the good Monsignor's umbrella would become a glittering sword, his adversaries not customs men but soldiers and his package not the Countess Villani's sausages but seditious papal bulls. As it is, however, without the feverish Browning imagination, but with Helen Parry Eden's gentle playfulness, the Monsignor justifies the description "something of a wag." Isn't there one in every rectory? Well, there should be.

HELEN PARRY EDEN

The Duplicity of Monsignor Scalabrin

"One must never lie, of course," said Padre Innocento in English, "but there are an amount of people here in Italy we allow to deceive themselves: the gentry on the frontier, for instance, when it is a question of tobacco, and the *dazieri* who sit at the receipt of custom over there," and he waved lavishly at the toy roofs and towers of Borgo Sant' Ignoto three kilometres off in the valley. "There is a story of old Monsignor Scalabrin and how he outwitted the customs of his own town and took in duty-free the sausage of the Countess Villani. The incident was brought about in the first place by a scene with the officials of the city customs over some marionettes. So I think I had better go back to the beginning and tell you about the marionettes first.

"One warm afternoon in mid-October our good Monsignor was re-entering Borgo Sant' Ignoto on foot by the station gate. He had not been preaching in the country, for a wonder. He had been over for the day to see his brother — a count if you believe me — in Venice. In his right hand he carried a striped umbrella; in his left, a parcel as big as a hunter's bird-cage, but heavier — a parcel wrapped up in brown paper. So, inevitably, as he drew up to the barrier where tolls are taken, two good fellows in grey-blue who were sitting a little outside under the thinning chestnut trees, laid down their newspapers and asked him with respect what he had in the parcel.

"Now as a matter of fact, the parcel contained a boxful of mario- nettes which Monsignor Scalabrin had bought years ago in a little shop on the dirtier side of the Rialto to amuse his small penitents. But as one of the names for marionettes is *burattini*, which is more commonly used in Borgo Sant' Ignoto to denote abuse, as you might say 'blockheads,' Monsignor's testy enunciation of this single quadri- syllable touched the official pride to the quick. They had often been called *burattini* before, the two *dazieri*. But never, never by a priest!

" 'Come, come, Monsignor!' said the elder good-temperedly. 'It is no more than our duty. You had only to say what is inside and we will take your word for it.'

"The younger man, evidently an anticlerical, muttered '*imposture religiose!*' and spat indignantly among the chestnut leaves.

" '*Burattini*,' repeated Monsignor Scalabrin firmly.

"A small crowd collected. Two *carabinieri*, cocked hats, white gloves and red striped trousers, strolled gracefully up and took the part of the State. A little bevy of black-scarfed women, on their way from a pilgrimage to Sant' Ignoto, sided with the Church. All gesticulated violently. One of the women took out her pocket- handkerchief to sob into and the strongest *carabinieri* removed his white gloves and gave them to his colleague to hold. If an arrest had to be made . . .

"There was no help for it. The elder *daziere*, still keeping his temper as the civic code requires, invited Monsignor to step inside his office. Monsignor went, *agnello in mezzo di lupi*, 'a lamb among the wolves.' This was the expression of the lady with the pocket- handkerchief, who was left outside. The two *carabinieri* guarded the door. Click! The anticlerical ruffian turned on the municipal electricity. Nothing should be left undone to throw light on this dark business. Monsignor put his parcel down on the table. '*Burattini*,' he repeated. But even then the elder official had polite qualms about cutting Monsignor's string, and carefully unpicked it.

"It was a good selection of *burattini*. There was a Harlequin, a comic peasant, a court lady in a sacque and a black mask, a Capuchin with a cord round his middle, Pinnocchio with his long nose and Toby frill, a thin little Jesuit with a crooked biretta, and a half a dozen more. Monsignor straightened the biretta tenderly and sat the little Jesuit down next to Pinnocchio. 'That completes the company,' he said, and lifted out a handful of shavings to show there was no deception. 'There isn't a *monsignore*. Perhaps one is enough.'

"The sympathetic women were still waiting outside like the Babylonian king in the story of the Prophet Daniel, when Monsignor, carrying his reconstructed parcel, emerged from the office. They saw at a glance that their companion was not only unscathed but triumphant. It was a veritable victory of the Faith. 'Good evening, my children,' said Monsignor Scalabrin, and went quietly home to his house in the Contrada Reale." Padre Innocento paused, and I thought he had forgotten the sausage sequel altogether. But looking up at his eloquently wrinkled face, I realized that he was only disentangling the matter from a medley of similar reminiscences too vivacious for publication, even in England. So I waited patiently for the space of a *Salve Regina*, at the end of which interval he began again of his own accord.

"I suppose Monsignor forgot all about the *dazieri* as soon as he reached home. Adventures of this kind happened to him so frequently that he had no time to think about the last episode before the next began. Indeed, it is the mark of a truly great man that he cannot remember his own sayings and doings, and nobody else can forget them. Moreover, the two officials were hardly given a chance to let Monsignor slip their minds, for that day three weeks later they met him journeying towards them again in the same train from Venice, chatting pleasantly — having finished as much of his Office as conscience prompted — with his cousin the Countess Villani.

"The Countess was a tall, dignified woman in the graceful black costume and little black turban hat affected by devout ladies in Borgo Sant' Ignoto. Monsignor Scalabrin sat opposite to her, their carriage, an overheated second class, having been otherwise emptied at Padua. On the rack above the Countess's head reposed a square brown-paper parcel, almost as large as the box of the famous *burattini*.

" 'Yes, it's a sausage,' said the Countess with a deprecatory glance upwards. She used the word *luaneghe*, which means a large, ribbed, cylindrical sausage, three times as thick as a man's arm. 'Emilia, my husband's sister at Treviso, thrust it upon me, and I could not hurt her feelings by refusing it. At least the box has no tell-tale contours; and if I have no trouble at the *dazio* . . .'

" 'Leave that to me,' said Monsignor Scalabrin.

"There were no chairs under the chestnut trees as the Countess and her chivalrous escort approached the city boundaries. The trees themselves were leafless, the ground was strewn with gold as for a procession of King Midas, and the *dazieri* themselves were invisible. Invisible, but not absent; for with one eye apiece on their windows and one eye apiece on their evening papers, they sat inside their little office in serene anticipation of their prey.

" 'It's that buffoon again!' said the anticlerical zealot, releasing his window eye from its vigil and turning to his companion.

" 'What buffoon?' said the latter somewhat irritably, for he was half-way through a Milanese murder trial and did not want to lose his place.

" 'Monsignor *Burattini*;' replied his colleague with withering scorn.

" 'Any parcel?' queried the elder man resignedly.

"The anticlerical strolled to the door and took a long look down the road.

" 'The same parcel,' he sneered, 'and one of his rich penitents come to see it opened.'

" 'Don't open it,' said his senior. It was not a suggestion. It was a command.

"The Countess Villani could not make out at the time, why, as she stood beside Monsignor Scalabrin blushing for the sausage whose plebeian circle her sister-in-law had so tactfully squared, the two *dazieri* appeared together on their doorstep and with gestures of sublime hauteur ushered the parcel and its proprietors uncatechised and unexamined through the gates of Borgo Sant' Ignoto. Of course, later on, she told one or two confidential friends about their un-hindered passage — a thing without precedent in the municipal annals of Italy; and somehow, from the conversation of the two *carabinieri*, the marionette story got about, and the whole town exercised its wit piecing the tales together. Luckily the Countess moved to Treviso shortly afterwards and Monsignor Scalabrin translated himself mysteriously to Venice. I saw him not long ago at a Congress in the Piazza S. Marco, holding an old Capuchin by the beard while he kissed him on both cheeks. There will never be a merrier monsignor in any of the Three Venices. But I am afraid he is not likely to return to Borgo Sant' Ignoto."

RONALD KNOX

A Val-iant Effort *

I confess I am rather a pal
Of Cardinal Merry del Val.
    He expresses the hope,
    I will deign to be Pope,
But I doubt, on the whole, if I shall.

BRUCE MARSHALL

The Clergy and the Cinema

It was in 1910 that the first cinema came to the town. Paolo Sarno took a chance on things and converted the old bus stables next his

* This verse was written when Monsignor Knox was still a High Anglican. Since his conversion he may have re-versed his stand.

ice-cream shop, which was bang opposite the site on which Father Smith had already built the skeleton of his new tin church. The priest could see the advertisements from his presbytery window. They changed twice a week too, on Mondays and Thursdays: sometimes they were about a man called John Bunny and sometimes they were about two men called Gerald Ames and Stewart Rome, but the advertisement saying that afternoon tea would be served free of charge to patrons between three and four was always the same. People said that it was rather sporting of Sarno to be so enterprising, because the craze mightn't last any longer than the one for roller-skating in which the Italian had taken such a hard knock two years ago.

The canons of the chapter of the pro-Cathedral, however, didn't think it sporting at all. They were perturbed because weekday attendances at Benediction of the Blessed Sacrament began to fall off and the evening devotions in the month of May were performed only by the elderly, and even some of them hadn't been above popping in for an hour's Vitagraph and a wee free tea during the holy season of Lent when they thought none of the priests were looking. It was in vain that Monsignor O'Duffy had thundered from the pulpit, "It's no by sitting in red plush airmchairs watching a lot of silly gowks sauntering and daundering about a lot of helter-skeltering moving-picture postcairds that any of ye'll ever see the bonny Blessed Virgin Mary face to face in the kingdom of heaven"; the attendances at Benediction during the month of the Sacred Heart were as poor as during the month of May. Some of the canons at the chapter meeting maintained that it would be prudent not to condemn the cinema until His Holiness Pope Pius X had made an official pronouncement, but Monsignor O'Duffy had said that that was all havers and clavers and nonsense, and that if they had to wait on the official verdict of the Church, they might be argy-bargying till Doomsday, and that the Church had taken nearly nineteen hundred years to make up its mind about the doctrine of the Immaculate Conception and that they couldn't afford to dilly and dally like that while young folk aye and auld folk, too, were walking straight into the jaws of hell at sixpence a time and children half price.

It was decided, therefore, to send a deputation to attend a performance. This was possible because, as Monsignor O'Duffy pointed out, although local ecclesiastical law forbade priests to attend theatrical performances, the cinematograph was a very different cup of tea, indeed, and so could not be held to fall within the ban. He said, too, that if the members of the chapter didn't mind, he intended to go himself as there was no clergy in the diocese who knew more about wickedness than he did, and that he would take his old friends the Reverend Fathers Bonnyboat and Smith with him, because it wouldn't be fair on Signor Sarno to be letting only austere and wise canons have a peek at his newfangled toboggan slide down to the depths of the nethermost pit.

Paolo Sarno seemed to have heard of their intended visit, for he was there in the vestibule to greet them, standing underneath a large framed photograph of a lady called Flora Finch. Father Smith wondered why he hadn't come right out into the street, because that would have been even more polite, but Father Bonnyboat said that he mightn't have heard of their intended visit at all and that it was just by chance that he was standing there, and Monsignor O'Duffy said it was only because he couldn't very well have let them pay for themselves through yon wee hole in the wall into the lassie's face if he had come right out on the pavement, ha, ha. Anyway there he was on the purple carpet with his thick light-brown fingers looking just like the advertisement for Palethorpe's sausages on the railway embankment.

"*Buon giorno, reverendissimi signori,*" he greeted, because he thought that they all spoke Italian. The priests said "*Buon giorno,*" back, except Father Bonnyboat, who had studied in the Scots College in Valladolid instead of the Scots College in Rome, and who said, "*Buenos dias,*" instead. This made Paolo Sarno laugh and say "*Per Bacco!* The reverendo father speaka the Italian like a Spanish cow, *vero,* no offence meant, reverendo father. You coma to see my show. Very good, very elevating, very pious. The reverendi fathers coma this way."

The reverendi fathers came this way, carrying their inverted black hats in front of their faces like soup-plates, and as they trooped along, Monsignor O'Duffy said to Paolo Sarno in a loud voice:

"Wicked or elevating, shameful or pious, this new craze'll no last, Mr. Sarno, and in my opinion you'd have done much better to open one of yon miniature shooting ranges with wee celluloid balls dancing about on jets of water, which are without the suspicion of sin."

It took Father Smith's eyes some little time to grow accustomed to the darkness, so that at first he seemed to be sitting in an immense black hole with Father Bonnyboat's overcoat on one side of him and Monsignor O'Duffy's overcoat on the other. Gradually, however, the darkness lightened to an amber haze in which he could make out lines of heads all about him like rows of chocolates in a box. On the screen they were showing a blue river meandering along beneath green bridges and an old mouldering church or two, which didn't seem to Father Smith very wicked, because the old mouldering churches were almost certainly Catholic churches with the Body of God safe inside them, and a piano was playing away most politely, tra-la-la-la-la-la.

The same thought must have struck Father Bonnyboat, for he said across Father Smith to Monsignor O'Duffy, "Nothing very irreverent about that, Monsignor."

"Just you wait till we get to the acting," Monsignor O'Duffy said. "They tell me it's worse than yon machines you turn the handles on and look down on on piers." He brought his ear very close to Father Smith's and whispered: "Tights. Tell him," he said.

But before Father Smith could pass this information on to Father Bonnyboat, a hat with a large pin stuck through it in the row in front of them turned round and said "Sssh," and Father Smith was left to wonder in silence how Monsignor O'Duffy knew so much about what was inside the machines you looked down and turned the handles on on piers. Then the piano suddenly stopped playing and there was a noise in the air just like the buzzing the rotary brush made in the barber's, and the green bridges and the mouldering old churches went on for a moment or two and then they stopped, too, and the lights went up and the rows of heads in front of Father Smith had ears on them and the screen turned out to be not a hung-up sheet at all, but hard and rectangular and glossy with high lights on it here and there as though the paint had run.

"Most edifying, really," Father Bonnyboat said.

"Just you wait, I tell you," Monsignor O'Duffy said.

The lights went down again. This time the film was about a convict in prison. The convict wore a uniform striped broadly like a football jersey, and at first Father Smith was very sorry for him, because he seemed to be so miserable. But then the convict escaped and ran round a lot of street corners and the policemen ran round a lot of street corners after him, but the convict always managed to escape, even when the policemen came at him from both directions at once, because he dodged behind doorways and the policemen ran into one another and knocked one another over. When Father Smith laughed, he knew he wasn't doing anything wrong, because he could hear Monsignor O'Duffy and Father Bonnyboat laughing, too.

Then the convict ran along a beach, and there were a lot of pretty girls in bathing dresses eating chocolates on the sand, and the convict ran in among them and upset the chocolates, and Father Smith was wondering what Monsignor O'Duffy was going to say about the bathing dresses when down the gangway came a flashlight crying, "Chocleets, cigarettes and matches." Then the flashlight turned into Angus McNav's face above two sprays of gold buttons leaning across Monsignor O'Duffy's waistcoat and saying to Father Smith, "Do ye no ken me, Father?" "One of my altar boys," Father Smith was going to explain to Monsignor O'Duffy, but up on the screen the policemen and the convict and the pretty girls were throwing tarts and pies at one another's faces and Monsignor O'Duffy was laughing too hard to be able to listen. The pie-throwing didn't seem very funny to Father Smith and it didn't appear to strike Father Bonnyboat as very funny either, but the rest of the audience roared their heads off and Monsignor O'Duffy laughed enough for both of them.

"Yon fellow's a right comic and no mistake," he said as he sat wiping the tears from his eyes. Then he caught sight of a pretty waitress in a black frock and frisk of apron coming up the gangway. "Hi, laddie, what about yon free tea?" he asked.

"It'll be served during *Death or Dishonour*, sir," she said.

And served during *Death or Dishonour* their tea was, right bang in the middle of the Sheriff's speech, "Boys, I kinda reckon there's dirty work at Red Gulch and we're going to put out that dirty skunk of a double-crossing horsethief Ned Tranter's lights for him so that our God-fearing women-folk can sleep safe in their beds o' nights and our maidens wander happy and careless 'neath a myriad stars," flashed across the screen just like that, without any commas, but with lots of dots at the end to make up. There was a tray for each, with a teapot and a cup and saucer and two hard little biscuits with ribs running along the back. Monsignor O'Duffy said that if the management had wanted to do the thing really well, they would have given them a boiled egg to their teas as well, but he seemed to enjoy the biscuits all right, soaking them in his cup of tea before he ate them and making great appreciative gurglings, champings, and suckings.

On the screen, above the cups of tea, Ned Tranter had captured the Sheriff's pretty daughter, lassoing her while she was saying her prayers by bedside and riding off with her on his horse to his mountain fastness. "Ned Tranter," she said to him in a great paragraph through her gag, "you may starve me, beat me, flay me, but never shall I consent to befoul's God's great gift of love by becoming the mother of your children, nay, nor shall I cook for you, sew for you, dust for you. Death rather than Dishonour, Ned Tranter, for my heart belongs to clean-limbed Patrick Hogan of Lone Ranch." At this there was great cheering and clapping and stamping of feet, and Father Bonnyboat said that with a name like that Patrick Hogan must surely be a Catholic and Monsignor O'Duffy said that that just showed ye that even on the fillums the great Holy Catholic Church played a royal and triumphant role. Father Smith was too intrigued with the drama to say anything. With eager eyes and beating heart he watched the Sheriff and Patrick Hogan and the other boys of Red Gulch set out to rescue Molly Kintyre, whose eyes were like forest pools with the ineffable glory of the stars mirrored in their purple depths, at least that was what Patrick Hogan had said when he was playing snooker in a saloon bar with Mickey Riley.

As they set out on horseback, they all fired their pistols into the air to let Molly Kintyre know that they were coming, but of course

Ned Tranter didn't hear, because he always slept with his dirty head under the blankets. Up hill and down dale they rode, firing their pistols all the time. Sometimes it looked very much as though they were riding up the same hill twice, but Father Smith was too excited to care. With the others he clapped, groaned, lost heart, and clapped again, but at last it was all over and Molly Kintyre was restored to the arms of Patrick Hogan, who swore, colleen bawn, that he would never play snooker in saloon bars again, and the Sheriff said, pointing his revolver at Ned Tranter: "Nix on the gunplay, Tranter. Put 'em up. You're cornered."

The three priests clapped with the rest of the audience. And Father Bonnyboat said that he hadn't seen anything so edifying for a long time indeed, and Monsignor O'Duffy said that he was never afraid to confess when he was wrong and that it looked very much as though he had been wrong in what he had said about the cinema, and that if the remainder of the programme contained no unpleasant surprises, he would have to make amends to Signor Sarno by buying tickets for all the members of the Saint Vincent de Paul Society.

There was, however, no remainder of the programme, for as soon as the lights were lowered, the blue river and the green bridges and the mouldering old churches started all over again, with the piano going tra-la-la-la-la-la and all. Father Bonnyboat said that he supposed that they really ought to be going, but Monsignor O'Duffy said that that was all havers and nonsense and that "continuous performance" meant that folks could stay in as long as they like and that he was going to see yon bit again where they threw pies at one another, but that of course Father Bonnyboat and Father Smith could do what they liked. Even when, at the end of the blue river and the mouldering churches, they flashed an orange notice on the screen, "PATRONS WHO HAVE SEEN THE FULL PROGRAMME ONCE ARE REQUESTED TO VACATE THEIR SEATS IN FAVOR OF THOSE WAITING FOR ADMISSION," even then he still held out, maintaining that it wasn't as though he were trying to get served with an extra free tea, but only that he wanted to see them fling yon pies again. But when he had seen them flinging the pies, he found that he wanted to see them setting out to round up Ned Tranter again as well, so they all stayed to the end of *Death or Dishonour* and tried not to think that the spectators standing up in the passage were staring at them.

"Of course, it's just a craze and it'll no last," Monsignor O'Duffy said when they stood outside again on the unenchanted pavement.

Father Bonnyboat said that he thought somehow it was more than a craze and even wondered whether the blessed in heaven might not be treated to a similar entertainment, since it was so uplifting; but Father Smith said that in heaven the blessed would have our Lord to look at and that nothing could be more uplifting than that. Whereupon they all took off their hats, saluting the priesthood that was in one another, and went back to their churches, because it was the first Thursday of the month and they had confessions to hear.

SEAN O'FAOLAIN

The Confessional

In the wide nave the wintry evening light was faint as gloom and in the shadows of the aisle it was like early night. There was no sound in the chapel but the wind blowing up from the river valley, or an occasional tiny noise when a brass socket creaked under the great heat of a dying flame. To the three small boys crouched together in a bench in the farther aisle, holding each other's hands, listening timidly to the crying wind, staring wide-eyed at the candles, it seemed odd that in such a storm the bright flames never moved.

Suddenly the eldest of the three, a red-headed little ruffian, whispered loudly; but the other two, staring at the distant faces of the statue, silenced him with a great hiss like a breaking wave. In another moment the lad in the centre, crouching down in fear and gripping the hand on each side of him, whispered so quietly that they barely heard: "She's moving."

For a second or two they did not even breathe. Then all three expelled a deep sigh of disappointment.

It was Monday afternoon, and every Monday as they had heard each other tell over and over again in their homes, Father Hanafin spoke with the Blessed Virgin in the grotto. Some said she came late at night; some said in the early morning before the chapel was opened; some said it was at the time the sun goes down, but until now nobody had dared to watch. To be sure Father Hanafin was not in the chapel now, but for all that the three little spies had come filled with high hope. The eldest spoke their bitter disappointment aloud.

"It's all my eye," he said angrily. The other two felt that what he said was true, but they pretended to be deeply shocked.

"That's an awful thing you said, Foxer," whispered the boy in the middle.

"Go away, you, Philpot!" said Foxer.

"God! I think it's a cause for confession, Foxer!" whispered Philpot again.

"It's a mortal sin, Foxer!" said the third, leaning over to say it.

"Don't you try to cod me, Cooney, or I'd burst yer jaw!" cried Foxer angrily.

Philpot hushed them sternly and swiftly, but the spell was broken. They all leaned back in the bench.

Beside them was Father Hanafin's confession-box, its worn purple curtain partly drawn back, his worn purple stole hanging on a crook on the wall inside, and as Foxer gazed into the box with curiosity, the Adversary tempted him in his heart.

"Come on, Cooney!" he invited at last. "Come on, and I'll hear yer confession."

"Gor! Come on," said Cooney, rising.

"That's a sin," said Philpot, though secretly eager to sit in the priest's chair.

"You're an awful ould Aunt Mary!" jeered Foxer, whereupon all Philpot's scruples vanished and the three scrambled for the confessor's seat. But Foxer was there before either of them, and at once he swished the curtains together as he had seen Father Hanafin do, and put the long stole about his neck. It was so nice in there in the dark that he forgot his two penitents waiting beyond the closed grilles on either side, and he was putting imaginary snuff into his nostrils and flicking imaginary specks of snuff from his chest when Cooney's angry face appeared between the curtains.

"Are you going to hear me confession, Foxer, or are ye not?" he cried in a rage, eager for his turn to be priest.

"Go back, my child," said Foxer crossly, and he swished the curtains together again. Then, as if in spite, he leaned over to the opposite grille and slowly and solemnly he drew the slide and peered into the frightened eyes of Philpot.

"Tell me how long since your last confession, my child," he said, gravely.

"Twenty years," whispered Philpot in awe.

"What have you done since then?" intoned Foxer sadly.

"I stole sweets, Father. And I forgot my prayers. And I cursed, Father."

"You cursed!" thundered Foxer. "What curse did you say?"

"I said that our master was an ould sod, Father," murmured Philpot timidly.

"So he is, my child. Is there anything else?"

"No, Father."

"For your penance say two hundred and forty-nine Rosaries, and four hundred and seventy Our Fathers, and three hundred and thirty-two Hail Marys. And now be a good obedient boy. And pray for me, won't you? Gawd bless you, my child."

And with that Foxer drew the slide slowly before the small astonished face.

As he turned to the other side his hand fell on a little box — it was Father Hanafin's consolation during the long hours spent in that stuffy confessional listening to the sins and sorrows of his parishioners. Foxer's awkward fingers lifted the cover and the sweet scent rose powerfully through the darkness as he coaxed the loose snuff down from the cover. Then drawing the slide on Cooney, he gravely inhaled a pinch and leaned his ear to the cool iron of the grille.

Outside a footstep sounded on the marble floor, and peering out

Foxer saw the priest walk slowly up the farther aisle, turn and walk slowly down again, his breviary held high to the slanting radiance of the Virgin's altar.

"It's Father Hanafin," whispered Foxer to Cooney; and to Philpot: "Keep quiet or we're all ruined."

Up and down the solemn footsteps went, and high above their heads in the windows of the clerestory and along the lath and plaster of the roof the wind moaned and fingered the loose slates, and now and again they heard the priest murmur aloud the deep, open vowels of his prayer, *Gaudiamus Domine,* or *Domine, Domine meo,* in a long breathing sigh.

"He's talking to the Virgin," breathed Cooney to Foxer.

"He's talking to the Virgin," breathed Foxer in turn to Philpot.

"Amen," sighed the priest, and went on his knees before the candles that shone steadily and were reflected brilliantly in the burnished brass.

The three spies had begun to peep from their hiding-place when the snuff fell on Foxer's lap and the grains began to titillate his nose. In agony he held his mouth for a full minute and then burst into a furious sneeze. In astonishment the priest gazed about him and once again Foxer held his breath and once again he sneezed. At the third sneeze the priest gazed straight at the box.

"Come out!" he said in a loud voice. "Come out of that box!"

And as the three guilty forms crept from the three portals he commanded again: "Come here!"

Awkwardly they stumbled forward through the seats, trying to hide between one another, pushing and upbraiding one another until they stood before him.

"What were you doing in there?" he asked Foxer.

"I was hearing their confession, Father," trembled Foxer, and half raised his arm as if to ward off a blow.

For a moment the priest glared at him and then he asked: "And what penance did you give?"

"I — I gave three hundred and thirty Hail Marys, Father, and I think it was four hundred Our Fathers, Father, and two hundred and forty-nine Rosaries, Father."

"Well!" pronounced the priest in a solemn voice, "go home and let each one of ye say that penance three times over before nine o'clock tomorrow morning."

Stumbling over one another's heels the three crept down the dark aisle and crushed out through the green baize door and into the falling night that was torn by the storm. The street lamps were lit and under one of these they halted and looked at each other, angry and crestfallen.

"Nine hundred and ninety Hail Marys!" wailed Philpot, and Cooney squared up to Foxer with clenched fists.

"Yerrah!" said Foxer. "It's all a cod."

And he raced suddenly away to his supper, followed by the shouts and the feet of the other two.

In Church and Rectory

(These anecdotes, like those at the end of Section I, are from the humor page of *The Apostle* magazine.)

As unfortunately happens sometimes, the young choir members were not as attentive as they should be during the sermon.

The pastor paused in his sermon and said: "There are some young men up in the choir who are joking with the girls. When they get done," he added, glancing severely in the direction of the culprits, "perhaps they will give me a chance."

And only then did he realize why the congregation smiled.

A burglar who had entered the rectory of an impoverished little parish at midnight, was disturbed by the awakening of the pastor. Drawing his gun, he said:

"If you move, you are a dead man. I'm hunting for your money."

"Let me get up and strike a light," said the priest, "and I'll hunt with you."

The recently ordained young priest had been appointed assistant to his first parish. On his first parochial call, he was making every effort to be friendly to the parishioners and to appear interested in their family. He enthusiastically admired the baby, and asked how old it was.

"Just ten weeks," the proud mother replied.

And then without thinking, the young priest inquired with great interest:

"And is it your youngest?"

The president of a Catholic college, attending a banquet in Boston, was surprised to see that the colored man who took the hats at the door gave no hat-checks in return.

"He has a most remarkable memory," a local resident explained. "He's been doing that for years, and has never made a mistake yet."

As the priest was leaving the banquet, sure enough, his hat was passed to him. Smiling, he asked the old man, "How do you know that this hat is mine?"

"I don't know it, Fathah," admitted the attendant.

"Then why did you give it to me?"

" 'Cause you gave it to me, Fathah."

Priest (at baptism of a baby): "What is the baby's name, please?"
Sponsor: "Patrick Paul Anthony Joseph Leo John McCarthy."
Priest (to server): "A little more water."

There is nothing humorous about the far too prevalent ill feeling between people of different religious beliefs, but the following little story gives the lighter side of the differences between Protestants and Catholics:

A Protestant minister unconsciously speeding in his car, was embarrassed to notice a motorcycle policeman rapidly gaining on him. The minister stopped, and the policeman drew up alongside the car.

"Why didn't yez pull up when I hollered at yez back there?" the angry officer asked, with a brogue that must have come from the Golden Vale of Tipperary.

"Oh," said the minister, with great presence of mind, "I thought you just called out 'Good morning, Father.'"

"Shure and I did, Fhather," smiled the policeman. "But I wanted to warn yez about the next town — there's a Protestant cop on duty there."

Father Tom Burke, the famous Irish Dominican, was once riding atop a bus in Dublin. He had just completed a long service, and, as he rode, was deeply engrossed in reading his Breviary.

Another passenger, well-known for his anti-Catholic prejudice, was loudly commenting:

"The Lord tells us," he said, "that when we pray, we should not be as the hypocrites who love to pray in public and at the corners of streets that they may be seen by men. When I pray, I enter into my room, close the door and pray in secret."

Without looking up from his Breviary, Father Burke replied in a voice loud enough for all passengers to hear: "Yes, and then you get on top of a bus and tell everyone about it."

4. THE OLD PARISH

4. THE OLD PARISH

*"I raise my paean of praise to those who,
through a hundred continuing years or more
in the United States, have built simple parish
churches into cathedrals of great archdio-
ceses."*

— Doran Hurley

The dictionary says that a parish is "an ecclesiastical district having its own church and clergyman." This just proves that even dictionary makers make mistakes. They haven't mentioned the most important part of the parish, Mrs. Patrick Crowley.

Mrs. Crowley is that towering symbol of parish life whom Doran Hurley brought out of the obscurity of a New England town in his "Old Parish" stories. She is everybody's scolding stepmother, kindly grandmother and solicitous aunt, to whom the pastor and curates look for guidance in secular matters in much the same way that they look to Rome for guidance in spiritual matters. The good Fathers may know the canon law, but Mrs. Crowley knows the equally important parish lore. In the story included in this section, Mr. Hurley shows us the key position Mrs. Crowley holds. The Bishop rings her doorbell hopefully, and the new pastor looks out over the congregation for her nods which tell him that she is behind him "every inch of the way." With her support the new pastor solves an ancient dilemma, how to make the people see eye to eye with him on redecorating the church.

Though Mr. Hurley is undoubtedly in the forefront of Catholic writers etching the human side of parish life — in the tradition of Canon Sheehan and Maurice Francis Egan — there are others. And, as the selections here may indicate, no matter where the "Old Parish" is located — New England, Old England or Ireland — it is basically the same everywhere, like the Church it is a part of.

Catholic life in general, and Catholic parish life in particular, has a flavor which is indigenous to it, and which, as Father Galvin points out, in many instances is packed with phrases and doings and atmospheres which cannot be caught exactly by an outsider. The non-Catholic reader may be especially conscious of that in this section, as well as in the preceding one. But what can be understood by everyone is the mixture of human frailty amid striving for higher things.

In the case of altar boys, for example, Father Galvin shows that they are a "teasing paradox of ecstasy and monkeyshines." He writes from the viewpoint of America.

In Father Basset's "Old Parish," which is in "Old" England, we meet parishioners not too unlike those elsewhere on the globe. There is Miss Smithson, the schoolmistress in charge of the "angels" in the Christmas play. There are the parents demanding that the Archangel Gabriel leave rehearsals since it is long past his bedtime. Then there is Peter, the parish "character," who saves the day when confusion threatens to ring down the curtain prematurely.

Albert Eisele writes of a parish undoubtedly somewhere near Blue Earth, Minnesota, where he has a farm place. But his not too sharp Mrs. Keene, the "Oh, dear me!" type of card player, is not merely a Mid-western parish phenomenon. Neither is Mr. Schmidt who sings by ear and plays cards the same way, nor Mr. Wetternich, the insurance man whose policy is to make as much noise as possible.

Francis MacManus writes from the vantage point of Ireland, but you'll have to look twice to make sure that Augustine L. Fahy, the distinguished looking, black-coated, silver-haired orator and scholar, isn't the same fellow you met at the tavern last week after your parish Holy Name meeting. He "knew everything about everything." There's one in every parish!

There is no indication as to the location of Melfort Dalton's parish. This will undoubtedly lead to a lot of confusion, for many parishes, here and abroad, will claim him, especially if there is a St. Joseph's

Old Maids' Home in the neighborhood, as there is in Oliver Gogarty's poem.

In the chronicles which follow you'll meet not only these few people mentioned but many others. You'll also get a fuller view of some of the parish problems and arguments which assure a pastor of a shorter purgatory hereafter by giving him advance installments here and now.

BERNARD BASSET

"And Seeing, They Understood"

There is nothing like a good Christmas Play to fray the nerves, especially if it is a Nativity Play involving a choir of Angels.

Miss Smithson, the schoolmistress, was in charge of the Angels who were all of the tiresome age that can only understand songs about oranges and lemons, with an occasional apple thrown in. Hence, quite apart from the initial difficulty of making them stand still for three minutes and leave their wings alone, there was the appalling task of teaching them to pronounce Emmanuel as one word, not as a sentence.

By the time this had been accomplished, one or two in the rear rank had slipped off to play with the lights, and blow the fuses, and then an irate parent would arrive to demand the Archangel Gabriel, as it was long past his bedtime, and he would catch his death of cold if his feet were wet. That his feet were always perfectly dry never made any difference. He was carried away screaming, and the whole choir of Angels was thrown out of work. Poor Miss Smithson!

Father O'Riley had a much easier time with the leading actors, for Peggy took the part of Our Lady with great ease and dignity, and

Harry was good enough as St. Joseph, though he nearly ruined every-thing at the dress rehearsal because his beard made him sneeze.

Marjorie could be relied on as St. Elizabeth, and Jimmy as the innkeeper of Bethlehem was a great success. We were very lucky, then, with our principal actors and all would have been easy but for the shepherds. Any volunteer who proved useless in other parts, and who could not help with the lights, was detailed off as a shep-herd, and Father O'Riley made me commanding officer, or, better, regimental sergeant major, of the black sheep.

The greatest trouble about the shepherds arose from the fact that they had no words to say. When they first appeared they were sup-posed to be tending their sheep, and you have no idea how difficult it is to show anyone how to tend sheep when there are no sheep, no words, nothing. The promise of crooks, camp fires and distant sheep bells on the night of the performance improved their morale a little, but it did not help us at rehearsals, with a sack of paper taking the part of the sheep. The shepherds just stood about staring at the ground as though watching road-mending operations, until I asked them to hold their heads up, and then you might have thought there was an air-battle in progress up above. Their awkwardness com-pletely upset the Angels, who delivered their Christmas message as though they were reciting the multiplication tables, and then burst into tears.

To make matters worse, old Peter had somehow enlisted as a shepherd, though, had I been consulted beforehand, I'd have found him work elsewhere. Ideal as a distributor of tickets or programmes, his pastoral accomplishments were negligible, and he nearly drove me mad. Ask him to take the plate round, to scrub the porch, to act as godfather at a baptism, and you might be sure that no penny, dirt, or rubric would be missed, but put him to tend imaginary sheep and the play is over as far as you are concerned.

He always began each rehearsal by instructing the other shepherds in their different tasks. If I appealed for silence he would first rebuke the company in general for inattention, and would then go round to each one individually to explain in a whisper that the producer could not hope to succeed if the cast did not listen to him. This finished, he might return to his own post for a few minutes, but more often he'd come to the front of the stage and offer advice or information.

"I 'ave 'eard said," he would remark blandly, "that in the 'Oly Land you just can't tell sheep from goats."

"Very likely," I'd answer, trying not to lose my temper, "now would you mind standing more to the right, Peter, and turn towards the star. You are supposed to be gazing at it."

Such a remark gave Peter the chance of explaining to the others that what was right for me was left for those on the stage. He would then assume a most rigid pose for a few moments while gazing at the star. He might have been mistaken for a statue on the Artillery War Memorial, certainly not for a shepherd on the hills. Within sixty seconds he would be back by the footlights.

"I 'ave 'eard said as that it wasn't a real star," he'd announce casually, "something more in the nature of one of these 'ere comets, if you follow my meaning."

"It is going to be a star in this show, anyway," I'd answer fiercely. Peter would wave his hand.

"Quite right, sir; you do what you think's right, and don't you go bothering about what other people say. They don't know much, most of 'em, though I 'ave 'eard said as that there weren't no sheep on the 'ills at that time of the year with the snow and all about."

In the end I had to talk very severely to Peter. He was bad enough on the hills outside Bethlehem, but when he reached the cave itself I felt like the assistant in the china shop after the bull had arrived. He moved the position of the Angels, impeded St. Joseph, upset his fellow-shepherds, and finally broke the prompter's spectacles with a fine double-handed gesture of adoration before the Holy Child.

"I've pictured this scene to meself for over sixty years," said he magnificently, "and it always seems to me as that there ain't enough going on. I ask you, sir, would a crowd of shepherds just kneel in the blooming corner on such an occasion? Of course they wouldn't. I can see it all as though it were 'appening in me own back yard, and I 'ave 'eard said as that — "

"Look here, Peter," I broke in vigorously, "you really must leave things alone. You're getting in the way all the time."

"No 'arm intended," said Peter apologetically, "to me it always seemed as though perhaps the shepherds did get in the way."

Here Father O'Riley came to my support.

"Well, Peter," he said, "we can't have that here anyway. If you want to remain a shepherd you must stay at the back and keep absolutely quiet. If you interfere any more, out you go. We don't want an accident with the lamp, do we? You stay at the back and do what you're told or you'll wreck the whole play."

Poor Peter.

The Town Hall is more imposing in name than in appearance, but, nevertheless, it *is* the Town Hall. On the night of our performance it was packed. Some came because they liked a Nativity Play at Christmas, others because Mgr. Robert Hugh Benson was the author, many because the performance was given in aid of the schools. In the front row sat His Lordship the Bishop, the Canon, and many priests from the district; directly behind were the parents of the angelic choir, and proud relations of the shepherds and the kings. I saw the mother of the Archangel Gabriel sitting there smiling, as though she was responsible for the coming success, and under cover of the curtain I thought uncharitable thoughts.

Behind the scenes there was much subdued excitement and confusion. Miss Smithson was hunting for the herald angels, who in turn were hunting for their cardboard trumpets, or playing aeroplanes in everybody's way. In the green room the shepherds were being made very biblical and hairy, for with few words to say we felt we could let ourselves go on their beards. Peter was there, but he was not talking with the others. He was sitting on an up-turned soap box when I saw him, struggling to fasten his massive Old-Testament whiskers with twentieth-century glue. There was a book open on the table before him, and peeping over his shoulder I caught a glance of the title, the Gospel according to St. Luke. Peter saw me and pointed at the book.

"I 'ave 'eard said as that this Father Benson wrote our play," he mumbled through a fringe of whiskers, "but I ain't very certain. 'E may 'ave added a few words, but the plot was made up by God. 'Ere it all is in the Gospels, quite up to date and all, might be 'appening before our very eyes."

There is something fascinating about a Nativity Play. Often one has hurried through the Joyful Mysteries of the Rosary, but as the imagination wearies the scenes no longer live. A Nativity Play corrects the hastily constructed pictures of our imagination, and to length and breadth it adds depth. As I watched the first scenes of our performance, I became gradually less and less conscious of my surroundings, less distracted by familiarity with the actors, more attracted by the significance of the plot. As Peter had rightly said, the whole story was up to date and needed no alteration, it might have been happening before my very eyes. As Our Lady travelled across our humble stage on the journey from Nazareth to the cave of Bethlehem, she seemed to unite the past with the present so that one felt with lively emotion that our redemption was, in fact, at hand.

Standing in the wings with Father O'Riley, I had intended to keep a paternal eye on the shepherds, but as the story developed I became more and more engrossed in the play. I knew the words by heart from much rehearsing, but somehow they were charged with a new meaning for the night. The audience sat silent and attentive, and one felt that the play was changing into a prayer. Then suddenly I was disturbed by a whispered conversation beside me, and one glance over my shoulder convinced me that something had gone wrong. Miss Smithson was talking to Father O'Riley in an anxious way.

"What's happened?" I asked quickly of the others, and was informed that some of the Angels had rubbed against a newly-painted back-scene and were not fit to appear. Gabriel had torn his wings off and the damage would take several minutes to repair.

A glance at the stage brought home to me the gravity of the disaster, for the Holy Child was already lying down in the manger, the Shepherds were kneeling down in adoration, and the Angels should enter in a few seconds to add their share of praise. Already I could see that look of hesitancy on the faces of the actors which easily spreads to panic when it dawns on them that something has gone wrong. Father O'Riley and I looked at each other in misery, mumbled something uncomplimentary about the Angels, and wondered what we had better do.

Then, of a sudden, I caught sight of Peter kneeling obediently in the background behind the other shepherds, quite close to where I stood. Great decisions have to be taken quickly, so without dwelling on the terrible consequences which might follow from my action, I crept across to the wings and whispered urgently in his ear.

"Peter," said I anxiously, "for the love of the Lord do something, there's been a hitch."

Peter did not look my way but he seemed to have understood.

"Quick," I went on, "get up, move, say something, fill up the gap. Show us what you think the shepherds would have done."

Father O'Riley was crouching down beside me, and when he heard my orders he looked aghast.

"Sunk," he muttered murderously, "we'd better drop the curtain," but I, for some reason, stopped him and signalled him to stay where he was.

Somehow I felt less anxious now that the decision had been taken, and I watched Peter's movements more with wonder than concern.

Peter rose up from behind the other shepherds, cleared his throat and then tried to push his way on to the stage. The others were alarmed at his performance, and remembering the injunction that he was to stay in the background, they tried desperately to hold him back. Peter was having none of it.

"Don't be shy, mates," he said in a tremendous whisper and then sweeping aside all opposition, he pushed into the centre and tip-toed to the place where Our Blessed Lady knelt.

The shepherds cast anxious glances at each other, but from the audience there came no whisper of surprise. Our Lady looked up when she saw Peter standing beside her, but if she felt alarmed she did not show it, for she graciously pointed to the crib. Peter looked at the Holy Child with a reverence which no actor could have attempted, a reverence which had resulted from sixty years of prayer. Then he stooped towards Our Lady and said in another terrific whisper:

"May I take Him in my arms?"

For a moment I could see Our Lady's consternation, but she arose with complete confidence and placed her Child in Peter's arms.

"He'll be quite safe," said Peter, looking at the infant, "we shepherds understand."

Then, without warning, there was a noise of hurried footsteps and the Angels crowded in the entrance all flustered by the delay. Luckily Our Lady saw them, and with supreme graciousness she beckoned to them to enter, and led them over to where Peter stood, whispering to His Lord. Down they all knelt in profound adoration with Mary kneeling at their head.

His Lordship the Bishop said later that he had never seen a better performance in the diocese, and he congratulated all those responsible for the success. He commended us for choosing Mgr. Benson's libretto, for Benson had such a striking gift of originality that one could read the same book several times and still find plenty that was new.

"Take this play, for example," said His Lordship, warming to his subject, "I must have seen it acted many times, and yet, tonight, coming back to it after some twenty years, I noticed many moving details which must have escaped me in the past. What genius, for example, to allow one of the shepherds to carry the Lord of Heaven and yet that is an incident which must have happened on the first Christmas night. When we see the Holy Child in the arms of His dear Mother, her very excellence tends, perhaps, to lessen our appreciation of God's humility when He became a Man. Put the Infant Jesus in the arms of a rough shepherd, one who understands about babies, and we begin in a faint way to grasp that He had a body like ourselves.

"We begin to penetrate the mystery of the Holy Eucharist, for in Holy Communion, we come forward like that worthy shepherd and reassure the great Mother of God that we can be trusted with so tremendous a gift. Above all, we priests begin to realize the awful dignity of our office, for when, as shepherds, we hold the God-Child before us even Mary and the Angels bend their knees."

The Bishop smiled.

"That was the part I liked best," he said simply, "for I've often meditated on the Christmas mystery and I've sometimes felt that there was something missing. Your little play this evening has shown me better how to pray."

The Bishop drove away, and returning to the Hall to help clear away the rubbish, I found old Peter sweeping up clouds of dust.

"Well done, Peter," said I gratefully. "You were just marvellous. I can't think how you ever thought of it."

Peter looked puzzled.

"Why," he said abruptly, "I've been doing it for well nigh sixty years. He became Man for that."

ALBERT EISELE

The Farewell Party

Mr. Henry Vollmer had sung in the choir for more than thirty years and it was only natural that now, with the Vollmers moving away, the choir members should give him a surprise party.

And this was the night. Mr. Vollmer stood at a window and watched a long line of cars approach along the curving road that led to the farmplace, the cars following one another closely and studding the road with their lights. A lump came into Mr. Vollmer's throat.

"Emma," he said in an unsteady voice, "I'm just afraid that when these good people go home tonight I'll break down and cry like a baby! I always do. Such things get me."

"Well, that's the way the Lord made you, Henry, and you can't help it. And besides, 'tain't no disgrace for a man to cry."

The choir was composed of eight men. All had brought their wives or sweethearts, and so the Vollmer house was filled. Decks of cards were tossed on tables, and soon everybody was playing progressive five hundred.

"Now, then!" said Mr. Gassonade, the choirmaster, as he seated himself for the second game. He raked in the scattered cards, herded them together and deposited the pack in front of the lady to his right, Mrs. Keene. "Visiting lady deals!" he said politely.

"Oh, dear me!" exclaimed Mrs. Keene, "must I deal?" Her shoulders shuttled and her head wagged.

She dealt the cards gingerly, pausing at intervals to check up and assure herself that all was well. "Have you too many cards?" — "Oh, what have I done!" She looked to Mr. Vollmer, her partner, for advice and comfort.

And when finally she had decided to play a card she would pass it slowly to the center of the table, hesitate another moment, relinquish her hold on the card and then look at Mr. Vollmer and say, "Oh, I never should have played that!" Mr. Gassonade seldom engaged in side talk while at cards, but during this game he suddenly looked at Mr. Vollmer and said, "I see by the paper where beer has come back to Kansas after being gone fifty-six years."

"It was gone long enough," said Mr. Vollmer solemnly.

Mr. Vollmer lost this second game, as also he had lost the first. "Oh, you couldn't expect to win, with me for partner!" purled Mrs. Keene in agitation. Her head bobbed and wagged in little bows of apology and regret.

Mr. Gassonade and his partner, victorious, moved on to the next table, Mr. Vollmer remaining but shifting to another seat.

He lost the third game, and also the fourth and fifth. His luck began to draw attention; players at other tables were saying, "Mr. Vollmer hasn't won a game yet!" His fame spread.

He went around and around the table like a horse around an old-fashioned feed grinder. He tried to take his fortunes philosophically; but something, it seemed, had settled in his breast and was beginning to ferment. He tried to console himself with the feeling that he was permanently staged at a fixed point of vantage from where, like the person who stands on a street corner, he could get a good view of things.

Everyone, it seemed, passed before him. There was Mr. Kosmoski, a tenor. Mr. Kosmoski had a fine-timbred voice, very effective on the lower ranges, but inclined to thin out on the upper. Mr. Kosmoski, as an aid, ate peppermint candy — he always had a fresh supply of it, and would pass the bag around and then place it on the organ, where it was open to general foraging.

Opposed to Mr. Kosmoski and his theories was Mr. Hermann, a basso. Mr. Hermann bolstered up his voice with elderberry wine. He carried a bottle with him, and would usually take the necessary swig while ascending the dark stairway that led to the loft. "Nothing tunes up a man's sounding-board like a good drink of elderberry wine," he was fond of saying. Mr. Kosmoski, however, stood his ground, and Sunday after Sunday publicly passed around his peppermints, a tactic which was somehow closed to Mr. Hermann and his bottle.

Mr. Vollmer, in the meantime, had lost the sixth, seventh, and eighth games. His face was red, his mustache bristled, and he was now definitely angry.

And there was Leo Fleming, who had brought his girl with him. The two billed and cooed and tickled each other under the chin. Mr. Vollmer glared at them.

And tenor Philip Kesseling, a good singer and a demon at cards. He played to win; and it was ironical that the two ladies of that ninth game were Mrs. Kosmoski and Mrs. Wetternich, the two most lackadaisical players of the entire gathering. Mrs. Kosmoski played a card and then addressed Mrs. Wetternich: "Did you hear that Lincoln program over the radio the other night?" "No," said Mrs. Wetternich, "I didn't hear it." "It sure was good," Mrs. Kosmoski continued; "it gave everything from the time he was born till he was shot." "Well, for goodness' sakes!" Mrs. Wetternich exclaimed; "and did he live long after he was shot?" "I really couldn't say," replied Mrs. Kosmoski; "there was a lot of music in between, and talking. Is it my play now?"

And Mr. Schmidt, a tenor. Mr. Schmidt was getting old and shaky. He sang by ear, and held a score in his hands merely for the looks of things. It took him a long time to learn his part, but once he learned it he had it. As a card player he was fumbling and inept, the cards falling continually to the table, to his lap, and to the floor. In some strange way he acquired, as the evening wore on, an aura similar to that of the magician who makes cards tumble from armpits and other unseemly places.

It was Mr. Keene, a basso, who opposed Mr. Vollmer at the eleventh game. Mr. Keene was an inveterate latecomer at Mass, and for that matter the choirmaster never bothered much about teaching him the *Kyrie* or even the *Gloria*. But Mr. Keene could play cards, and he gave Mr. Vollmer a fearful walloping. It was Mr. Vollmer's

eleventh straight defeat, and he was now boiling inside like a thresh-
ing engine.

Then came the twelfth game, the last of the evening. "Everybody
keep their seats after this game!" someone announced, this being a
promise of sandwiches and coffee.

Mr. Vollmer's partner for this final game was Mrs. Schmidt,
and his opponents Mr. Wetternich and Mrs. Hermann. Mrs.
Schmidt was a very preoccupied sort of person. She wore strong
glasses, which gave her deep-set eyes an oscillating appearance, but
her gaze at the same time was fixed and staring. She went seemingly
into trances, and when in this condition there was nothing for the
other players to do but wait till she came back.

"I have always maintained," she addressed Mr. Vollmer in her
slow and measured speech, "that the Catholic Church should make
better provisions for its young people to meet one another and become acquainted. A mixed marriage is nothing but a joy and a delight to the devil. The devil is as much a partner to a mixed marriage
as is the bridegroom." Her eyes, made manifold by the strong lenses,
were on Mr. Vollmer like those of a myriad-orbed apparition.

"A mixed marriage," she went on, lost to the card game, "begins
its journey without the blessing of God. There is no Nuptial Mass,
and any marriage that is contracted without the blessings of a Nuptial Mass is not a marriage at all, but merely a farce." She moved
her head slightly and for a moment her eyes came into focus: they
were steady and unblinking like those of an owl. "What we Catholics
need are gathering places for our young — study clubs, recreation
halls, basket socials, and, under the proper supervision, of course,
dances."

All of which was a perennial subject with Mrs. Schmidt. The
woman had three unmarried daughters at home, and none of them
had a husband in sight. Several desirable young men of the parish
had in recent years been married out of the Church, and the villain-
ous injustice of all this loomed so mountainously to the mother that
she could hardly understand why public demonstrations did not
manifest themselves — she felt that there should be uprisings of
the populace; revolution; bloodshed. She brooded intensely over
the matter.

She came out of her trance and played her cards. She and Mr. Vollmer won the deal. Mr. Wetternich dealt afresh; the cards shot out from under his hands like grain from an end-gate seeder. Mr. Wetternich was an insurance man, a vapid and blustery fellow who played cards with a vast enthusiasm. He strove always for a noisy table. "You do the playing and I'll run the rake!" he would shout whenever his partner took a trick; and when the opposition won he would exclaim in tones of surprise and dismay, "Oh, oh! Oh, oh! Oh, oh!"

"You got the jump on us," he addressed Mr. Vollmer, "but things'll look different after this next deal. You watch us go! — Oh, boy!" He gathered the cards together and slapped them loudly on the table in front of Mr. Vollmer. "Your deal!" he said, "shoot 'em around!" Mr. Vollmer shuffled the cards and then presented them to Mr. Wetternich to cut; Mr. Wetternich removed the top half of the pack and slapped it to the table with another resounding clap. "Just right!" he beamed; "cut just the way I want 'em. Ha, ha, ha! Now watch my hand! Attaboy!"

He did draw a good hand, and the score was evened. The score then seesawed until the time for the bell drew near. Mr. Vollmer, in what was undoubtedly the final hand of the game, drew a strong run in hearts; he bid eight in the suit, and was not over-bid. He had the cards to win, and now if the play could be completed before the bell rang, he would have won a game.

Mr. Vollmer suddenly perked up. For the last hour or two he had been sullenly and bitterly resigned to the bludgeonings of vile fate, but now with the smell of victory in his nostrils he was a new man. He would yet win a game.

But the bell was imminent, and so it was strategy for Mr. Vollmer to rush the playing. He quickly threw away his discards and led. Mrs. Hermann, to his right, played promptly in turn. But Mrs. Schmidt had her gaze on Mr. Vollmer, and she was talking. "We hear so much nowadays as to what is wrong with the world," she said, "but how seldom do people put their finger on the real cause. It is in the mixed marriage that all evil has its root." Her hands were resting on the table, and the cards in them were pushed together in compact form.

"If you will play your cards quickly, Mrs. Schmidt," said Mr. Vollmer, "I think we can still win this game."

"We must bring our young men and our young women together," said Mrs. Schmidt firmly, " — we must take steps in these days and times which it was not necessary to take years ago. It behooves us — "

But here the bell rang, at which Mr. Wetternich bellowed, "We win!" and reaching across the table shook hands violently with his partner, while Mrs. Schmidt turned her head and stared long and studiously in the direction of the ringing, as though she had heard something suspicious.

Refreshments were served, but Mr. Vollmer merely nibbled at his food.

And then came the booby prize — a little fuzzy rabbit that jumped and squeaked when one pressed a rubber bulb attached. Mr. Wetternich, the insurance man, slapped Mr. Vollmer on the back: "We beat him twelve straight! — it shouldn't have been a rabbit at all, but a skunk!"

And presently everybody went home. Mr. Vollmer stood at a window and glared at the disappearing headlights.

"Oh, Henry," spoke Mrs. Vollmer softly, as she laid a hand on her husband's shoulder, "I'm so glad that you didn't break down and cry tonight when the people left!"

JAMES J. GALVIN

In Faint Praise of Altar Boys

There are many combinations of simple English words that to the non-Catholic make no sense at all! For an instance, the common question: "Is anyone *hearing* this afternoon?" or "Who was it *said the seven* this morning?" There are scores of such innocent phrases packed with meaning for the initiate, and proving that as Catholics we do not speak the same language as do our countrymen. But one such phrase is just packed with delicious naiveté and bewildering hyperbole: the expression "on the Altar"!

"Isn't that your Willie *on the altar* these mornings, Mrs. Wycliffe?" It ingenuously suggests that little Willie, who peddles papers in the afternoons, and breaks windows in his spare time, has by some incredible *ex cathedra* been sainted in this vale of tears, so that for all his freckles and dusty corduroy, and the lilac in his cap and the jack-knife and marbles in his noisy pockets, he stands among tulips and tall candles in a marble niche above the spotless linen of the High Altar. Of course "on the altar" simply means that little Willie Wycliffe is an altar boy; that he has been chosen by the Pastor or the Sister in school to serve at Mass.

Altar Boys have been accused of many pranks and failings . . . and many may be true. It has been said for instance that they sometimes sleep in their laundered surplices . . . and even snore during vespers; that they play tag during the sermon, and wrestle each other to kindle the charcoal for Benediction. Sacristans have reported them for spilling hot wax on the carpets and conning Comic books in the sacristy . . . but sacristans are cranky folk anyhow and are always finding fault! Sometimes old ladies say that they rubberneck during Mass; but I seldom believe them. I call to mind an ancient saw: that it is not the cowl that maketh the monk . . . nor a surplice, a saint or an acolyte! Strange how a naughty Altar Boy can circumflex our eyebrows, almost like finding a nun playing poker; like catching a Cardinal lapping a lollypop!

Mischief they do, but they have many virtues. What other schoolboy is there who is out of bed before his mother; who is up and dressed and out of the house before his father leaves for work? Who other than the little boy who serves the six o'clock Mass! In the summer he is up before the sun and the sparrows; and in wintertime he crawls from his warm feather comforter with the whistling sleet clawing at his bedroom window, and the air piercing cold.

And as for Latin! Tell me what other little lad in the sixth or seventh grade can talk the solemn language of the Pope? Perhaps they can parse a sentence like sixty; or tell you the principal products of Yucatán, but they could never repeat the *"Suscipiat,"* if you gave them the whole Sunday collection, not in a million years!

Then, too, Altar Boys transfer the big red book with the gold edges and the colored strings; and you sometimes wonder how they do. For their eyes just barely peep over the altar-cloth, and the missal as big as themselves! But somehow they manage to set the bookstand and missal in position for the Gospel without a major mishap. Of course now and then they may suffer a minor contretemps, such as tripping or spilling the missal or tobogganing headlong down the altar-steps; but they speedily gather composure and bow for the Gospel and answer the prayer albeit with a grinning bump on their foreheads, and all out of breath.

Still Altar Boys do not learn Latin, and how to ring chimes, and when to move the missal and bring up the wine, by sheer intuition. They must have rehearsals. And rehearsals mean that they cannot ski or play Scrub. So you might call this another of their virtues; that they freely forego an afternoon or two in the week to master the fine-points of Ritual. And for a little lad who likes to fly kites and climb lamp-posts, it is not easy at all.

But they have their compensations too! Funerals, for example, when in order to serve, they sometimes escape a spelling bee or a test in fractions and are free from school for almost sixty minutes. And weddings! where they hold the ring in a silver platter, and hear the Bride whisper her trembling "I do." . . . and afterwards stare the Best Man into yielding up a large piece of silver or a crisp dollar bill.

If one likes to be worshipped with envy and meek admiration (and what little boy does not?) then the Altar Boy has more than his wish. For little girls follow him breathlessly with wide blue ravenous eyes as he minces and marches and bows during High Mass. They dote on his glamorous wardrobe: his cassocks of white serge and Cardinal red and imperial violet, and his surplice like a bride's veil, and his satin capes to match the color of the Mass. Many little girls wish that they were boys just to parade such beautiful raiment.

And his school fellows envy him too. For ringing those teasing snatches of music on the chimes, and for leading processions with

candles and cross; but especially for swinging the censer, and knowing that magical trick of producing a great cloud of sweet-smelling
smoke with seemingly nothing but a pass of the hand.

The age-limit for Altar Boys is generously elastic. You might
safely place it as between the ages of seven and fifty-nine complete.
But there are exceptions. I know of a man in Guayaquil who has worn
a surplice for the last seventy-three summers; and in Montefiascone
they tell me there is an Altar Boy who remembers Michaelangelo!!
Be that as it may, the common garden variety of acolyte ranges
between seven and seventeen; and of these there are three classes
depending on their length of time on the altar. For brevity let us call
them the Green Horn, the Big Shot and the Old Timer.

When a youngster is first made an Altar Boy he is thoroughly
awed by the sacred nature of his office. He walks with folded hands
and downcast eyes and never opens his lips. He seems half afraid to
be so near the Sacred Host. He feels almost like Moses coming down
from Sinai, like St. Joseph beside the crib! But to the Sacristan he
is more like the ox or the ass. With the best of holy intentions he
seems to stir up pandemonium. He brings up wine when it's time
for the Gospel; and unless the priest is alert he may suddenly shuttle
the missal from under his hand. And the chimes! When he rings
them, they sound like a clatter of egg-beaters, and he rings them
whenever the spirit moves. It is a galling, embarrassing, heart-
rending, dreadful apprenticeship; but it passes like everything
else!

Next comes the Big Shot era. Many Altar Boys skip this stage
completely; but the majority of them pass through it for at least a
time. If you walk into any sacristy you can instantly single them
out from their fellows by their breezy devil-may-care demeanor.
They seem to meet your casual glance with a curt *So what?* in the
eyes! The fidgety jitters have vanished. Their cassocks now reach to
their ankles; and all the short cuts and fine points of serving they
know. They could serve Mass in their sleep . . . and often do!

When the coast is clear they lounge in their cassocks, and twiddle
their thumbs, barking orders at the smaller lads. They browbeat the
Greenhorns into serving all the extra Masses. When charcoal is
needed, only they can light it, spraying sparks into everyone's face.

Thurifer at Benediction: that too is their right; and they swing the censer like a flying pendulum.

Every priest in the parish is rated as fast or slow; and should one of the latter be vesting for Mass, presto! they are out of their cassocks and nowhere to be found. And when they do serve, they muster a jaunty how-am-I-doing appearance that gives one ulcers to behold. They utter the Latin in war-whoops. They handle the chimes with the modesty of carnival drum-majors, with sudden sidelong peeps at the pews to be sure of their public.

And lastly come the Old Timers, the Altar Boys of High School age. These are trim now as new candles and very clean. They sit sedately in the sacristy on a Sunday morning filing their nails as they wait for the 10:30 Mass. They walk with a noiseless unassuming gait into the sanctuary. They bow with genuine liturgical courtesy. They answer the Latin in clear soft-spoken syllables. And betweenwhiles they pace the priest with a small pocket missal of their own. There is a stately reverence, a quiet unobtrusive dignity about them.

Whether they sense it or not, acolytes are creatures apart. There was a time when they even bore the Blessed Sacrament from Mass, hung in little silken bags about their necks, as did Tarcisius through the streets of Rome. By right they should be consecrated clerics, for the order of acolyte is the highest of the Minor Orders in the Church. No woman, no matter who she be: a queen of Spain, a sister of His Holiness, even a Mother Superior, can ever usurp the glory of the Altar Boy. True, she may answer the prayers, and tinkle the bell, when the Altar Boy is absent; but she may not mount the altar, and pour the wine and change the book. She must stay outside in the pews.

So important is this little surpliced jumping-jack, that Canon Law forbids the priest to start the Mass without him. Because the Mass can never be a private devotion that the priest can say alone, but always and ever a public act of solemn worship offered in unison by the universal Church.

In this unruly scatterbrain with the itching dust of dreams still sticky on his eyelids, the sacrosanct Catholic Church is concentrated for the space of half an hour. Pius the Twelfth is here, and the cardinals in gorgeous *cappa magna,* and mitered bishops with rings of blazing emeralds, and nuns with clicking beads, and rough-shod monks! The whole work-a-day world is here in the person of this tousled acolyte, farmers at their ploughs, and pilots in their planes; miners with soiled coats and lighted caps, and surgeons in spotless smocks and rubber gloves; mothers warming breakfast for their children, and children tagging schoolwards, and babies chuckling in egg-stained bibs. The entire Mystical Christ is here at the altar in unsuspected miniature.

Such is the mystical function of the Altar Boy: to substitute for all the living sons of Adam on whom water and the Holy Ghost have wrought their shining miracle; to be for a fleeting thirty minutes the Bride without spot or wrinkle, the City of the sparkling streets and golden spires that St. John beheld on Patmos . . . the dazzling, ineffable creature that is the Church!

And so it strikes me as passing strange that Altar Boys do not figure more prominently in the Christian Arts. Musicians have been inspired to towering melody by the March of the pagan priests, and by meditations in a convent garden. They have never to my knowledge been stirred to forge a single chord of music entitled the Procession of the Acolytes — or a sacristy sonata! I wonder was Petr Ilich Tchaikovsky ever an Altar Boy?

The great painters too have passed them by. Still Leonardo with his busy pencils must have spied their possibilities. Surely there must be a pad of his rapid sketches somewhere in Florence, done perhaps in the great duomo while Savonarola thundered from his pulpit: acolytes with the heads of angels and the seven imps of mischief twinkling in their eyes! Or Murillo of Seville. He if anyone could have wedded in immortal colors their teasing paradox of ecstasy and monkey-shines: sliding down a sacristy balustrade, their cassocks flying like batwings behind them; wrestling to swing on the bell-ropes at the hour of the Angelus. But Murillo of Seville never did!

The quill drivers at least give them mention. Belloc flips them the tribute of a sentence in his *Path to Rome*. Agnes Repplier remembers in her "Convent Days" how a whole school of smocks and pig-tails once fell desperately in love with mysterious dark-eyed Marianus who served at the convent Mass. Then someone or other tells a fetching yarn of a lad who suddenly vanished until his testy pastor confessed that he had bashed his skull in with a candlestick for mispronouncing the Confiteor.

Someday a learned Doctor of Philosophy will take pen in hand and write a thesis on "The Acolyte in Art and Literature." When it is published be sure to read it, for it will be a priceless document. Meanwhile let this be by way of ever so delicate suggestion to the groping doctorandus, a subtly given fillip to the dreaming poet, a gentle innuendo to the artist and the writer to stir their brush and pen in faint praise of Altar Boys.

OLIVER ST. JOHN GOGARTY

To an Old Tenor

Melfort Dalton, I know you well
With your frozen eyes and your spastic stance.
Ah but your voice was clear as a bell
When you tenored the ladies into a trance;
The finest tenor in town you were
Finest; but those were the days of yore,
Oh, but weren't you arrogant then
Weren't you arrogant, Chanticleer,
When you told each hostess to go to hell:
"I'll sing what I like and I'll read the score"?
Little they knew; but I knew what you meant:
Yourself you first had to magnify
Before your notes into Heaven were sent —
(Peacocks and tenors and G.P.I.)
I knew it, and that is the reason why
I now am recording the wonderful tale
Of how you received an offer to come,

Though your eyes and your legs were beginning to fail,
And sing at St. Joseph's Old Maid's Home,
And all the honors you gained therefrom.

We sat in the nearest respectable bar
Waiting the message of how you fared;
And, though we wished it, we were not for
Success overwhelming quite prepared.
Sitting we waited and tippled the ale;
In came the scout with the wonderful word
Of how they tittered and how you scored:
"Called back four times." And we roared *"Waes-hael!*
Melfort has done it again, good Lord!"
We were not allowed in the Old Maid's Home;
And rightly so, for they might be scored;
But "Here, boy, here. Tell us all How Come?"
"He shuffled at first then he came to a stand,
He did not bow as a fav'rite should
(He knew that his balance was none too good)
But he stared with visage inane and bland."
"But how did he merit such great applause?
Be more explicit, you poor recorder?"
"Once for singing, and thrice because
His dress revealed a quaint disorder."

Moral
(*Non Nobis*)

A moral lies in this occurrence;
Let those who have too much assurance
And think that public approbation
That comes from songs or an oration
Is due but to their own desert,
Remember Melfort Dalton's shirt.

———————

DORAN HURLEY

Artistic . . . but Very Plain

When the new pastor came to the Old Parish, he brought with him very decided ideas about the remodeling and redecoration of the interior of our church. In fact, as old Ned Meehan remarked a little later, with a tinge of bitterness, the man was hardly used to the steps of the pulpit before he was announcing special collections for that purpose.

It was not the added contributions from our none too wealthy purses that bothered us . . . we have never been stingy with God in the Old Parish; and to tell you the truth we were tickled to death to have the church fixed up. No. It was the way the man went about it. That hurt us. For he all but intimated from the high altar that as far as taste went, the Holy Rollers could show us a thing or two.

It was not that we expected to be consulted every inch of the way. We know our place and our province; and the beautifying of the church was his province, not ours. But even before the plasterers came in to fix the crack in the north wall and the painters to set up their scaffolding, what did the man do but rise up at the Gospel and say very firmly that we must have noticed that at least three atrocities had already been permanently banished . . . that he was glad to report that a start had been made toward liturgical correctness.

The things you are used to seeing you never notice when they are gone. Not for a while anyway. You feel that they are there because they should be there. Indeed, it took Ned Meehan staying through two Masses and staring hard while he said his beads to find out what was in the church that had been taken out.

It was he who brought the report to the men of the Old Parish seated sunning themselves in Angels' Fold, although Mrs. Patrick

Crowley had spread the tale among the women hours before. Mrs.
Crowley missed them at once . . . the twice life-sized statue of
the Sacred Heart painted most lifelike, the one of the Blessed Virgin
all blue and gold, and the beautiful representation of Saint Patrick
that the Ancient Order and the Knights gave the old pastor on
his jubilee.

To say that we were shocked would be putting it mildly. We
were scandalized. Dinnie the Bow Shea and Larry O'Toole were
all for going to the bishop at once and telling him that the man was
a Protestant. James Kielty, whose son is himself Bishop of the Wild
West, said that he would appeal to Bishop Dan to take the boat right
over to the Holy Father and stop such goings-on. All the elder statesmen made up their minds very firmly that hereafter for Sunday Mass
they would go down to the French. And they did, for the two succeeding Sundays.

They might still be worshippers at Notre Dame de Pitié had
not the old bishop reached Father Beauprêtre's church on his con-
firmation round and, as he passed down the broad aisle, seen not one
but two pews filled with the stalwarts of the Old Parish. The angels,
they say, whisper to the old bishop as he sleeps and bring him all
the news of the diocese that needs his attention.

It was not in the least by accident, then, that he decided to walk
up from Notre Dame to visit the new pastor, after luncheon with
Father Beauprêtre, and that he took the short cut from Saint Mary's
Street through Angels' Fold.

His walk had tired him a bit, he told the old men with a faint
smile and a gentle wave of his hand that they keep their places.
Would they mind if he sat down with them for a bit?

He envied them, he went on, the lovely spot they had for themselves. Everything had been kept so simple, and simplicity was so
close to God. With a twinkle he added mischievously that he supposed if the women of the parish had had the arranging of the little
park all the benches would have sofa cushions and gay umbrellas
over them.

"Doilies," chuckled Ned Meehan with deep relish. "They'd have
doilies and tidies and leetle bits of bows of ribbon here and there."

"I'm sure of it," sighed the old bishop humourously. "It's we men appreciate simplicity and cleanness of line and honesty of workmanship."

"We're the ones does," eagerly agreed Larry O'Toole. "If it was only two red bricks laid together, if they were laid clean and neat it would please the heart of a good workman. But you can't tell a woman that . . . she wouldn't understand. Frills and fripperies they set such store by . . . the poor things."

"I know," murmured the bishop, "I'm afraid poor Father will have a hard job convincing some of our own women that good art is simple art and is unmistakably stamped with its own integrity. You men will understand, but the women!" He lifted his hands.

"Would you say now, Bishop," James Kielty put forth the question tentatively, "that the statue of the Sacred Heart we have in the church yonder isn't a little bit overdone? I mean no irreverence, but would you say it was a little bit on the loud side?"

"As a good workingman, as a craftsman, what would you say, Mr. Kielty?" asked the bishop.

"It was never to my taste, anyway," Larry O'Toole spoke his mind. "To tell you the truth, it always had a 'foreign' look to me. Something plain . . . like in white marble . . . would, I think, be much nicer."

"If you wouldn't put its like on a grave," said old Ned Meehan who at eighty-odd is cemetery conscious, "then you'd have no business putting it up in a church. I think that statue was very disrespectful."

"Hmnh," Dinnie the Bow Shea bit off his question slowly, "but a statue of Saint Patrick now, you'd like to have the green showing on that, wouldn't you? 'Twould be more patriotic."

"Not in church, you wouldn't, Dinnie," Larry O'Toole was very shocked.

"A statue like that, though, would be not out of place in a meeting room, I would say." The old bishop smiled.

"Holy Name hall would be the place for a statue like that, Dinnie." Ned Meehan spoke categorically. And as the bishop rose to go, "Er-r, I wonder would the new pastor, do you think, leave us have the loan of Saint Patrick from the new church for our own hall?"

"I'll mention it to him," said the bishop, "when I tell him how interested you all are in his plans."

"Oh, we are, we are," protested Ned Meehan, "and if you can say a word to him, have him keep it very plain . . . artistic but very plain."

Of course no one knows what passed in conversation between the old bishop and the new pastor that afternoon; but that was not the only visit the bishop made in the Old Parish. For he very gently tugged at Mrs. Patrick Crowley's bell later that afternoon and announced that he had come for tea.

Now Mrs. Patrick Crowley, for the past fifty years president of the altar and rosary society, is an authority on church decoration. The fixing of the altar was ever an art with her, and she was considered in the parish as a very artistic woman. Next only to Sister Felicita, who is a real oil-painter and who can hand-paint a yard of flowers as good as the next one.

But it was not until later that week, when the new pastor called a parish meeting to present his plans for the redecoration of the church to the people and ask their approval, that we knew that there was a name for artistic knowledge about a church, like that possessed by Mrs. Crowley. "Liturgical" was the word, and it was a great treat to all of us to hear it explained. The new pastor knew it from A to Z, and you could see by the nods Mrs. Crowley would give him that she was right behind him every inch of the way. But then so were we all, for it was just what the old bishop had to say without actually putting a name to it.

The church is completed now, and we are more than ever proud of it. The new pastor, too, has firmly ensconced himself in our hearts for having made our House of God so beautiful, and so correctly so.

But there is one thing bothers us all. Ned Meehan is thinking of speaking to the old bishop about it. John McCarthy's boy was ordained in May, and you may be sure that the Old Parish went down to the cathedral in a body. We all talked about this on the way home. After the dignity and simplicity of our own Old Parish church as it stands today, we are afraid that the interior of the cathedral leaves something to be desired.

"Isn't it too bad," said Ned Meehan sadly, "that the rector and the people of the cathedral parish haven't better taste? It struck me today that the high altar at the cathedral was very unliturgical."

FRANCIS MacMANUS

The Professor

Augustine L. Fahy was known in our town as a very learned man, a scholar whose mere presence made all the citizens glow with vicarious distinction. When you saw him sauntering, stick in gloved hand, across the town towards the river-path, along which he took his constitutional every morning, hail, rain or snow, you could return to your counter or your office chair feeling that the town was no hole-in-the-corner provincial place, but a centre fit to rank among the nations. Where he got the title of professor, like many another thing about him, was unknown; and although there were at least ten or eleven hard-working poor devils in the colleges who also bore the title, it was always implied that they, in comparison with the Professor himself, were only imposters.

The Professor didn't work at all. Because he had no visible means of subsistence and could, at the same time, dress decently, regard for him was all the greater. He lived in lodgings over by the White Abbey, was never known to be in trouble about debts, took his constitutional, dropped into the Hotel Metropole occasionally for a nip of whiskey that restored a uniform flush to his benign, otherwise purple-veined face, and generally appeared to be on the very best terms with God, the town, and, perhaps more important, with himself. What he had lived on, who were his people, how he came into the town, nobody knew.

He was not to be questioned. Indeed, no one ever thought of being so impertinent. His carriage, voice, dress and gesture forbade anything as imprudent as that. For he was a good-looking man, so portly, however, that he seemed to be leaning backward from the hips to maintain balance. His mass of fine silver hair, curling over his collar at the nape of his neck, was in itself impressive enough as a crown of glory, without speaking of his black, very broad-trimmed hat at all. He wore dark, even clerical black, clothes and these, with his white shirts and soft necktie fashioned in a flowing bow, set him apart from the townsfolk, and especially from all the very ordinary college-men who mistakenly called themselves professors. There were two other effects which indisputably allowed him full and solitary possession of his title, and they were his rimless pince-nez anchored to his person by black ribbon, and his magnificent voice, bass, rich in tones, attractively accented, the very voice of learning itself.

Now, what was the nature of his learning? That was another impertinent question that only a fool, reckless with folly and ignorance, would dare to put. Didn't the Chief Librarian say once, after a conversation about books, that he had never met a man who knew as much about embalming as the Professor? Embalming was presumed to be a small insignificant portion of his knowledge. Since nobody could fix for him any branch of learning in particular, it was assumed — wasn't it proved by the title? — that he knew everything about everything. He would have been in the mental asylum with sheer cleverness, it was said, but for the restraint he kept on himself.

There were some real facts. It was vaguely remembered that once he had condescended to engage in a long-winded controversy with the Town Clerk about the deplorable, uncivic and unseemly state of the sewerage in his lodgings. He had written columns in the *Tribune* demanding new pipes or a new corporation, and the editor, himself suffering from the decrepit arteries of drainage, had backed him up, referring to him as "the eminent well-known scholar" in caustic footnotes about the City Fathers. It was also remembered by one of the college-men — jealousy this was, of course! — that the footnotes were necessary to explain that the Professor, through his verbiage, was asking for new pipes. At any rate, it was admitted that Augustine L. Fahy was a scholar, a great one, far above the heads of the townsfolk, and stood as an institution as cherished and as worthy as the grey, mouldering, charming seventeenth century town clock-tower, or as the Aldermen who played Lord Mayor in turn, or as the Cathedral with the birds circling above it for generations.

II

A local discovery brought the Professor into the unenviable position of leader.

Some workmen, digging up a garden on the river-bank for the laying of new pipes after all the years of controversy, unearthed a few stone compartments containing broken pots and stone implements. You yourself probably can recall the discovery, for it created a stir, archaeologists travelled down from Dublin, and our town figured largely in the daily papers, which it hadn't done since the time the Aldermen locked themselves in the Council Chamber and went on hunger-strike as a protest against the criticisms of the *Tribune*. (But that's another story!) The town had its own way of dealing with the discovery, which only confirmed what they had always believed, that the town was very ancient. The *Tribune*, naturally, published what was said by the archaeologists, but only after the special correspondent had given the considered opinion of Professor Augustine L. Fahy from the scene itself. He declared that it was a discovery of the first magnitude, that the broken vessels and stone implements suggested the work of human hands and that it was time for the town to have a new drainage system. He, complete with pince-nez and ribbon, graced a page with his photograph.

Then the whole thing would have faded away, leaving the Professor with another leaf to his laurels, if Canon Kinch, on the lookout for more funds for the Boy Scouts' Hall in St. Michael's Parish, hadn't taken it into his head to invite from Dublin an old friend — a very famous archaeologist whose name mustn't be mentioned. The idea was to put the Professor on the same platform, or even in the chair, and what with the discovery, the renown of the Professor and curiosity about the issue of the debate, the hall would be filled. The day was fixed and the hour appointed, and the Canon himself said a word from the pulpit.

The town was in no doubt as to the outcome if the lecture developed into a debate between the Professor and the man from Dublin. The *Tribune* looked forward with eagerness a month before the time, and said that while it would be unfair to the visiting lecturer to anticipate the results, all honest citizens knew what to expect.

But the same *Tribune*, a week later, was to announce, with the deepest regret, that the eminent scholar, Professor Augustine L. Fahy, had been taken ill with a form of contagious fever — due, it maliciously added, according to some reports, "to the deplorable, uncivic and unseemly condition" of the drainage. (The Editor rather overworked that phrase!) While the lecture at which he was to preside would not be postponed, it was sincerely hoped that his absence would not incommode the energetic Very Reverend Canon Kinch.

Apparently there's nothing on earth that ever will incommode the Canon. He went blandly ahead, advertising his lecture, persuading people who wouldn't attend to buy tickets, and enticing likely people into buying more seats than they could sit on, all with the plea that it would be a help for archaeology, the Boy Scouts and the Church. I'm afraid that his business during the weeks before the lecture earned him, for the time being only, of course, the ill repute of being a hard-hearted cruel man who pushed on a lecture even while the principal figure lay prostrate, at death's door, preparing to impoverish the earth and to enrich heaven with distinction. The principal figure, big-hatted, dark, benign, crowned with silvery hair, wasn't seen crossing the town towards the river. For two issues the *Tribune* still regretted to announce the illness of Augustine L. Fahy who, it explained again, was to have lectured, and so forth; but the plea for recovery became agonised. The honour of the town, her claim to a place in the sunlight, as the Editor, picturesquely put it, would be safe only in the hands of a man of such eminence and learning as Professor Augustine L. Fahy.

On the day of the lecture the silvery head lit up our town once again. He doffed his hat, raised his gloved hand and stick, to the many salutes he got and to the good wishes for his health. A king, who occasionally makes a surprise sally without escort among his subjects, couldn't get more smiles and good-mornings.

"Yes!" said he to one citizen, "I'm not quite recovered, I must say." The pince-nez were removed and the gloved hand twiddled the black ribbon. "But this matter arranged by my friend Canon Kinch, you know! It had to be met, and I think — " The cough was polite, the voice deep and musical, the accent just tinged with slight scorn as if the lecture were a mere children's party. "Dear, dear! My friend the Canon insisted. A remarkably energetic man, remarkably! That's a fine little boy you have, if I may say so. Ha! I see the hour is advancing to twelve. Good morning."

Canon Kinch should have been satisfied. He nearly filled his hall, a rare thing for a performance of the kind, with people who cared little for the Boy Scouts and nothing at all about archaeology. Curiosity brought them. They civilly clapped the expert from Dublin when, punctual, fussy and smiling, he passed up the hall between the Canon and one of the college-men. The Canon and his company seated themselves behind the table, covered with green baize, on the platform, and appeared to get into an earnest conversation that didn't interest the Canon at all, because he spent his time pulling out his watch and glancing at the clock, then past the time, on the back wall of the room.

The Professor made his entry. It was obvious that no archaeologist, however renowned, had a dog's chance. The clapping rolled up to the platform, proud, cocksure clapping, increasing in volume while the Professor, bowing, brushing back his silver hair, retrieving his pince-nez and patting children on the head, made his lone triumphal progress to the platform. He shook hands with the expert, then seemed to protest, with large smiles, that he would not take the chair which, in the end, he did with the gesture of a man forced to ascend a throne. He looked pale as he arose to introduce the lecturer.

It was the usual kind of introduction: the lecturer was eminent, the discovery on which he would speak was known to one and all, and he, the Chairman, was sure that everybody would have a most enjoyable evening. The voice and man made the usual speech seem very unusual, very brilliant, very weighty.

The lecture, which doesn't matter much, was all about the Stone Age and the Bronze Age and long-headed and short-headed folk, the art of the potter and the building of stone forts in pre-historic Ireland. The expert knew too much about it to make it simple, and besides he foostered with papers, lost himself in the middle of sentences, and behaved generally as if he were conversing with himself. He was rewarded with a polite clap, led vigorously by the Canon.

The Professor called on the Canon to put the vote of thanks, and added that he himself would second it. The Canon, good man, was brief. Anyway the audience had got an hour and a half of it already, counting the delay caused by the Professor. The Professor was also brief.

"May I add," he said, coughing and fingering his pince-nez, "May I add my appreciation to the good Canon's. You indicated by your applause" — a slight silence here was significant — "that-eh-I-what you thought of the lecture. For many, many years" — he dropped his voice — "I have been a citizen of this town, this magnificent city, set like a jewel in a valley where river and woodland afford us some of the finest scenery, I say it without fear of contradiction, some of the finest scenery in the world. I had thought to retire from any kind of active life many years ago, and only for the good offices of the dear Canon and the repute of our visitor, I should have refused to appear. Besides, as you know, my illness, my recent illness — " Warm applause with hear-hears, and furious scribbling by the *Tribune* reporter. "Ours, if I may say so, and I'm sure I may, since I have sojourned so long amongst a kindly, good, and talented people whom I regard as my own, ours is an ancient as well as a beautiful city. Ancient, do I say?" His voice boomed. "It is more ancient, more historical, more well-supplied with links with the past, than any stranger can ever know. We have lived here. Here we hope to die. Who can tell us more about this landmark or that old ruin or about the latest discovery than ourselves? And I say it without offence, without any desire to hurt feelings, but in the full knowledge that no judgments should be pronounced until we, the citizens of this fair city, have decided for ourselves." The pince-nez went back with a snap, the mouth smiled, the silvery hair was brushed back, and the Professor stalked back to his chair amidst such a burst of applause as must have somehow penetrated to the brain of the archaeologist from Dublin. The Professor had saved the honour of our town. He had kept the torch of learning alight. His renown was greater and he was almost sacred.

He died some years ago, greeting Saint Peter, you may be sure, with an imposing gesture that allowed no hedging or refusals. There was a magnificent funeral through the streets, and columns of pane- gyrics in the *Tribune,* which, out of respect for the dead, forbore to mention "the deplorable, uncivic and unseemly" state of anything in the town.

A solicitor's clerk who was given the Professor's papers to set them right, found, in a pathetic album of photographs, a few of those bill-heads, like the ruled sheets which traders send out to customers. You know the kind: across the top the name, business, address and slogans of the trader are printed. Across the Professor's bill-heads was written in large black type: "Augustine Lucius Fahy, Under- taker, Dublin; Funerals Arranged; Embalming; Moderate Charges." So ran the whispered story of the solicitor's clerk, a story that nobody would believe, and that I doubt myself, for Augustine L. Fahy's repute is formidable. But there are a few evil-minded peo- ple who cannot forget that the Chief Librarian once said that he never had met anybody who knew as much about embalming as the black-coated, silvery-haired, benign Professor.

5. MATTERS HAGIOGRAPHICAL

5. MATTERS HAGIOGRAPHICAL

"Good thoughts his only friends,
His wealth a well-spent age,
The earth his sober inn
And quiet pilgrimage."

— From "The Man of Life Upright"
by Thomas Campion

"The saints preserve us!" we sometimes exclaim. I often wonder why we don't give as much thought to preserving them as we want them to give to preserving us. I'm not trying to start an argument on hagiographical matters — the saints preserve us! — but the general notion long has been that a saint is an excellent person to pray to and an awful person to read about. That is why I am all for the growing movement among writers in the Church militant toward establishing a better liaison with the Church triumphant by writing interesting and believable lives of the saints.

There certainly is a middle ground between some modern "bi-ogre-phers," who make saints seem horrible people, and the "biog-ravers" who make saints seem too good to be people at all. And the happy medium has been struck by writers like Katherine Burton, Theodore Maynard, Aloysius Roche, Henri Ghëon, Thomas Lahey, Joan Windham, Mary Windeatt.

Another encouraging trend has been the occasional tilting of halos by Catholic humorists. This is a precarious pastime, unless done by careful hands. The proper angle which will emphasize the saint's humanity and at the same time preserve his dignity, is matter for an expert.

Helen Walker Homan's "Epistle to St. Paul" is gentle halo-tilting on a very high level. Monsignor Knox's quatrains are a bit more jostling jests. You might call them Hard Knox. But they are deft and clever. They are, as Gordon Albion pointed out in printing them in *Duckett's Register,* of the species "clerihew." Clerihew is the middle name of E. C. Bentley, creator of a severe and strong form of biography. Monsignor Knox said that his clerihews were "made up round the dinner table." So any carping critics, not certain of the authenticity of the details, will please remember that the rhymes are *ex tabula,* not *ex cathedra!*

St. Mochua and St. Imaginus are not in Father Butler's *Lives of the Saints,* nor on the Irish or Roman calendar of saints. The suspicion is that they belong, respectively, to the Sullivanian and Maguirean calendar. But away with hagiographical hagglers! I can't think of any other two saints who do a better job of reminding us the main difference between the saints and the rest of us is that they are wise enough to know how foolish they are and strong enough to overcome their weaknesses.

HELEN WALKER HOMAN

Epistle to St. Paul

Dear Saint Paul:

It will, perhaps, startle you to learn the desire to write to you was born of the suspicion that we shared at least two points in common — one, you were forever writing letters and nobody seemed ever to answer them; and two, you had weakness for making puns (don't try to deny it). I wonder if people were always jumping on you, as they are on me, for this *petite faiblesse?* It's a dreadful admission of egotism to confess that, when I discovered your puns were almost as bad as mine, it drew me even closer to you than years of listening, each Sunday, to your beautiful Epistles. There is, for instance, that atrocious pun you perpetrated in your Epistle to Philemon when you asked him to take back and forgive his runaway slave, Onesimus, who had not only decamped but had robbed his master as well, but whom you had recently converted. Now, Saint Paul, in spite of my little Latin and less Greek, I do know that the name Onesimus is the same in Greek as the word for "profitable." Thus translating, you are discovered shamelessly writing to Philemon: "I beseech thee for my son, Profitable, who hath been heretofore unprofitable to thee, but now is Profitable both to me and to thee."

What makes your life story so human is that the drama was not infrequently mingled with comedy.

Even though the joke was on you, Saint Paul, I think you will agree that there was comedy in your experience at Lystra, when you arrived with Barnabas to spread the gospel. You certainly began with a superb gesture, crying to a life-long cripple; "Stand upright on your feet." Whereupon he "leaped up and walked." But do you recall how the astounded townspeople declared that only Jupiter and Mercury could perform such miracles; therefore, you must be Mercury (since you were chief speaker) and Barnabas must be Jupiter? They joyfully shouted: "The gods have come down to us in the likeness of men!" Naturally, you were somewhat taken aback. There they were, as a result of your miracle wrought to bring them a new religion, lustily cheering for the old! And when you saw a jubilant multitude preparing a nice sacrifice of oxen and garlands to lay at your outraged Christian feet, your consternation must indeed have been great. Poor Saint Paul!

Reading over your wonderful letters, it has struck me as perhaps unfortunate that they have come to be known as the "Pauline Epistles"; and some of them, as the "Pastoral Epistles." Youth is woefully ignorant — and I know, rather too intimately, at least one person who, as a child, thought there must once have been a lady named Pauline who had been a great letter-writer and who was sure the Pastoral Epistles dealt only with rural life. Bored with the two ideas she investigated no further. Later, when an overdue enlightenment dawned on what you can see was a lamentable intellect, she was further deterred by the unjust charge that you were a violent antifeminist. Not that I think the charge utterly groundless, Saint Paul. But that a careful reading of your Epistles indicates it has been grossly exaggerated, with no allowance made for extenuating circumstances. I can even see you at times, a very sound feminist. You did not cheer too much for marriage in the first place (nor do our most modern feminists) but if entered into (you admit reluctantly that "it is better to be married than to be burnt") you uphold women's rights in the home, at least. "Art thou bound to a wife? Seek not to be loosed." Some of my sex have deemed it unfortunate that you saw fit to continue: "Art thou loosed from a wife? Seek not a wife." But I feel sure you would have stated the same precept to women, had you been addressing them.

As for your other alleged severities, tackling them as I do, a confirmed feminist, I think I can see a good reason for them all. Loath as I am to admit it — unique as your experience may seem — it must be conceded that women had given you no end of trouble. When you and Barnabas were going after the conversion of Antioch in a big way, and the Jews got the women of the town to arouse the authorities against you, it was the feminine clamor which caused your forced withdrawal. Also, there were those two ladies of your own Philippian Church, Evodia and Syntache, who, in that otherwise peaceful congregation, stirred up all kinds of dissension with their theological disputes. Even after all these centuries, their shrill arguments seem still to linger on the air. Their very names lay them open to suspicion. I can almost see Evodia pulling Syntache's hair, and Syntache scratching back. Your gentleness in rebuking them must have made them very much ashamed of themselves: "I beg of Evodia, and I beseech Syntache, to be of one mind in the Lord."

Did you know that the story had gotten around that there was also a damsel of Iconium — one Thecla — who caused you considerable embarrassment? It is related that she became such an ardent convert that she insisted on dressing up as a boy with a view toward accompanying you on all your missionary journeys! There is only one word I can think of to describe adequately your state of mind at this juncture. You must, in fine, have been flabbergasted! With some difficulty, you succeeded in sidestepping her; but later, I'm sure, must amply have forgiven her when you learned she had braved martyrdom for the faith.

Then there was that other lady who upset you considerably. You remember — the one who lived in Thyatira, and was possessed of a "pythonical spirit" which revealed the future to her. She "brought to her masters much gain by divining." How it must have irritated you, whenever she saw you walk quietly in the public streets — for then, we are told, she would quit her job, run after you and tag you up and down the town, all the time crying out loudly your name and mission. "And this she did many days." No one can blame you, that this unwelcome publicity got to be such a nuisance that you finally had to turn in your tracks and exorcise the spirit possessing her. It was most unfortunate, Saint Paul, that this also had the effect of ruining her commercial value. The spirit gone out of her, her masters soon found she was no longer any good at prophesying. Naturally, they had you arrested for interfering with their business — and you were beaten and thrown into prison.

Ladies all — and now after all these years, when you really should be allowed to continue, undisturbed, a well-earned peace from feminine botheration, here I come along with this epistle! Small wonder, that with a few such experiences, you felt like writing: "Let women keep silence in the churches — If they would learn anything, let them ask their husbands at home." (The less they bothered you the better.) I am a trifle encouraged, however, to read that women, if they lived long enough, might hope eventually for your confidence. You admonish Bishop Timothy, of the Ephesus Church, in selecting widows to help him, carefully to choose those not less than sixty years old. You take pains to add: "But the younger widows avoid." Since philosophers of succeeding centuries have concurred in the soundness of this caution, I'm sure Timothy must have seen sense to it.

RONALD KNOX

Saintly Limericks

St. Cyprian of Carthage
Sat down on the bath-edge
And wondered whether it would be a sin
If he didn't get in. . . .

St. Simeon Stylites
Left off the use of nighties;
But St. John Chrysostom
Said it would never do for HIS system.

When they told St. Gregory the Great
It was his turn to take the eight,
He replied, with a slight cough,
That he thought it was his day off.

Said gentle St. Francis of Sales
"I've converted the Prince of Wales."
 Said Francis Xavier:
 "Oh, 'ave yer!"

FRANCES M. MAGUIRE

The Ungrateful Bricklayer

It has been told how Imaginus was gifted with the power to work miracles, and how, on divers occasions, he brought about wondrous happenings to the edification of the multitude and the consternation of his Superiors. So much was this the case, that at last he was forbidden to work miracles, except by permission of the Abbot or the Prior of the Monastery where he lived.

Imaginus was in no wise cast down, for he had every confidence in the wisdom of those set in authority over him and he longed only to perfect his soul by the practice of a happy obedience. He asked permission to help those who were sweeping the city streets of the grain which he had caused by his miraculous power to grow along the pavements. This the Abbot granted him.

For many days Imaginus laboured and it may be thought that he sometimes regretted having brought about such an abundant harvest. This was not so. He saw only evidence of the power of God which had brought the corn into being and his labour he offered in thanksgiving.

One day while he was thus engaged he met a grasshopper. The little creature jumped through the air and alighted at the monk's feet.

"See how far I can fly," he boasted. "There is no one who has such strong legs and such fine beautiful wings."

Imaginus tried to teach him the value of humility, pointing out that his strength was due in no wise to any merit of his own, but was wholly dependent on the bounty of God. But the grasshopper would not agree and continued to praise himself and his accomplishments.

Imaginus saw that he would not learn in the pride of life, but he prayed that in misfortune more wisdom might come to him. "Remember," he said to the grasshopper, "if you ever are overcome with weakness and cannot fly, repent of your vanity and call upon God that His finger may sustain you."

The grasshopper gaily promised (for he was a cheerful fellow) and he hopped beside Imaginus as he set out on his return journey to the Monastery. Their way lay along the city streets where many people were moving to and fro. After a time the grasshopper found it convenient to hide in the folds of the monk's habit, for fear of being walked on by the passers-by. But he said nothing of this to Imaginus as he was ashamed that his fine jumping did not safeguard him from the traffic.

They had gone some distance when they came to a high building, on the top of which, some workmen were laying bricks. The building was so tall that from below the bricklayers looked no larger than the grasshopper himself.

As Imaginus and Chirripus (for that was the grasshopper's name) walked past the building, one of the bricklayers missed his footing and began to fall through the air towards the earth. "This man," said Chirripus to himself, "can fly through the air much further than I can," and he lost a little of his vanity.

The people in the street also watched the man and began to cry out loudly and to run together into a crowd. Seeing them point upwards with their fingers, Imaginus raised his head from the reverie into which he had fallen. When he saw the man rapidly approaching from above, he was overcome with dismay, for he realised that the man would be killed if he hit the ground. It was, however, not so much the bricklayer's death which concerned the good monk, as the fact that, if he should be killed, his soul would undoubtedly be lost for ever.

Never had Imaginus felt himself in such a dilemma. He longed to beg the mercy of God to save the man's life; but he would rather have died himself than commit the sin of disobedience by performing a miracle. It would be necessary then to obtain the permission of his Superiors. Crying loudly to the bricklayer to await his return, he gathered up the skirts of his habit and made off to the Monastery with all speed.

At the Monastery the Prior was instructing a class of catechumens in the merits of the Nine First Fridays. He sustained Imaginus's interruption with patience and received his request with equanimity.

"Were I to grant you permission to do as you desire," he said, "the time is already past for it to be of profit, for by now the poor man has fallen to the ground. May God have mercy on his soul."

"Amen," said Imaginus. "But indeed it is not as you think, Father Prior. For I dared not commit the sin of disobedience by working a miracle without your permission, so I bade the man wait for my return and came with all haste to the Monastery."

"What!" exclaimed the Prior, jumping to his feet. "Do I understand that you have left the man in mid-air?"

"That is undoubtedly the case," said Imaginus. Whereupon the Prior ran out of the house, followed by Imaginus and all the catechumens.

When they came to the place where the bricklayer was they found a large crowd of people. Some firemen were raising ladders.

Imaginus looked at the bricklayer and felt very sad, for he saw that the man's soul was dark with sin, and he longed to bring him to repentance.

"Have I your permission, Father Prior," he said, "to save the life of this poor fellow?"

"Yes, yes," said the Prior. "Bring him down."

Imaginus raised his hand. Very gently and slowly the bricklayer came to earth. Imaginus put his hand on the man's shoulder. "How grateful you should be," he said, "to the Infinite Mercy of God which has thus saved you from death."

But the man, in a rage at being, as he thought, made to look like a fool before so many people, would have struck Imaginus had he not been constrained by two policemen and a chartered accountant.

Now Chirripus, who had remained hidden in the folds of Imaginus's habit, had seen and heard all that had taken place. Becoming incensed at the bricklayer's ingratitude he hopped across and bit him sharply on the ankle. He then accompanied Imaginus and the Prior and all the catechumens back to the Monastery.

After a time the bricklayer found that his foot became red and swollen. Finding it easier to suffer repentance for his sins than the pain of his wound, he repaired to the Monastery to seek the aid of Father Imaginus. There he met the Prior and had perforce to listen to much good counsel concerning the state of his soul and the necessity of leading a Christian life. Then the Prior gave him absolution and a poultice for his foot and sent him away.

Imaginus, who in silence had seen all this, spoke to the grasshopper with loving benevolence. "Well done, little Chirripus," he said. "What I sought to do by extravagant means you have accomplished by lowly ones." But the grasshopper who had learnt his lesson would not accept the praise.

"Hold out your finger, Father Imaginus," he said. "I am weary of flying."

H. I. PHILLIPS

Saint Nick Visits the Salesgirl

'Twas the night before Christmas when all through the flat
Not a creature was stirrin' (include me in that);
My stockin's a little the worse for the wear,
Was hung on the back of a three-legged chair;
Outside snow was fallin' in beautiful flakes,
But I didn't care — I was too full of aches;
I'd worked in a store through the holiday strife,
And was plannin' to sleep for the rest of my life.

When up from the airshaft there came such a clatter
I leaped out of bed to see what was the matter,
(I thought at the time 'twas a nut down one flight,
Who starts up his radio late ev'ry night);
So I went to the window and loudly did cry,
"Is this Christmas Eve or the Fourth of July?"

When what to my dead-with-sleep eyes did appear
But a hinky-dink sleigh and eight tiny reindeer!
And who should be drivin' right up to the door
But one of them masquerade guys from the store!
I said to myself, "What can be the mug's game?"
When he clucked to his reindeers and called 'em by name:
"Now Dasher! Now Dancer! Now Prancer! Now Vixen!
On Comet! On Cupid! On Donner and Blitzen!"
An just as I'm dopin' what next he will do,
Right up to the housetop the whole outfit flew!

And then in a twinklin' I heard on the roof
The prancin' an' pawin' of meat on the hoof;
(Just imagine my feelin's with sleep nearly dead
And some sap with an ANIMAL ACT OVERHEAD!)

As I drew in my neck and was turnin' around,
Down the chimney my visitor came with a bound;
A big bag of junk he displayed with a grin,
And he acted to me like he'd like to move in.
He was chubby, good natured and oozin' with glee.
But I ask you, dear reader, what was it to me?
The point that I make is 'twas then 2 o'clock,
And a man in my room without stoppin' to knock!

I was thinkin' how noivy he was and how slick
When he says to me, "Lady, I'm only St. Nick."
Well, a poor tired store slave in no mood for fun,
I gave him a look and I asked him, "Which one?"
"As a Christmas rush salesgirl," I said, "you'll agree
That a look at St. Nick is no big treat to me;
This has gone far enough and this bunk's gotta stop —
Take the air with them goats or I'll yell for a cop!"

He spoke not a word but went on with his work,
And filled up my stockin's then turned with a jerk.
And layin' a finger aside his red nose,

And givin' a nod up the airshaft he rose. . . .
He sprang to his sleigh with a shake of his head,
And I pulled the shades down and fell into bed.
"Merry Christmas!" he called as away his deers flew,
And I just gave a yawn and I answers, "Sez you!"

———————

A. M. SULLIVAN

The Grief of St. Mochua

Mochua, wept without restraint
Beside a rowan tree. The Saint

Had three friends and they did die —
A cock, a mouse, and silver fly.

The cock had learned to crow in Latin
And rouse Mochua up at matin.

And if the hermit did not hear
A field mouse nibbled at his ear.

And when his eyes began to falter
The silver fly hummed on the psalter

Moving along the notes gregorian
To mark the cadences stentorian.

Not rash the sorrow he expended
For the happy days now ended.

The cock grew proud, and crowed in Greek
And a verb irregular, cracked his beak,

The field mouse, chancing on a cat
Blessed himself and murmured, "scat."

The fly who marked the psalter scale
Flew headlong into a dewy veil,

Thus Mochua's servants perished
And with them everything he cherished,

And mournfully he took his quill
Making complaint to Columkille.

"Once, I was rich, none can deny,
With a cock, a mouse, and silver fly,

No king of Eire, Greece, or Rome
Was rich as Mochua in his home

Of a cloistered grinian where the gold
Of sun and moon fell on my fold,

Now, poor am I, with a pride as scant
As the heart of a wayside mendicant."

Columkille, vexed as a druid oracle
Hurried to Mochua in his coracle,

And said, "Thou art guilty of heinous sin
O Mochua, for pride was in

Your worldly heart. Now may the salt
Of anguish shrive the bitter fault

And for your penance, search until
You find three gillies on a hill, —

A bird to pluck grain from the eyes
Of a sleepy monk and make him rise,

And if he slumbers yet, a bee
To rouse him somewhat urgently,

And for his psalter, search the thicket
Until you catch a basso cricket.

Seeking them, Mochua, pray that I
Find a cock, and mouse and a silver fly."

6. OUR ENGLISH COUSINS

6. OUR ENGLISH COUSINS

> *"The English amused themselves sadly after the fashion of their country."*
>
> — Froissart

Our English cousins are scattered throughout this book, imparting their rare and, paradoxically enough, well-done humor to various sections. But at this point there is a pause and a definite doffing of the jesters' caps in deference to the British Comic Muse.

There is no doubt that the British Comic Muse has had her face lifted lately. The changes in her physiognomy have resulted primarily in a more versatile mouth and tongue. In pre-First World War times, the Muse would part her mouth in a genteel smile, à la Addison and Steele, or cluck her tongue, à la Gilbert and Sullivan, making funny but harmless noises.

But nowadays the Muse has discovered that her tongue also can be made to fit very nicely into her right or left cheek, with excellent risible results. Thus we have in this section J. B. Morton solemnly describing an imaginary visit to the Soviet Union, and all the while there is that bump on the right side of his face. The Muse has also learned that there are times when the tongue is most comfortable when protruding from the mouth to an extent of several inches, a kind of peninsula of impertinence. D. B. Wyndham Lewis' sketch exemplifies this posture, as he irreverently treats of false pride in matters of genealogy and nobility.

Under Evelyn Waugh's tutelage the Muse has learned not only to place her tongue artfully, but also to thumb her nose, use brass knuckles and deliver swift kicks with spiked shoes. He has also taught her that the mouth can be opened not only for genteel smiles

but for hoots and hisses. When with him the Muse is frequently very
unladylike.

The reason for the change in British humor, from Old World
charm and ease to slickness, caustic sophistication and tension, is to
be found in the American influence, as D. B. Wyndham Lewis has
admitted. The flow of wit from Hollywood and New York to London has greatly surpassed the flow from London to Hollywood and
New York. English humor has caused a mere ripple on the periphery
of America's iconoclastic comic culture. But the fresh hurricane of
humor from the West has laid low many ancestral English castles
of wit, where the slow-moving, snuff-box and spotless-waistcoat
comics made merry in their own quiet way.

Mr. Waugh is one of the bridges between the two humors. His
urbanity is English, his satiric incisions are American. The irony
of the matter is that in his book, *The Loved One,* Mr. Waugh pays
tribute to American humor by as alum-inating a portrayal of Hollywood as any of that town's denizens could have done. A portion of
this book is reprinted here, showing Dennis Barlow, the frustrated
English poet with movie ambitions, carrying out his duties at the
Happier Hunting Ground, a dog crematory in Hollywood. Barlow
acts in defiance of the British-in-Hollywood dictum that "there are
some jobs an Englishman doesn't take."

Monsignor Ronald Knox (*See* sections III, V, XI) is a comic
Waugh-rior in clerical garb. His lance is lively and sharp, but not
quite as cutting and flamboyant as Mr. Waugh's. D. B. Wyndham
Lewis and J. B. Morton, get a lot of their flippancy from their
American cousins. Douglas Woodruff, like Father Basset (section
IV) and Bruce Marshall (sections II and III), is a bit out of the
stream of British-American humor. His writings are in a more quiet
vein. Mr. Woodruff, in fact, frequently brings you back to an at-
mosphere which has the aroma of the scholar's midnight oil and
the panorama of Oxford's cricket field and quad. He is just as likely
to title a joke, as he does in this section, "In Partibus Infidelium?",
or to throw in a casual side remark, referring to Cicero's *De Amicitia.*

But Mr. Woodruff is not a phenomenon among English writers.
Scholarship and humor may make startling companions to American
eyes, but in England writers have found that the jester's cap fits

very comfortably underneath the scholar's mortarboard. Belloc could pen an amusing farrago or write an historical treatise, and Chesterton could roar on merrily about the rolling English road, or sing inspiredly of Don Juan of Austria. J. B. Morton can tell us of Sobieski, King of Poland, of Louis XVII, but, when the serious work is done, of Captain Foulenough and the Belle of the Southern Command. D. B. Wyndham Lewis is equally at home with François Villon, Charles the Fifth, James Boswell or Aelfgyva Rigthorpe. Evelyn Waugh can write glowingly of Edmund Campion or gloweringly of Aimee Thanatogenos and American crematories. Ronald Knox can rewrite the New Testament with a pen dipped in the honey of eloquence or cut down an opponent with a scythe dipped in the gall of satire.

This eclecticism is one accomplishment English humorists have, over and above anything they may have gotten from America. And when the English humorist combines his scholarship and his humor for a strictly humorous effect, as D. B. Wyndham Lewis does in his sketch in this section, the results are sometimes especially fresh and appealing to the American taste. It is too much to expect many American humorists to compete in this field. I refer now particularly to many comedians of stage, screen and radio, as well as to many in the book field. To them the Renaissance sounds like the name of a restaurant, and they'd expect to find the Bayeux tapestry in Macy's home furnishings department.

D. B. WYNDHAM LEWIS

A Personal Matter *

For some time I have been brooding, not without enthusiasm, over a recent news-item concerning the unveiling of a mural tablet to

---

* Reprinted from *Welcome to 'All This,* by D. B. Wyndham Lewis, published by E. P. Dutton and Co., Inc.

the memory of Arlette of Falaise, mother of William the Conqueror. The tablet, affixed to a pillar of the ruined abbey outside Honfleur where Arlette is buried, is the gift of two descendants of the Conqueror, Mrs. Stober and Mrs. Jones, both of America.

The incident interests me chiefly because I myself am also, in my way, a descendant of the Conqueror through a great-great-great-great-great-great-great aunt, who was herself engaged to the Conqueror for a time. No student of the Bayeux Tapestry can have helped being puzzled by the odd and hitherto enigmatic group which is placed exactly between the scene of William's interview with Harold and William's departure for the Mont St. Michel. This group is of two figures: a woman, standing between two pillars, and a man in the dress of a learned clerk, apparently striking her on the head. Over this is inscribed:

VNVS: CLERICVS: ET: AELFGYVA

That is, "A clerk and Aelfgyva." No authority on the Tapestry has yet produced a satisfactory explanation of this incident. I can do so, however. The female figure is that of my aunt, Miss Aelfgyva Rigthorpe. The clerk who is beating my aunt about the head is J. O. Smith, private secretary to the Conqueror. The whole story is rather sordid, but I owe it perhaps to my aunt's and the Conqueror's memory to state the facts. I take them from private archives.

My aunt was walking with her maid in Falaise one day in 1060 when a stranger with a clerk's tonsure approached, saluted her courteously, and asked the way to the Castle. She told him. He said, "Thank you so much. I am a stranger in Falaise. And in any case," he added through clenched teeth, "I love you, you little bronze-haired Norman duck."

My aunt gave him a cool, level glance and turned away.

"Wait," said the stranger, biting his lip. "They tell me you are engaged to the Duke."

My aunt haughtily inclined her head.

"Let me tell you," said Mr. Smith (for he it was) bitterly, clutching his shaven head, "that I'm just mad about, mad about, mad about you; but I think you're just a gadabout, gadabout, gadabout, too."

He then lifted his right hand in a passion and struck my aunt;

and at that moment William, Duke of Normandy, her betrothed, came riding past. The Duke at once reined in and called out rather angrily, "I say, you can't do that sort of thing here!"

"Yes, sir, I can," said Mr. Smith, and struck my aunt again. "I can also," he added, "write in cursive and uncial script, illuminate MS., clean and polish hawks, and do sums in my head."

"What," said the Duke sharply, "is fifty-nine times thirty-million-eight-hundred-thousand-and-sixty-four?"

"An awful lot," said Mr. Smith. "Nevertheless," he added more gently, "I love this girl."

"So do I," said the Conqueror. "Don't I, Gyva?" he said to my aunt.

"In a way," said my aunt shyly.

"Well," said the Conqueror, "hum something." So my aunt hummed a favourite song of the Duke's which went:

> I never seemed to know what love meant dear, till I met you,
> I never thought that two hearts as one could beat so true.
> You gave me sunshine and gladness all the day, sweetheart,
> And should there come a day when we two must part:
> *Refrain*
> Boys of the Empire, brave and bold and free (etc.)

The Duke and Mr. Smith both hummed the refrain very feelingly with my aunt, and the result of the whole incident was that Mr. Smith that day became the Duke's secretary. My aunt broke off her engagement soon afterwards and later married William Rufus; at which the Conqueror observed merely, "God's splendour!" (*Par le splendeur Deux!*) — which was his usual comment. The early portion of the family tree, therefore, stands thus:

WILLIAM THE CONQUEROR — Matilda

William Rufus ── Miss Rigthorpe (my aunt)

Charlotte — H. J. Shakespeare, George, d. 1178. Odo d. 1145
('Nasty,' as he was called). (Good)

William — Anne Hathaway

Baby — G. Washington Shaw

Bernard

So all turned out fairly well. My aunt Aelfgyva, as she appears in the act of being hit by Mr. Smith in the Bayeux Tapestry, was slim, petite, cultured, passionate, but a great needlewoman. She took a sincere interest in the Norman Conquest, and seemed affected when offered the crown. For some reason the words "Anglo-Saxon" always made her laugh quite terribly; but so they do me, for that matter. She also thought there were far too many Smiths about.

This is all I have to say here about Miss Rigthorpe. She died in a serene old age, in possession of all her faculties, and on meeting old Mr. Smith in Rome one day in 1126 was able to rally him gently on his technique with women. There was then, of course, no Air Force, or she would undoubtedly have brought into her rallying something faintly satiric about "Air Force methods."

Any other descendant of the Conqueror, whatever her name, who would like to commemorate my aunt may communicate with me, care of Barclay's Bank. Cheques may be crossed "Rigthorpe Memorial"; or, better still, left open.

J. B. MORTON

Mr. Milk Goes to Russia *

Among the party of distinguished writers and politicians now visiting Soviet Russia is my personal friend, Mr. Roland Milk. His impressions of his tour are so interesting that I have decided to publish them at once, partly because if I wait for his return I shall have to pay him for them, and partly because there is a chance at last for the public to know what is really happening in Russia.

I give the first extracts today.

October 14

Everyone in Moscow was most kind to us. I asked one of the guides if there was any scarcity of food. He laughed at the mere idea, so that disposes once for all of the wicked propaganda of those at home in England who do not understand this great and noble experiment.

We visited a school, and were amazed to find the children as clean as pins and very alert. The guide suggested that we should ask some of them about England. At once a chorus of voices repeated the names of the leading politicians and writers of England. We were quite embarrassed to find our own names in the list. What intelligent children!

Mrs. Thunderstroke, the Socialist worker, strayed from the party, and explored some of the narrow streets. She thought she had discovered a bread queue, and was most indignant, until it was explained to her that it was only a Russian outdoor game. They stand in single file for quite a long time, muttering and shouting various sentences. So utterly Russian!

* This was written some years ago, in 1933, but is still a good peek inside the Iron Curtain.

October 15

We attended a cultural lecture in a large building. The lecturer was a prominent official of the Party, and his subject was the New Consciousness of the Worker-State.

The audience was composed of workers who were brought in from one of the rest-homes.

We could not understand the lecture, as it was in Russian, but it was interesting to note that there was not a single interruption or adverse criticism.

At the end of the lecture our guide brought up a man, and suggested that we should question him through an interpreter. Mrs. Thunderstroke asked him if he was happy. He mumbled something which the interpreter said meant, "I am deliriously happy. The Soviet regime has freed the workers. On to World Revolution!"

Before we left England we were told by reactionaries that the workers were, in some cases, discontented with their lot. I would like to make it clear that we have discovered none of this discontent. The wireless programmes contain nothing hostile to the Soviet, nor do the loudspeakers at street-corners criticize the regime adversely.

When we asked our guide about it, he said that all this talk of discontent was capitalist propaganda.

One of our party very indiscreetly repeated a story about a small town in which all the churches were burnt down and the priests massacred, and pointed out that this led people to say that religion was persecuted.

"It is not encouraged," said the guide, "because it is the opium of the people. But how can you say it is persecuted, in a place where there is nothing to persecute? If the churches do not exist and the priests are dead, there can be no religion going on. Therefore it cannot be persecuted."

October 16

On our way to visit the old summer palaces of the Czars, on the Black Sea, we called at a collective farm.

The guide explained that under the Czar the peasants were slaves, and that many of them were forced to till their own land instead of tilling communal land for the State. Each family lived separately in a very primitive dwelling, instead of having so many cubic metres of space allotted to it in a communal barrack.

He said that those peasants who do not like working on state farms were given a chance of taking a long journey, often as far as the Arctic regions.

We asked the man on a state farm, through an interpreter, whether he enjoyed his work. He said that he did, and that Lenin had freed the Workers. We asked him how much money he was allowed to earn, and he replied that money was not everything, and that Lenin had freed the Workers. We asked him about his religion. He said that religion was the opium of the people, and that Lenin had freed the Workers.

We visited one of the old summer palaces on the Black Sea Coast. It had been turned into a rest-home for the workers.

In what was once the banqueting hall, the workers were being lectured on the capitalist tendency of the pictures and the furniture — both of which remained.

The interpreter told us that all art before the Revolution had been propaganda for the capitalist classes. He said that the idea of families living in their own homes, instead of in communal flats or barracks, was an invention of the Capitalists to emphasize the gulf between one man and another.

The guide said that many of the workers resting here could not read or write, but that, in order to remedy this state of affairs, a certain sum was docked from their pay as an annual subscription to a newspaper, and further sums as subscriptions to the various Worker's societies.

We asked if we might question some of the workers, but the guide said that to-morrow would be a better day, after he would have had time to prepare them for the shock of meeting such distinguished visitors.

October 20

We had almost made up our minds that the Soviet system was flawless, and that the world must adopt it wholesale in order to survive, when we saw an official, a burly man in leather jacket and peaked cap, maltreating a skinny horse. Such a sight brought a cry of anger from Mrs. Thunderstroke, and Mr. Milk protested to the guide. The incident has considerably modified our opinion of Soviet Russia.

We had to wait two days for a train. The guide explained that in capitalist countries everyone is so eager to amass money and to exploit the proletariat that trains have to be punctual whereas in Russia other things are considered more important.

The train, when it arrived had not enough fuel to go to the place we had intended to visit, so we had to get out after twenty minutes, and walk a long way to the nearest town.

EVELYN WAUGH

The Happier Hunting Ground

Presently the telephone rang.

"The Happier Hunting Ground," Dennis Barlow said.

A woman's voice came to him, hoarse, it seemed, with emotion; in other circumstances he might have thought her drunk. "This is Theodora Heinkel, Mrs. Walter Heinkel, of 207 Via Dolorosa, Bel Air. You must come at once. I can't tell you over the phone. My little Arthur — they've just brought him in. He went out first thing and never came back. I didn't worry because he's sometimes been away like that before. I said to Mr. Heinkel, 'But, Walter, I can't go out to dine when I don't know where Arthur is' and Mr. Heinkel said, 'What the heck? You can't walk out on Mrs. Leicester Scrunch at the last minute,' so I went and there I was at the table on Mr. Leicester Scrunch's right hand when they brought me the news . . . Hullo, hullo, are you there?"

Dennis picked up the instrument which he had laid on the blotting pad. "I will come at once, Mrs. Heinkel; 207 Via Dolorosa I think you said."

"I said I was sitting at Mr. Leicester Scrunch's right hand when they brought me the news. He and Mr. Heinkel had to help me to the automobile."

"I am coming at once."

"I shall never forgive myself as long as I live. To think of his being brought home alone. The maid was out and the city wagon-driver had to telephone from the drugstore. . . . Hullo, hullo. Are you there? I said the city wagon-driver had to telephone from the drugstore."

"I am on my way, Mrs. Heinkel."

Dennis locked the office and backed the car from the garage; not his own, but the plain black van which was used for official business. Half an hour later he was at the house of mourning. A corpulent man came down the garden path to greet him. He was formally dressed for the evening in the high fashion of the place — Donegal tweeds, sandals, a grass-green silk shirt, open at the neck with an embroidered monogram covering half his torso. "Am I pleased to see you?" he said.

"Mr. W. H., all happiness," said Dennis involuntarily.

"Pardon me?"

"I am the Happier Hunting Ground," said Dennis.

"Yes, come along in."

Dennis opened the back of the wagon and took out an aluminum container. "Will this be large enough?"

"Plenty."

They entered the house. A lady, also dressed for the evening in a long, low gown and a diamond tiara, sat in the hall with a glass in her hand.

"This has been a terrible experience for Mrs. Heinkel."

"I don't want to see him. I don't want to speak of it," said the lady.

"The Happier Hunting Ground assumes all responsibility," said Dennis.

"This way," said Mr. Heinkel. "In the pantry."

The Sealyham lay on the draining board beside the sink. Dennis lifted it into the container.

"Perhaps you wouldn't mind taking a hand?"

Together he and Mr. Heinkel carried their load to the wagon.

"Shall we discuss arrangements now, or would you prefer to call in the morning?"

"I'm a pretty busy man mornings," said Mr. Heinkel. "Come into the study."

There was a tray on the desk. They helped themselves to whisky.

"I have our brochure here setting out our service. Were you thinking of interment or incineration?"

"Pardon me?"

"Buried or burned?"

"Burned, I guess."

"I have some photographs here of various styles of urn."

"The best will be good enough."

"Would you require a niche in our columbarium or do you prefer to keep the remains at home?"

"What you said first."

"And the religious rites? We have a pastor who is always pleased to assist."

"Well, Mr. ——— ?"

"Barlow."

"Mr. Barlow, we're neither of us what you might call very church-going people, but I think on an occasion like this Mrs. Heinkel would want all the comfort you can offer."

"Our Grade A service includes several unique features. At the moment of committal, a white dove, symbolizing the deceased's soul, is liberated over the crematorium."

"Yes," said Mr. Heinkel, "I reckon Mrs. Heinkel would appreciate the dove."

"And every anniversary a card of remembrance is mailed without further charge. It reads: *Your little Arthur is thinking of you in heaven today and wagging his tail.*"

"That's a very beautiful thought, Mr. Barlow."

"Then if you will just sign the order . . ."

Mrs. Heinkel bowed gravely to him as he passed through the hall.

Mr. Heinkel accompanied him to the door of his car. "It has been a great pleasure to make your acquaintance, Mr. Barlow. You have certainly relieved me of a great responsibility."

"That is what the Happier Hunting Ground aims to do," said Dennis, and drove away.

DOUGLAS WOODRUFF

Just Jests

THE SALAMANCA SYLLOGISM

Lord John Russell when in Spain had dinner with a Spanish Canon, and refused a second glass of wine. "What," said the Canon. "You refuse? You do not know the Syllogism of Salamanca: *'Qui bene bibit, bene dormiet. Qui dormit non peccat. Qui non peccat, salvatus erit.'* "

IN PARTIBUS INFIDELIUM?

Of all the many fine titles which are a spur to ecclesiastical ambition, I think few can have such a lure as the Vicariate of Bulge, in Bolivia. I can think of more than one churchman, and St. Thomas Aquinas among them, who might have seemed cut out for the post.

EX NIHILO NIHIL FIT

Ronald Knox said that when in a broadcast sermon he once said that man had been created out of nothing, he received a number of indignant letters from people who resented the slight. Presumably they thought he would demonstrate in his next sermon that they were necessarily nobodies, if they conceded the first fatal step in the argument.

At the Cinema

"Madame," said the attendant at the entrance, "you cannot take that dog in with you; it is not permitted."

Lady (most indignantly): "How absurd! What harm can the Movies do to a little dog like this?"

Who Said?

An American and an Englishman were arguing about the authorship of the tolerant saying, "We cannot expect old heads on young shoulders." The American claimed it for P. T. Barnum. "No," said the Englishman, "it was a favourite expression with Henry VIII."

Universality of Charity

Some Italian nuns of a nursing order printed this on the cover of their prospectus in English: —

"We harbour all kinds of diseases, and have no respect for religion."

"Compell Them to Come In"

Another notice put up by an Italian congregation read: "Home for Abandoned Old Men."

The Art of Scoring

In the north I heard of a Lancashire man who asked a friend if he would give him a hand, to help push a horse into the house. In the best tradition of Cicero's *De Amicitia,* the friend only sought to prove useful, and did not question but pushed; nor did he ask questions or blench when in the narrow hall he was asked to help get the horse upstairs. When that had been achieved, not without bad moments with the linoleum, the next stage of the operation was to get the horse into the bathroom, and, finally, standing in the bath. Then the friend could not refrain from asking why.

"My brother-in-law," explained the man, "is one of those clever chaps, always knows everything. He's coming to stay with me to-night, and when he comes he'll go to the bathroom to wash himself, and he'll come down and he'll say, 'Bill, there's a horse in your bath,' and I'll say 'Yes, I know there is.' "

FATHER GANNON COMES TO TOWN

On three occasions in the last week, finding myself at lunches in honour of Father Robert Gannon, S.J., the President of Fordham, I have been entertained by a master of after-luncheon speaking.

When he wanted to tell one party what needs to be done to encourage in the States the settled and universal conviction, which he finds over here, that Britain and the United States have more in common than either has with any other country, and need no artificial stimulations to recognize the truth of their interdependence, he told a pleasant tale of an American business man in Florida reaching the beach just as his drowning wife was pulled ashore unconscious. "Artificial respiration," they cried; "send for someone who understands how to give it!" "To blazes with artificial respiration," he retorted, "I can afford to pay for the real thing."

Nor did I know the story of Archbishop Williams of Pittsburgh, to whom an ill-bred, aggressive man said, "Where in hell have I seen you before?" and was answered, "What part of hell do you come from?"

He tells of examination questions he has seen set — but not, indeed, at Fordham — for second-year students of religious knowledge. One went to the heart of things, directing the student to "describe the process of the Creation, touching lightly on its causes and effects." Another was "How would you define blasphemy? Give two examples."

RELIGION AND POLITICS

The following story is sent to me from the States: An American girl summoned to evening prayers said "I don't need to say any prayers tonight because we had a Bible lesson in school today." "Oh," said her mother. "What did you learn?" "About George Washington; how first God told him that he'd got to kill his son, and then he told him that he needn't after all, and sent an angel to clear the muddle up." "Surely," said the mother, "you don't mean

George Washington, you mean Abraham?" "Yes, that's it," said the daughter, "Abraham Lincoln."

The Art of Meditation

A Dominican and a Jesuit resolved to seek permission to smoke at meditation. The Dominican asked whether he could smoke while he meditated, and was curtly told "Of course not." The Jesuit asked whether he could meditate while smoking, and was told there could be no possible objection.

7. THE IRISH — HERE AND ON THE OULD SOD

7. THE IRISH — HERE AND ON THE OULD SOD

All Irishmen can be divided into four parts — head, tongue, heart and hands. The head is held high, proud symbol of the dreamer of dreams, the architect of "clever dodges," and the author of inspired ingenuity. The tongue is another strong point, frequently in prominent use, an organ of lilting circumlocution, colorful metaphors, rousing repartee. Sometimes it drips with the oil of charity, other times with the acetic, not ascetic, acid of sarcasm. The hands, those sad symbols of "toilin' an' moilin'," are usually wisely hidden in ample pockets. Or else they are even more wisely occupied fingering a pipe and tobacco or doing justice to a pint of ale or the "pint" of a good story.

I think that you'll not have to look far for these traits of head and tongue, heart and hands, in the stories in this section. You'll see Mr. Pirrie, seemingly solid as a beer keg, yet a wild dreamer of dreams. You'll see the ingenuity and tongue acrobatics of The Spaeman, and of Patch and Fan, and of Thomasheen James, all fleeing from the harsh world of life and work, to the pleasant world of words and ideas. How much more fun to duel with words, like Patch and Fan, than to help cut rushes in the bog. How much better to do some hard labor with your tongue, like handyman Thomasheen James, than to push a heavy barrow filled with mountains of leaves.

To an Irishman work is the symbol of that very stupid world of fact and reality willed to him by Adam and Eve. He has head enough to recognize the existence of this world but heart enough to despise it. At very most he tolerates it while he "ardently aspires after life, light and emotion, to be expansive, adventurous and gay, to be sociable, hospitable and eloquent, admired for figuring away brilliantly."

H. V. Morton, author of the delightful travel book *In Search of Ireland*, is one outsider, and an Englishman at that, who has caught the real significance of the Irish spirit.

"The charm of Ireland," Mr. Morton wrote, "is partly due to the delicious slowness of life. Ireland is a Catholic country and you feel, as in most Catholic countries, . . . that the material world is rendered unreal and rather childish because it is overshadowed by the spiritual . . . Perhaps it explains why the Irish laugh at things which we consider urgent and why they cannot become excited about things which we believe are important. I wonder how many Irishmen have been called 'lazy' by Englishmen when in reality they were simply 'metaphysical.' "

PATRICK J. CARROLL

*A Fog on the Hill**

It was a foggy morning. Johnny and Dick were cutting rushes in the bog. . . . Fan and myself were on the hill picking mushrooms. Dick saw us dimly when he looked up to straighten his back; but because of the fog we were so misty he wasn't sure. He saw us and he didn't. He looked back at his father and they both stopped working.

* Condensed.

"I'll bet you," Fan said, "they want us to help with the rushes."

"Are ye the Carroll children?" Dick shouted.

"What did you say?" And Fan changed her voice so you'd never know her. She hadn't studied elocution with Mr. Murphy for nothing.

"I'm saying, if ye're the two small Carrolls we want ye to come down to us."

"We're from the west and we're picking mushrooms."

And she wasn't telling a lie either. We lived west of Sheehy's. Johnny and Dick talked some more, and then Dick roared.

"Wait where ye are — I'm coming to ye."

He put on his shoes, pulled down his trousers and started around the bog. When he reached the base of the hill he lost sight of us.

"Let us hide," Fan had whispered. We ran back and found cover in a clump of bushes that grew out of a cairn of stones. Dick climbed the hill very slowly and when he reached the top the two strangers from the west were gone.

"I can't see! Where are ye?" Dick cried.

"We're adjacent," Fan called in a nice Dublin accent.

"Adjacent — where's that?"

" ' 'Tis beside the road to yesterday!' "

Fan was quoting from a poem she had memorized. I was sure Dick would let out a streak of curses, but he didn't. He thought we were genteel young people visiting the Whites of Nantenan.

"I don't know where ye are or how to get there."

"Is there something we can do for you?" Fan's accent left me dumb.

"There isn't, if ye aren't the young Carrolls. I thought ye were the Carrolls."

"And who are the Carrolls?"

Dick stood very straight and made a speaking tube out of his half-closed fist.

"They're neighbors a bit west across the fields. I thought ye were the two young ones. I was going to ask ye for to help my father bring some rushes to dry land."

"And would the young Carrolls help you?"

"Would they help us? Why the devil wouldn't they! They do

nothing but gallop all over the parish when they aren't at school."

"Are they boys?"

"They're not. They're a boy and a girl. And the boy is as lazy as the devil, with the appetite of a horse."

"And the girl?"

"She's kind of weak-like, and will never grow up to be a woman with big hands to do hard work."

"So that's what Dick thinks of us after bringing him the pane of glass!" I said in a fierce whisper to Fan.

"You can't count that against him. We were doing a good turn," Fan whispered back. Then she called to Dick, "Come on up and talk to us."

Before Dick could answer Johnny shouted.

"Why are you roaring, Sonny? Is there a strange donkey trespassing upon our land?"

"Whoo-hoo-whoo-hoo." Fan's owl cries raced across the valley and came back in echoes.

"Or is it an owl you're chasing? And is that why you're screeching?" Johnny called.

"Lave me alone will you, till I find out the people I'm talking to!"

There was a silence after this, during which I pushed my cap into my mouth to keep back the laugh that was choking me. At last Dick shouted,

"Am I to go where ye are, or am I?"

"Come to us." It was Fan again.

"But where are ye? How am I to know where ye are when I can't see e'er a sign of ye?"

Fan chanted some of her memory poetry as if she were a banshee.

"When her voice calls to you through crowding shadows
Follow her voice, as sweet as moving waters.
And when you pass from shadows into light —
Lo, she is there!"

Johnny heard her voice way down in the bog, "What is she saying, Sonny?"

"How the devil do I know!" Then to us, "Am I going up to ye, or am I?"

"Come, my beloved, come!"

Dick never came up with us. We played Jacky the Lantern in a confusion of tongues. We went from hiding to hiding, Dick chasing the voice but never catching up with it.

Later that morning we walked down the east slope that skidded into the bog valley. Dick was back again killing the rushes with his scythe, Johnny bundling together what Dick had killed, and carrying them to dry land on his back.

"God bless the work!" I said, as if I were a gentleman farmer looking over my properties.

"Where were ye and where are ye coming from?" Dick asked.

"God bless the work!" I said a second time because 'tis bad luck not to answer a blessing.

"An' you too — where were ye?" Johnny was trying to kill two birds with one stone.

"God bless the work, Dick." I wanted Dick to answer too.

"An' you too," he growled. "But why the devil don't you answer the question my father put to you? . . . Are you a son of the gentry, by the way!"

"Everybody answers 'and you too' when you say 'God bless the work,' because we're Christians in Ireland."

I saw at once that my single blow had downed both of them, but they were up again in no time.

"Fan, my little girl" — and Johnny's voice was as jam — "we want to know — Sonny and myself — for good reasons, where you and your brother came from."

"We came from the east." And she gestured beautifully in that direction.

"And how did ye get over to the east?"

"We got there from the west."

"Ay." While Johnny thought of his next question, Dick thundered in. "Didn't ye hear somebody roaring up upon the hill a while ago?"

"Yes, we heard somebody roaring like a circus animal," Fan answered.

I laughed outright.

"There's nothing to laugh at — you little fool!" Dick was getting mad. "Now" — and he came nearer to Fan — "me and my father thinks that . . ."

I broke in — I couldn't help it — "*My father and I think* is what you must say."

"Will you shut your puss and keep your tongue out of this and mind your own business!"

"I was only correcting your grammar. Ireland will never be a cultured nation until we quit talking bog grammar." I was using the language Mr. Murphy used so often.

"Will you shut up so my father can talk to your sister!"

Johnny scratched his head and then shook it.

"I forget where we were and what I was going to ask you. Sonny, do you remember what I was going to ask her?" He looked at Dick.

"How the devil could I, and you asking so much that had no sense to it!"

"Well, you do the asking — if you're so smart!" Johnny was hurt.

Dick looked at Fan. "I'm going to ask you some questions and I don't want you to tell me no lies."

"I don't think that's a proper way to speak to a lady," Fan said. And that stirred me to say something. "And neither do I. In the old days a lady travelled the whole length of Ireland with a gold ring pushed into the point of a stick and nobody put a finger on her. . . .

"O lady dost thou not fear to stray
So lone and lovely through this bleak way?
Are Ireland's sons so good or so cold
As not to be tempted by women or gold?"

"Sir Knight, I feel not the least alarm,
No son of Ireland will offer me harm,
For though they love women and golden store,
Sir Knight, they love honor and virtue more."

"That's beautiful, and you rendered it beautifully," Fan said. "Rendered" was a favorite word with Mr. Murphy. There was a little pause, until Johnny faced Dick.

"Well, are you finished — or what?"

"I amn't. I haven't hardly began yet."

"Begun," I said, to keep his grammar straight.

"Keep out of this. You have no call to be sticking in your word. . . . Now Fan, be a good girl. Tell me, did you hear a great screeching up upon the hill?"

"Sure you asked her that already," Johnny broke in.

"Can't you lave me alone, so I'll get something out of her, seeing you couldn't! Fan, you heard me, didn't you?"

"Why, yes. All Ireland heard you." I laughed outright and Dick's temper went up a few points.

"Where were you when you heard me?"

"You mean, exactly where was I?"

"Yes, exactly where were you?"

"Do you mean, where we were *every time you shouted?* Or do you mean only *one time?* And which one of the times do you mean?"

"I'm asking you if you heard me when I screeched till I was hoarse up upon the hill."

"But sure you asked her that already, Sonny?"

Dick got sulky. "Well, then you try it again — if you're so smart!"

Johnny did and took a new tack, "Where were ye all morning?"

Fan began with seven o'clock, when she got up. Then she planted the whole family down to breakfast, naming off every one of us.

"Don't bother with all that. We don't want to hear it. Tell us where ye were when ye were up upon the hill."

"We were on the top of the hill."

"Did you hear Sonny calling ye?"

"Didn't I ask her that myself, and didn't you jaw about it!"

"Wait now, Sonny. Don't stop me, and I'll catch her." It was Johnny's loud whisper to Dick.

"Was there anyone else up upon the hill besides you and your brother?"

"We heard Dick shouting upon the hill, Mr. Sheehy."

"I know. But didn't you see any more?"

"There was a fog, Mr. Sheehy."

"Yes, a heavy fog, but 'tis rising now," I said. And I was right.

The fog climbed up the sides of the heather hill and rose slowly into the low sky. And away to the south the sun pierced the vapor with arrows of light.

Johnny pointed a finger at Fan as if he were an attorney examining a witness at one of the court sessions in Rathkeale.

"Now, I'm going to put a question which you're not going to coogle out of, my smart lady. Sonny and I want to get at some points about where you were this morning — without any hum or haw. Tell us plain — and don't coogle out of it — did you and your brother, this very morning, standing up upon the hill and the fog rising out of the bog like smoke out of a burning heap of wet weeds, when the weather is . . ."

"Why don't you get to the point and not be beating around the bush!" Dick shouted.

"Can't you lave me alone! I had the very question on the tip of my tongue which would hit the bull in the eye — and now 'tis gone like a frightened bird . . ."

From Sheehy's gate, before Sheehy's yard, came the bang, bang, bang of a small stick on the bottom of a dishpan.

"Hoo . . . hoo . . . hoo . . . Dinner!" And even the Pope wouldn't dare keep Mrs. Sheehy waiting.

"Well, we'll have to go." And Dick mooched off.

"And my point is gone. Clean gone." But then by way of no harm Johnny added, "Will ye come up for a bite of dinner?"

"Thank you, Mr. Sheehy, but our dinner is waiting at home."

Fan was afraid Johnny might hit the bull in the eye during the meal.

———————

PADRAIC COLUM

The Spaeman

Once upon a time and a very good time it was, though I had neither hat nor shoe, nor coat nor cloak, with a stick in my hand and a stone under my foot I went on my way to the Parish of No-sense where everyone has a goose for a gossip. Up hill and down dale and through the boggy, miry places I went, for it was only in the Parish of No-sense that I could better the state I was in. But when I came to Goose-green that is in the middle of the parish the doors were closed and the rushlights were dowsed, and there was no one in sight that I could crave shelter of. I walked between the mill and the moat and the moat and the mill, harkening for the watchman's "All's well! All's well," but they had neither watchman nor warden in the Parish of No-sense. I went through a broken door and into an empty house and I lay down to sleep upon the cold hearthstones. And while I was lying there in the deep darkness three knaves came in. They were carrying bags and bundles of stuffs they had stolen and they had come to hide them in the empty bins that were left in the house. And they went tiptoeing and whispering and telling each other that they would bring the brown mare and the gray horse and the spavined jennet and load the stuffs upon them and get out of the town next day when the dusk was falling.

When daylight came I got up from where I lay and went and warmed myself at a hearth I was asked to and ate out of the porridge-pot, and then I made my way to Goose-green which is the center of the parish to hear of what doings might be in the town. And no sooner had I got there when the Bellman came up and ringing his bell gave out that goods had been stolen and that a reward would be given to whoever discovered the thieves. All on Goose-green talked about this happening: some said that and some said this,

"What we want in this town is a Spaeman who could know by his own insight where stolen things are taken to. If we had a Spaeman we'd have no robberies here, and the town should hire one." And they all said, "Hear, hear!" to this, and so I went where the Bellman was drinking his dram, and I took up the bell that he had laid down on the ground, and I went through Goose-green crying, "A Spaeman am I, a Spaeman am I, and what town wants to hire a man with insight enough to know where stolen things are hidden!" They said I would have to prove I was a Spaeman before they hired me, and they took me to the warehouse that the robbery was made from (Peter's in Duck Street) and they asked me what my insight showed me. "It shows me," I said, "that three robbers took bags and bundles of stuffs from this place, and that the same robbers will be leaving the town at dusk carrying their loads upon a brown mare, a gray horse, and a spavined jennet."

They set a watch upon the bridge, and as dusk fell along came a brown mare, a gray horse, and a spavined jennet with loads of stuffs upon them and a man walking beside each load. The watch with their staves in their hands surrounded the beasts and the men, but the robbers jumped over the bridge and ran away. The stolen goods were found in the packs that the mare, the horse, and the jennet carried, and they were brought back to the warehouse. "The best Spaeman that ever was," the people said about me, and they gave me a house to live in and a penny a day pension and a candle to light my chamber in the night-time and free entry to all the games and cock-fights that might be on Goose-green. So there I lived in comfort and security, not having to make any more discoveries, for when they knew that the town had a Spaeman wrong-doers went to other places.

But I got tired of a place where there were no doings, for although I had free entry to the games and cock-fights upon Goose-green it was no good, for none ever took place there. So when the Squire asked me to come to his place and be Spaeman for him, I left my house with its candle-light and my penny a day pension and went to his mansion. His silver was being taken, spoon by spoon and plate by plate, and there was no way of finding out who was taking it or where it was being taken to. And when I came to the door, there were the butler and the footman and the groom, all with long faces on them, telling the Squire that the potato-ring and the salt-cellar had disappeared. "This day must not pass," said the Squire to me, "without your discovering for me where my silver is being taken to."

I was sorry I came, for the insight I had wasn't likely to tell me where the Squire's silver was being taken to. Howsomever, I thought I should get a meal out of my visit to the mansion. So I told the Squire that I couldn't engage in the matter until I had a meal with no less than three pots of ale to go with it. So a dish of duck was set before me in a room next the pantry. I took up knife and fork and looked for the pot of ale that wasn't there. And just then the butler came out of the pantry with the pot in his hand. "Here comes the first of them," I said aloud, and the butler gave a start and put the pot before me with a shaking hand.

I heard him talking to the footman and the groom in the pantry and it seemed to me that his voice was very failing. Then the footman came in with a pot in his hand. "Here comes the second of them," I said aloud, and he gave such a start that he spilled the ale on me as he set it down and went out of the room before I could give him a second look.

I drank my ale and I ate my duck, and I could hear them talking in the pantry and their voices sounded strained as two were saying to the third, "You go to him now." So the groom came in carrying the ale-pot, and I said aloud, "Here comes the third and the last of them." The groom let the pot fall and the ale went on the floor. He went back to the pantry without a word, and the next thing I saw was the three servants standing before me. The butler spoke to me and said, "You know us and we were foolish to think you would not discover us as you discovered us before when we stole the bundles of cloth. And now what will you take not to inform on us?" "All I want," I said, "is to see the place where the silver's hidden, and if that's shown to me you can go from the mansion without my informing on you."

They took me to the cellar then and there and they showed me where they had hidden the silver until such time as they could get it safely away. I waited until they had gone helter-skelter, and then I sat down at the table, picking a bone and drinking a dram from the pot. The Squire came to me. "What have you to tell me, Spaeman?" he asked. "Go down to the cellar, move over the biggest of the hogs-heads, and you'll find an opening under it and there's where your silver is, if I amn't mistaken." So he went down with the coachman and moved over the hogshead, and there was his silver, plate and spoon, salt-cellar and potato-ring.

The Squire declared that I was the best Spaeman that ever was, and he gave me a gate-lodge to live in and sixpence a day and leave to come in and talk with the gentlemen after dinner and drink what they offered me. And one night when I was in the dining-room drinking a punch with a gentleman I heard the Squire making a bet with another gentleman that I could find out anything about any-thing that was put before me. "I lay you five thousand pounds that he will not be able to find out what's in the dish that I'll put before him," said the gentleman. "Done," said the Squire, and then he turned to me and said, "Spaeman, my fortune's wagered on your insight. Win you must, and when you do I'll reward you well." I was very frightened to hear this, and I would have stolen away from the place only the Squire had me stay in the mansion that night so as to be ready for the trial that was to take place next afternoon.

I lay awake all night. I knew the name I had for being a Spaeman wouldn't last out the trial that was before me, and I knew that the Squire was going to lose his fortune, and that I would lose my six-pence a day and my place in the gate-lodge. I didnt' leave my bed until all was ready for the trial. The gentleman had prepared a dish of meat and I was to taste it and then tell all present what beast it was cut from. The Squire and his friend and the gentleman who had made the bet were all seated at the table when I came in, my knees knocking together. I had a look of great anxiety from the Squire, and I was afraid to give him a look back. Then, I can tell you, I cursed the day when I had given myself out for a Spaeman.

The cover-dish was taken off and there in the dish was a stew of meat. "Speak up and tell us what it is," said the gentleman who had made the bet. What was it? Beef or mutton, pork or goat, veal or venison, rabbit or hare? I was less able to tell than anyone in the world, for all sense of smell or taste had gone from me with the fright I was in. "You can't tell what it is," said the gentleman, looking at me as if the Squire's five thousand pounds were in his pocket already. "Your honor," I said, "the old fox is caught at last." At that he dropped the cover-dish he was holding. "No one else could have known," he said, "that this is the fox that was caught yesterday, for I cut him up and cooked him with my own hands." And when he said this the Squire came up and took my own two hands and shook them until the blood was nearly squeezed out of them.

More than before I had the name of being a Spaeman. But my last feat did me little good, for, with the money he won, the Squire went traveling, and when he was gone a full year the steward stopped my sixpence a day, and in a while after that he turned me out of the gate-lodge to let a young couple who were relations of his live there. So back I went to the Parish of No-sense and stood upon Goose-green and cried out that I was a Spaeman and that I could be hired. But the young people who were there asked me what a Spaeman was, and when I told them they laughed and said that they could make discoveries by insight themselves. As is the way with people, they had become more foolish than their fathers. So I said, say I —

> Let them go to the Devil and shake themselves,
> And when they come back, behave themselves.

So without hat or shoe, coat or cloak, and with a stick in my hand and a stone under my foot I went from the Parish of No-sense. Over hills and down dales I went, and through miry, boggy places, and came back to where I started from —

> The Tree that withstood
> The Big
> Wind — The
> Big Tree
> of Bunlahy.

ROBERT I. GANNON

Truth Is a Fixed Star*

"The Day We Celebrate" — that is again my title assigned.
But to speak to this group on the significance of the seventeenth of
March is certainly carrying peat to Kerry. So we always announce
the title with formality and talk about something else. At first I
thought that the Soggarth Aroon would make an appropriate topic,
dear old Father O'Flynn, his umbrella under his arm, shrinking and
downtrodden, as Irish pastors always are, humbly taking his orders
from everybody in the parish. But then I realized how many left feet
there are among the Friendly Sons, to say nothing of the Medes and
Elamites and inhabitants of Mesopotamia who are here as guests.
To be polite and bring them all into the picture, we should have to
begin by saying that there were once three Soggarth Aroons —
Patrick, Elmer, and Irving — who all got along like Kilkenny cows,
though they didn't play the same kind of bingo. And that I'm afraid,
would call for more delicacy and tact than I possess.

Then it occurred to me that there was some unfinished business
about the Kellys of Staten Island, and I hate unfinished business. So
I thought, since so many Friendly Sons have asked me year after
year, "How's herself?", meaning Mrs. Kelly, of course, you might
want to take up the threads and finish the story, as far as human
stories are ever finished.

Poor Mrs. Kelly, God rest her soul, was forty-five when I was
five and is dead and gone to her glory these many long years. The
last I saw of her was the day herself and all her children, including
the old man, were dispossessed from their tar-paper shack by the
railroad and passed our house in single file on their way to the
promised land in Bergen Point. Her parting words were these:

* A speech, here condensed, given before the Friendly Sons of St. Patrick, 1944.

"Gossoon, beware the horn of a bull, the tooth of a dog, the stallion's hoof and the smile of an Englishman." I have thought of her good advice many times since, especially a year ago today in London, when I celebrated the Feast of Feasts in the House of Lords at lunch with the Duke of Norfolk. But I knew that she did not mean the smile of every Englishman at all, but only those too blind to appreciate the peculiar genius of the Irish. So Mrs. Kelly is gone, and the old man, and the family is scattered now; but Mary, the daughter who came between Barney and Jim, has done very well by herself. In fact, I met "Marie" the other day.

She told me her start in life had been slow enough. Her first husband was just a Democrat, but he managed to pick up a crumb here and there, as a poor man will, and they were able, in time, to move to the Bronx. Being slightly sensitive about it, they said that the place was Riverdale. But Jimmy Lyons says it's as much the Bronx as the Grand Concourse.

Still, Mary was happy up there for years, and when her husband died he left her well fixed, fixed with eight beautiful children. The last two were twins named Morris and Sidney, after his favorite Sachems in the Hall. He left her, besides, a jewel of wisdom straight from the Book of Kells. "Before you marry again," said he, "take a look at Mr. Gallup's latest poll on the Presidential candidates." And she did. It happened to be the year of our Lord ninteen hundred and forty and the third Olympiad was about to begin. So she married a Republican and moved into the Fifteenth Assembly District — but she still goes to church. In fact, she has a pew in St. Vincent Ferrer's, where her boys are learning from the good Dominican Fathers to serve the wine and water at the strangest times and shout "Hurrah for the Jesuits."

Now Mary is the only Kelly I have actually met in recent years. But she tells me about the rest, and thank God it is the usual comforting story of the Irish-American, one generation removed. Danny is a Monsignor, Birdie is a school principal, Kate entered the convent but couldn't stay on account of her health and keeps house for Barney, who never married but owns a slice of Far Rockaway and is grand to the Sisters. Jimmie is a missionary Father and has a colored parish in the South, which the rest of the family has to support. Tim is the poorest of the lot. He's a college professor — and from what I can gather, a great and distinguished scholar of most discriminating views. He is never done shooting holes in Progressive Education. There's one they never mention and I won't mention him either. I don't know what's the matter with him. He may be down in Washington. But one out of seven is a fair enough record. The tragedy of the American home is that too often there's only one, and they would just as soon overlook him.

So that's the story of Mrs. Kelly brought up to date, a story which can be multiplied thousands of times throughout the land. A story of a family keeping close to God, close to truth, keeping close to their own very definite principles. And being a simple Irishman, I have told it with an ulterior motive.

We owe as much to this country, gentlemen, as any other group — and more than some. We love this country as much as any other group, and a great deal more than some that could be named. But we have given as well as taken; we've built as well as shared. When we came to this strange and happier land a hundred years ago, we did not have the Yankee gift for trading, the English gift for compromise or the Scottish gift for rubbing the face off a sixpence. At our worst we were loud, pugnacious, and insolent; extravagant, too, and, like the Scotch and the English, too fond of strong drink entirely.

But with these faults went some of the finest qualities of the human heart, and eternal principles, gentlemen, qualities and principles which the United States needs most desperately today. Our ancestors were first of all models of supernatural Faith — simple, direct, and complete. They wanted no splitting of hairs and distinctions without a difference. They had stood up in the face of seven blood-drenched centuries, and no mere snubbing or petty discrimination by the immigrants who had come before them could shake their fierce devotion to the truth.

When Molly Maguires came around to warn them away from church, they laughed in their faces. When well-meaning friends suggested that all they needed for success was a little cheese knife to wear on their coat, they roared with anger. As a result, of course, some doors were closed in their faces and some doors are still closed today in the faces of their descendants. Some doors that for the sake of the country ought to be open now. For the country needs men who keep faith with God and faith with other men. Men of conviction. Men who believe in absolute truth and will suffer for a principle.

OLIVER ST. JOHN GOGARTY

Mr. Pirrie, Pyrophile *

In a side street by the river the old houses leaned like gossips, wise in their generation, to converse with one another. One of the houses "belonged to the Ryans," the husband and father of whom was Mike Ryan, Captain of James's Gate Division of the Dublin Fire Brigade, for so the Fire Department is named in Dublin. Captain Mike Ryan's section included the eighty acres of the great Brewery of Guinness, and Stevens Hospital as well as the lunatic asylum called St. Patrick's which was left to the nation by Dean Swift. South and east it was bounded by the river and Winetavern Street.

George Pirrie occupied the top story of the house of the Ryans for fourteen years, from the days when he had to be up at five in the morning to check the casks as they left the Brewery on lorry or lighter for cross-channel ships or the cellars of the city, to the present time when, a man of authority and substance, he went to his office in the Brewery at the more human hour of eight o'clock.

George Pirrie was a little man, short and trim, but no one would think of him as a small man, for his connection with the Brewery gave him, if not height, status. Small men are either geniuses or eccentrics. No one thought of his size. They regarded only his position, for the Brewery, being a Protestant institution, emanated the respectability

* Condensed.

and authority of the Ascendancy. Each Brewer as he sat at his post felt this authority, for he was a product of Winchester and Balliol. He felt himself a *vates* as he sat at his vat brewing the best ale in the world, a brew that could bring quarrels, mirth or the prophetic phrensy, spiritual conditions these; to the material body it could bring health and strength — a food for invalids.

Mr. Pirrie had a small library off his living room on the top floor. It consisted mostly of books on fire-fighting with the histories of the development of modern apparatus; pictures of the lofty scaling ladders of the New York Fire Department with steering wheels fore and aft to direct them through the streets. He knew all there was to be known about fire brigades or departments from the first in the New World to the quaintest of them all, the Fire Brigade of Constantinople which the merchants of that city buy off if it threatens to extinguish a burning store and thus interfere with the will of Allah. Only Mr. Pirrie's lack of inches prevented him from being a fireman and not an official in a brewery. He was as closely associated with fire as he could well be. Did he not live with the family of a fire captain with a wife and seven children?

The Captain was not an imaginative man, that is to say, he was a bad historian. It took years before Mr. Pirrie discovered that Captain Ryan had been to New York, and when he did discover it, it took much questioning to get a clear picture of how they fought fire in that great metropolis. Accounts of the receptions the Captain attended and the speeches Captain Purcell, who led the Delegation, made were substituted for what really interested Mr. Pirrie. "What do they do when one of their skyscrapers goes on fire?" he asked.

"They don't," was all he got from Captain Ryan. Mr. Pirrie was a mild little man. He did not like to press a question.

"Strange," was all he said, and he said it like a sigh.

"Fire-proof," the Captain retorted.

So the evening would wear on: Mr. Pirrie avid for information; the Captain taking for granted what meant Life and Adventure to Mr. Pirrie.

One evening he ventured to ask if it were true that the fire-stations in New York had steel pillars down which the firemen could slide to save time when answering an alarm.

"Sure," said Captain Ryan.

No; there was not much to be got out of the Fire Captain. There was another disappointment that troubled Mr. Pirrie. The Captain was accustomed to sit at home after dinner in his stockinged feet. Gone was his uniform with its brazen helmet, his belted ax, and his thigh-high boots. It seemed a desecration. To the Captain it not only seemed but it was a relaxation from the weight of armor he had to carry while on duty.

"You were asking how we got on when the New York Fire Department invited us over to be their guests."

"I was interested," Mr. Pirrie affirmed.

"Well, them's the boys that can drive like blazes."

"Yes?" said Mr. Pirrie, his mind on tiptoe.

"I remember how we went to a place called the Antlers over a bridge miles long. We got there just in time. Them boys can drive."

"A fire?"

"No. A clam bake. They don't have things like that in this country. More's the pity. We went with bells ringing and sirens blowing enough to raise the dead. The Elks lent us the place."

"Talking of fires," the Captain continued as if making a concession to an amateur, "they have red cars that clear the way, and brass double hydrants, 'stand pipes' they call them, that can throw a jet ninety feet high."

But there was a far greater disappointment in store for Mr. Pirrie. At a fancy dress ball at Lord Iveagh's (his Lordship was head of the Brewery), Dr. Lumbsden, the doctor to the Brewery, had appeared dressed as a fireman. Where did he get the uniform? Captain Ryan lent it to him! Why had not Mr. Pirrie thought of that? And it was such a matter-of-fact gesture on the part of the Fire Captain that he did not even mention it when Mrs. Ryan was going through a list of the guests and the costumes they wore, until she came to Dr. Lumbsden. "Dr. Lumbsden, a Captain in the Dublin Fire Brigade."

Mr. Pirrie gave an exclamation.

"Show him the note of thanks," Mrs. Ryan requested.

"It's behind the clock." And Mrs. Ryan took it out and gave it to Mr. Pirrie.

"You are a bigger man than I," he read, "but it made things all

the merrier when they saw me floundering on the dance floor in
your boots."

Mr. Pirrie could have floundered just as well as Dr. Lumbsden;
and floundered in the privacy of his apartment.

Columbus died on land, having been land-locked in jail. What
irony there is in the fate of heroes! Some workmen were working
down in a manhole twenty feet below the surface of the street. Their
mates failed to get an answer when they signaled to them. One of
them grew alarmed and reported to the police, who promptly called
the Fire Brigade and dashed to the site of the accident. The Brigade
reached the scene as soon as the police. "Gassed," announced the
Fire Captain.

"I can't send men where I wouldn't go myself. Give me a line."
So saying he lowered himself down by the staples that were fitted to
the side of the shaft. A young constable followed. They never reached
the surface alive again. Thus in the dark and in the cold far under the
surface of the street died Mike Ryan, Fire Captain, fighting for his
fellow man.

Though Mr. Pirrie did not attend the wake, he was not remiss in
offering his condolences to the widow. He did not dare to give notice
that he intended to seek other quarters. Her loss was too recent to
add another to it. But he felt that sooner or later it would appear
unseemly to remain in the house of an unchaperoned lady. True, as
he suggested to himself, the children were chaperons. What would
the Brewery think?

Thoughts such as these were dispelled one evening when he was
invited in "for a minute" as he ascended the stairs. Over the mantel
piece hung the helmet and ax of the Captain! "With the compliments of the Brigade," he read. "I knew you'd like to see it," Mrs.
Ryan remarked, referring to the complimentary note attached to the
ax. Mr. Pirrie was thrilled. The helmet! And that ax had hewn
down blazing walls! Doubtless it was the attraction of the helmet
and ax that brought Mr. Pirrie down when he came in the old days
to talk with the Captain after the children had gone to bed. He
found that he could get more information from Mrs. Ryan. Women
have a way of seeing things as a series of images, which is more than
can be said for men of action, including the late Captain.

Mr. Pirrie gazed at the mantel shelf. Mrs. Ryan followed his eye. She simpered as she said, "That's of him when we were married. Of course he had to give up waxing his mustache when he joined the Brigade." But it was of no amateurish photograph Mr. Pirrie was thinking. What was the history of the helmet and the ax? The dinge on the helmet?

"How did he get that dinge on the helmet?"

"Oh, that! He was fighting a fire" (how the expression thrilled Mr. Pirrie!), "fighting a fire up at St. Patrick's and one of the loonies threw something at him. Only for that helmet it might have broken his head or thrown him off the ladder. So he says to me."

Mr. Pirrie pondered for many days. On another occasion as the evening wore into night he ventured to inquire into the history of the ax. Mrs. Ryan knew little of its history.

"He used it for breaking down windows and doors, mostly at night when a fire breaks out and the people in the house are asleep in their beds. There's no time to ask for a key."

Mr. Pirrie pondered and came to the conclusion that it must be somewhat hard for Mrs. Ryan and her seven children to make ends meet on the pension of a Fire Captain. Yet it would be indelicate to offer her monetary assistance. His object could be reached just as well were he to buy for a substantial sum the helmet and the ax.

Mrs. Ryan had been out "shopping" for the greater part of the day. The strain had evidently told on her because she required a little "spirits" to assure sleep. Mr. Pirrie who joined in "well, just half a glass" thought the moment favorable.

"I have been thinking that it might go some way in educating the little ones as well as helping household expenses, if you were to sell and I were to buy that helmet and ax."

Though couched with due consideration, the effect of the speech on Mrs. Ryan was considerable. She extended her hand to arm's length toward Mr. Pirrie and shook with silent tears. She rose and stood by the fireplace. She raised her head and gazed at the helmet above.

She was not an uncomely figure. That is what occurred at the moment, in spite of his confusion, to Mr. Pirrie. With Ellsie fourteen and that photograph of Ryan with waxed mustaches, Mrs. Ryan need not be more than in her middle thirties.

She turned from gazing and wiped her eyes.

"It's all I have," she said, a mother forgetful.

Mr. Pirrie was infected by the spirit of sympathy. He had a vision as he gazed at her swimming eyes and at the arms above her head. He saw far beyond the Fire Brigade and the streets of Dublin, far away over the ocean to the Fire Department of New York. He saw the scarlet fire engines and the Fire Chief's red cars, bells, and sirens! The roar and diapason on the way to a fire. Even if the skyscrapers did not catch fire, there were other buildings, maybe, just as high that did. He saw himself high in mid-air. The helmet would save his eyes as he smashed a window. "Jets ninety feet high!" He heard the Fire Captain's voice. He also heard his widow's voice, and in the flesh.

"It's all I have. Don't ask me to sell it."

"But . . . but . . . I did not mean to be unkind. I meant that if I had it, it would not be far away."

"Far away?" Mrs. Ryan looked over her handkerchief. Her tear-bright eyes pleaded for elucidation.

"Do you mean you would marry me, George?" she murmured. George Pirrie rose to the occasion for the house seemed all on fire. He had to assume that helmet and that ax.

"I do, indeed," he said.

DOYLE HENNESSY

A Kelly Spurns His Name

(A man named Kelly petitioned the court to have his name changed to Kellett. He said the name Kelly had been a handicap to him and his father before him, and that he was tired of people reminding him of Kelly with the Green Necktie, Kelly as the name of a hat, Kelly Pool, and Slide, Kelly, Slide. — News Item.)

Oh Molly, dear
And did ye hear
   The craziest news yet?
A madman wants to change his name
   From Kelly to Kellett!

Kellett, I said, sure I don't know
   Just how ye would pronounce it,
But may the Irish, high and low,
   Fervently denounce it!

Will such a one, devoid of shame,
Who spurns so great and fair a name,
Share with Ireland's saints in Heaven's thrill?
He may think so,
But I say "No!"
   I say like Kelly will.

For when he dies, St. Peter will ask
   "What is your name, my son?"
"Kelly, it used to be," he'll say,
   "But now I've a better one."

Then Peter will say to Kellett
   "St. Patrick should hear your story;
To him I'll let you tell it —
   That's him in his robes of glory."

St. Patrick hearing the tale, will boom:
   "Take this rascal away!"
"Has Anyone Here Seen Kelly?"
   The heavenly choir will play.

On the chutes to hell they'll seat him;
   On the slippery chutes of Pride,
And this is the cry will greet him:
   "Slide, Kelly, Slide!"

MARTIN QUIGLEY, JR.

Mark of the Gaels

The average Irishman has his deep sense of humor because he has developed and inherited a philosophy of life which permits him to enjoy living. While work is valued, leisure is elevated to a position unknown to America. Leisure in Ireland is not, as in America, a time for recreation in order to work better afterwards. It is an art and end in itself and it is so cultivated. What might be considered downright idleness in the United States is a highly developed activity there. This way of life provides time for wit and story-telling.

The Irishman's love of living and leisure would seem to be much more a dominant characteristic than the more accepted one of the fiery, hot-headed person. It is certainly true the Irish like to fight and argue but truer even it is that they like, and appear to know how, to live.

With all the leisure time carefully preserved, the Irish have developed an endless treasure of stories. They are the classic forms of humor in Ireland. The art of story-telling in Ireland goes back in an unbroken line as far as the days of Homer in Greece. As in all good humor, the age of an Irish story does not affect its value. The old story may be much the best one. Persons may be glad to hear the same tale or short joke again and again.

Irish stories are numberless. Professor James Hamilton DeLargy and his associates at the Irish Folklore Commission are devoting their lives to recording old Irish stories, especially those in the Gaelic. But even he is continually surprised by new, yet very old, stories of which he had no previous knowledge.

Justice can be done to a real Irish story, which might take an hour to narrate, only by an Irish story-teller. The bare outline sometimes suggests the humor of the whole; in other cases the delightful impression is created out of the infinite details, skillfully blended into the narration. Other Irish stories are brief and amusing, even when poorly told. The following brief stories, lately encountered in the country of their origin, illustrate a trifle from that great wealth of Irish humor:

A local patriot in West Clare — that wild and rough country — one Sunday afternoon during the Land League days — departed from his usual custom of delivering a lengthy political speech and said only the following: "Drink is the curse of Ireland. Drink made you shoot your Landlords . . . and drink made you miss."

Another Land League story tells how it was the custom, when it was decided a certain landlord's agent must be eliminated, four men would be chosen for the task. Each would be given a rifle but three would contain cartridges. None of the four would know who had the loaded cartridge. On one such occasion in County Cork when it was decided a particular land agent must be done away with, four "of the lads" took the rifles and concealed themselves behind a hedge which the tyrant passed regularly as clockwork every day at five p.m. The four lads consulted their watches and, as five o'clock approached, cocked their rifles and waited. The stroke of five came but no land agent. The men looked at each other in surprise. After waiting some more, in a worried and compassionate tone one of them said, "Now you don't think anything could have happened to the poor man?"

There are countless stories about farmers, and about pigs (even though the latter were very scarce during the war period). One of these tells about a County Leitrim farmer, named Patrick O'Donnell, who lived in a very wet section; the road was always deep in puddles; the path to his door was a morass. When the farmer died he was laid out in his Sunday clothes and his best pair of boots. Four of Paddy's cronies were the pallbearers. They had considerable trouble carrying the body down the path from the cottage and placing it in the carriage. Finally the job was accomplished. One of the pallbearers, wiping his brow, exclaimed, "Well, this is the first time Paddy ever came out of his house without getting mud on his boots."

Naturally the weather has received plenty of attention from Irish story-tellers. One of these tales recounts how a farmer had harvested his crops but was unable to gather them into the barns before the rains came. He prayed at first for the rain to stop, but it rained the harder. Finally, giving up all hope for a successful crop, he shouted, "Rain on, it's dung I want now."

Another story tells how a farmer prayed for rain because his fields were too dry. The rain came. But it would not stop. Soon there was too much rain and the crops were being ruined. The farmer prayed for the rain to stop. It did not. Finally, he looked up to the sky through the curtain of rain and exclaimed, "Now, don't be ridiculous!"

In case there is a question about the three immediately preceding stories, it may be noted that they are stories of a priest and excellent story-teller, Father O'Donnell of County Leitrim.

The longer stories, those which take fifteen minutes to tell, are the most characteristic of the story lore of the country. A man skilled in the art of telling such stories is Dr. Theo Dillon, National University medical professor and brother of Mr. James Dillon, the politician. One of his stories tells of a legendary character in County Monaghan, a Father Burke. While the whole tale requires much time for all the details, its outline runs like this: Father Burke went to the local county fair and purchased a pig. After the usual Irish trading about price the priest selected a large, fat animal. The farmer offered to drive the pig to the priest's home or to assist the priest in tying the pig up and placing it in the back of his car. Father Burke declined that and the spectators were somewhat mystified as to what he was going to do. Instead of keeping close control over the big pig, Father Burke deliberately let it get away. The priest then drew a long knife and started chasing the pig. Then there was a scene that even surprised the buyers and sellers at an Irish county fair. The pig ran around and around the market square with Father Burke (who had by this time taken off his coat) in hot pursuit. After a good fifteen minutes' chase the priest caught the pig. Finally, the knife was plunged home and the blood ran. Father Burke hoisted the pig on his shoulder and carried it back across the square and threw it into the back of his car. When asked the reason for the previous events, Father Burke explained that it was much too much trouble to take home a live pig. . . .

This is a story told by Dr. Richard Hayes, the film censor and noted writer on Irish history: "I was walking down a country road and saw in the distance three men and a cart approaching. The men were not walking along side of each other but were strung out in a line. As I got nearer I saw that there was a father and two grown sons. As the day was warm we stopped for a moment to chat. I said to the father, 'Those are two grand young men you have.' 'Yes,' the father replied, 'they are wonderful boys, — kind, obedient, thoughtful. Why, I never had to raise me hand to them — except in self defense'!"

The usual Irish "character" discovered by the English or American visitor is the jarvey, the driver of a jaunting car or vehicle. Jarveys are famed for enjoying life and meanwhile making wonderful remarks. The stories told about jarveys in Dublin, Killarney and other places, strange as it may seem, are in many cases actually true. There are many tales about jaunting car horses trained to pull up in front of pubs and refuse to go until they are refreshed by letting the jarveys have a drink. One who stays in Ireland any length of time is sure to have this happen to him. When the jarvey's horse or the jarvey decides to stop there is no disputing the point even if the destination is only a few hundred yards away. Only rarely does a jarvey lose patience. It is said that after the "troubles" an American was being taken around in a jaunting car and seemed to be taking too much of an interest in the struggles which the jarvey wished to forget. The visitor pestered the jarvey to know how some building was destroyed and who was fighting. The jarvey's answer was, "The I.R. Ayes and the I.R. Ahs."

MAURICE WALSH

Thomasheen James and
Thirty Pieces of Copper

On a certain Tuesday afternoon, after an absence over the long Easter week-end, I was sitting in my open-fronted summer-house when Thomasheen James came down the garden path behind the handles of a wheelbarrow that held nothing but his brush and two dead cabbage leaves. He set the barrow carefully down on the plot of grass fronting the house, and calculated me with a cold and wary eye.

"Get out!" I said, looking at him sourly over the top of my writing-glasses.

"You're back?" said Thomasheen James.

"Obviously. Get out!"

I was endeavouring to put a few profitable words on a writing-pad, and not succeeding very well.

"A bad time to talk to a man," said Thomasheen James distantly, "an' him with a sore head after his week-end in Kerry! But talk I will. I'm in trouble."

"I gave you five shillings last week — "

"The week before last — four and a tanner to be exack. The trouble concerns the both of us."

"The devil it does! How much do you want?"

"Do you recolleck them fishin'-boots o' yours?"

"The black rubbers? You can have them — they leak in ten places."

"Not them. The yellow boyos with the nails in the sole that come up below your oxters."

"My new waders? If you dare put as much as a finger — "

"They're in the pawnshop this solid minit," said Thomasheen
James solidly.

I was on the point of explosion, but took a second thought.

"Who put them there?" I enquired, mildly enough.

"I did — Holy Thursday evening."

"A holy evening, and a holy thing to do!"

Somehow my urge to explode vanished, and was replaced by an
unpleasant sinking feeling. Thomasheen James had broken trust.
The old careless tolerance that existed between us was in real danger
for the first time, and I was actually distressed.

"Am I to understand," I enquired patiently, "that you lifted my
only decent waders and pawned them?"

"I knew you'd be takin' the dam'dest view you could," he said
sadly. "I got nothin' for them anyway."

I found the relief of anger. The waders were first-class articles, and
could be pledged in any Dublin pawnshop for at least twenty
shillings.

"Don't say it," besought Thomasheen James. "Don't never say
I up and stole your waders."

"I'll say more than that." And I did. Unfortunately I can be
occasionally guilty of language to astonish even Thomasheen James.
I invented a family tree for him and detailed the fate of it, branch by
branch. No one, not even Thomasheen James's father, knew who
Thomasheen James's father was, but I traced that reprobate's progress as far as the hangman — and after — and drew pointed con-
clusions. "For," said I, warming to the subject, "any so-and-so nurtured in my bosom who would repay me by stealing my new waders
at the peak of the salmon-fishing — the only decent waders I had
— the only pair of waders that never soaked a drop of water — "

"Who declaims on such marvellous waders?" said a pleasant
voice at the garden gate behind my left shoulder.

"Heavens be me bed!" prayed Thomasheen James desperately.
"Me goose is cooked." He wiped his brow. "Becripers, sir! That
langwidge 'ud be worth a hundred quid to me if I had a witness I
could trust for slander."

I looked over my shoulder at the newcomer. He was my friend,
Father Charley Morrow, curate of the parish, a dark, handsome,

youngish man; a good enough Churchman, but the best man I knew to lay a fly over a feeding fish twenty yards across a pool.

"Who is mixing genealogy with fishing-waders?" he enquired.

"I have only just begun," I told him grimly.

"And a good beginning. I could hear you at the foot of the hill, and two respectable married ladies out on the road are wondering if they can remember and use some of the words. All right! Let us talk waders. Lent is over — "

"Small difference to you," I said.

"An' that's no lie," agreed Thomasheen James.

" — and I have a permit to fish a mile of water above Leixlip tomorrow evening," finished Father Charley.

I sat up.

"That means that you want to borrow my waders?"

"There's a pool I can't cover without them. Thank you kindly."

"Come away in and rest yourself," I invited. I was busy with a coward's thought. I was afraid of the issue facing me, and would put the onus on the broad shoulders of the Church.

Father Morrow plumped into a wicker chair at my side, drew forth pipe and tobacco-pouch, and settled his shoulders at ease.

"Do you resume where you left off?"

"Not yet. I want to call your attention to that thief there," I said pointing at Thomasheen James.

"No, no! You must not call a man a thief until you are sure that he is not one."

"You want my waders, don't you?"

"I do!"

"Then I will ask you to sit in judgment on this honest man, Thomas James O'Doran?"

"No, not in judgment — not on my fellow-man; but if the case concerns a pair of waders I am prepared to give an opinion in equity."

" 'Tisn't fair," shouted Thomasheen James bitterly, kicking at his barrow. " 'Tisn't dam' fair nohow. Sure isn't it known, and well known, that the priests and bishops and the Pope himself is on the side of the constitutional authority. What bloody chance have I?"

"You are trying to prejudice the opinion of the court in your favour," said the priest. "Sit down, Thomasheen James!"

Thomasheen James sat on a corner of the barrow and sighed.

"Very well so! But come-high-come-low I didn't steal no waders."

There was another interruption. Again a voice spoke from the garden gate — a quiet, strong voice.

" 'Tis treason broad high and low to usurp the authority of the courts of this nation."

"Me name is mud for sure now," said Thomasheen James resignedly, "an this bit o' a garden can go to hell for thirty days in Mountjoy jail."

The new visitor was my good friend Joe O'Dowd, a big placid man with the broad, ruddy, smooth face of the countryman. He was a detective-sergeant in the Metropolitan Police, and one of the best. He strolled across the grass, placed a foot on the wheel of the barrow, leant elbow on knee, and leant imminently over Thomasheen James, whose shoulders twitched and contracted. I am always glad to see Sergeant Joe, but at that moment I was not too happy.

"Waders ye were talking about?" he suggested, smiling encouragingly. "Let us resume."

"Four estates are met, and the usual one on trial," said the Church. "What do you know about waders, Joseph?"

"I'm after looking at a pair, reverend sir — in a pawnshop — Mullarkey's at Egan's corner."

"May the devil melt him!" cursed Thomasheen James fervently.

"They looked sort of familiar to me," said the sergeant. " 'Tell me, Mull,' I said, 'the lad that soaked these on you, what was he like?' 'A common corner-boy,' says Mull, 'only worse.' 'You're hot!' said I. 'A bit of the fox about him?' 'Crossed by a weasel,' says Mull. 'You're dam' hot,' I said. 'A skate-mouthed, fish-eyed, carrotypolled son of a Dublin Jackeen,' says Mull. 'Mull,' said I, 'you're on to him — ' "

"Is there ne'er a honest witness in me vicinity?" Thomasheen James besought of high heaven.

" 'I can lay my hand on him any minit,' I told Mullarkey." The detective turned to the priest. "Am I interrupting the illegal proceedings, Father Charley?"

"You are, Joseph. Are you thinking to dispute the verdict?"

"I will listen to the evidence without prejudice," said the policeman cautiously. "Carry on, reverend Justice!"

The priest leant back in his chair and smoked for a while. Then he turned to me.

"I am rather in the dark," he said. "Are you making a complaint?"

I had been thinking too, and I wanted the onus where it was.

"Complaint or not," I said, "there is nothing I can hide even if I wanted to — suffering as we do from interlopers. I was away for the week-end. Before I left I saw my almost new waders hanging in the tool-shed. Now this man informs me that he pawned them on Holy Thursday evening."

"I never said nothin' o' the kind," denied Thomasheen James. "I only said they was in the pawnshop."

"You are a fool as well as a rogue," I said warmly. "Did you or did you not lift my waders?"

"I only took a loan o' them, unbeknownst," said Thomasheen James.

"The distinction is a fine one," said Justice. "Would you care to elucidate, Jesuit in disguise?"

"Elucidate — elucidate!" Thomasheen James was stumped for a moment. "Oh, yes, becripers! I can elucidate all right, but what good'll it do me? Here I am betune the three of ye, and I might as well go to law with the divil an' the court in hell. But I was explainin' his bit of forgetfulness to this gintleman when all Dublin came in on top of us, and I'll go on doin' it. Gi'e me time now, will ye?"

I hastily sought in my mind for some possible lapse of my own, but could not find any to fit. Thomasheen James gathered his powers close about him, and looked round at the tiny garden where all the hard work had been mine.

"For six months — or a bit less," he began, "I been toilin' and moilin' in this place off and on — "

"Toiling and moiling?" I interrupted him. "For a year or a bit more, you've been idling and pandering in this place, but you will neither work nor idle in it for another day — and that's flat."

"Order in the court!" commanded Justice. "Go on, Thomasheen James!"

"Long or short, I been workin' in this garden off and on, and if

'tisn't a wreck and a ruin let him take the credit that wants it. An'
wan day I'd get a shillin', and in three days' time another shillin', and
a gintleman 'ud be feeling generous and a noble Christian the same
as if you martyred him. Mind you, I'm not complainin' at all. A
shillin' now and a shillin' then is all I ever wanted — and a bowl of
soup when it was goin'."

"These he got," I put in, "and more besides, yet where are the
waders that I want to loan to the reverend judge?"

"No special pleading, please! Cut the cackle and get to the
waders, Thomasheen James!"

"I'm workin' up to the bloody waders, amn't I? Holy Thursday,
after lunchin'-time an' the week's work put past me, I was saying
to meself that five bob would be as little as himself could be handlin'
out to get me over the Good Friday an' the Bank Holiday at Fairy-
house Races. An' did I get the five bob? Did I, I ask you? Did I hell!
A couple hours after meal-time, an' his snooze over him, out comes
himself and a friend with him — a fellow wouldn't come in a door
sideways — and the two wives chit-chatterin', and two bags strapped
on the heel of the motor car; and off with them laughin' and jokin',
full of food an' fun. 'We'll stop for a drink in Ard-na-Righ,' says the
stout fellow. 'No,' says his missus, 'we'll have tea in Mary-
borough' —

"That's where the jail is," said the sergeant suggestively.

"I know it. I was hungry in it once — and I was hungry Easter
Sunday as well. For there I was left, me mouth open, an' not one
ha'penny to rub against another; the long week-end before me, the
town empty — and no one in the house but the girl an' the two
young wans."

"No need for him to go hungry," I said quickly. "The servant
was in the house."

" 'Tis little you know her," said Thomasheen James.

"Moreover, I looked in the garden before I left, but he was not
about — "

"You looked dam' hard, I know. I was sweepin' out the hen-house
at the back."

"Or asleep in a corner?"

"Like me betters — and why not? If you lifted your voice above a whisper you'd ha' heard from me. Mind you, I didn't blame you, and I'm not blamin' you. You're your own master — outside the house — an' every man has the weight of his own conscience. 'Maybe he left something for me with that servant-girl,' says I to meself, havin' the best opinion of you in spite o' previous occasions. And in I went to consort her. 'What would he laive?' says she, the mopsy. 'Hadn't you your dinner, and there's a cup o' tay in the pot if you want it. An' look here, me boyo!' says she, 'you'll cut your hook out o' this place till the boss comes back, for I'll not be the subjeck of scandal in this end o' Dublin.' An' she with a face on her to stop a clock. 'Give me the tay,' I says, 'before I lose me timper.' And I took it, and it lukewarm, sitting outside in the tool-shed. An' even then an' after all, I didn't blame you. 'He never meant to throw me distitute this way,' I colloges with myself. 'He'll be worryin' the heart out o' himself when it crosses his mind every hour. It'll be troublin' the dacent man day and night, and him knowin' that I've run out me fourteen nights in the Vincent de Paul's shelter.' "

"Oh, dammit!" I exclaimed. Truth to tell, I had not thought of Thomasheen James for a single moment during that pleasant week-end in Kerry.

"Take it aisy," implored Thomasheen James. "There's no call to be usin' bad langwidge before a priest, and him not usin' it back at you." He drew in a long breath. "It was about that time that me eyes lodged thimselves on the yalla waders hangin' upside down on the wall. What am I sayin'? It wasn't me eyes saw thim at all, but the divil lookin' through me eyeballs, and him whisperin' in me ear: 'Mullarkey at Egan's corner!' I heard the whisper plain as I'm talkin' to you this minit. 'Mullarkey would advance you half-a-dollar on them fishin'-boots. They're worth more, but you'd ax only the half-dollar. You can manage on that be the dint of the hole in your belt till the boss comes back, an' with the five bob he'll hand to you and he no more than out o' the car you'll be able to redeem the boots an' no one a penny the wiser. Go on, you cowardly skrimshanker! 'Tis what the boss would be glad you'd do, and it to aise his con-science . . .' So I took the boots," said Thomasheen James briefly.

"And pawned them for your half-dollar?"

"That's what you think. To Mullarkey's I took them at Egan's corner. He is not me usual man o' business, but he was convanient — an' he don't know me. But, be the powders o' war! he'll have cause to know me one o' these days — if he has eyes in the back of his poll. He looked at the waders an' he looked at me. 'These are spang new,' says he cogitatenly. 'These things cost a fiver not so long ago. Where'd you get 'em, me dacent boy?' 'From a fri'nd,' says I careless-like. 'He was that,' says Mullarkey. 'Is he a fisherman be any chance?' 'So he says,' I says. 'An' has he given up the foolish game?' 'He has not,' says I, the dam' fool I was. 'He'd be fishin' a splash o' water in the track of a road after a shower o' rain, an' so he might as well for all the sprats he brings home.' 'Then he must be out of his mind to present you with these,' says Mullarkey, and he went on rubbin' 'em with wan finger. And there I was in front o' him, the hooks o' desp'ration buried in me, for I saw what was in his mind, the doubtin' divil.

"And then, without another word out of him, he stuffed the boots under the counter, an' cast a red eye at the telephone in the corner. 'How much?' says I. 'Come back on Saturday mornin' like a good boy,' says he coaxin', 'an' I'll see what I can do for you.' " 'Give me back me fishin'-boots, you so-and-so,' I starts on him. But he looked at me out o' that red eye an' reached a hand at the telephone, an' whether he got a hould of it or not I don't know, for I was skedaddlin' up the street as if the divil was after me — an' so he was. An' there I was, broke to the world, an' worse off than ever!"

"I gather that you did not accept the invitation for Saturday?" enquired Justice.

"An invitation to me own wake! What sort of a omadhaun do you take me for? Wasn't Mullarkey's intintion as plain as the nose on his face, an' he goes to bed be the red light o' that. Seein' the holy evenin' that was in it, an' Good Friday followin', he had no mind to put the hooks in me till the Saturday. Why the hell didn't I go to a Jewman instead of an oul' sanctimonous craw-thumper? Satur-day, how are you! an' Detective Dowd waitin' for me, the hand-cuffs up his sleeve. I wasn't in this end o' Dublin be Saturday. I wasn't in Dublin at all. Down be Navan an' round by Trim I was, slinkin' from door to door an' sleepin' under a hedge five nights — an' every time I seen a Guard in the distance me hair ruzz."

He lifted and shook a finger at the priest.

"An' let me tell you, me reverent gintleman, that this very minute I'd be in a safe place I know where Joe Dowd couldn't lay a hand on me, only I knew the boss 'ud be needin' his waders — and so are you. Ye know where they are now, an' me duty is done." His hand implored peace. "Don't let no wan be raisin' Cain. I won't. I'll go quiet, an' in thirty days I'll have lashin's o' time to forgive an' forget. That's me complaint, now — an' may the divil look sideways at me!"

Sergeant Joe O'Dowd thumped his massive thigh.

"Truth or lie — and I have my own opinion — that's as thorough a bit of special pleading as ever I heard in or out of court."

The priest and judge looked at me, and I noted that all the humour had gone out of his eyes.

"Joe might accept your opinion in equity," I hinted placatingly.

"I am glad you have some grace in you," said the priest.

He had stopped smoking long ago. Now he laid his pipe down and rubbed his hands through his black hair as if his thoughts pained him. There certainly was trouble in his voice.

"The Lord forgive us," he said. "I wonder are we Christians at all? Thirty brown coppers were all that this unfortunate rogue wanted; consider how many you spent over the same week-end."

"I am not the defendant," I tried to ward him off.

"You are, and I am. Thirty pieces of silver were a certain price, and thirty pieces of copper would have kept Thomasheen James from hunger and from cold in the days we celebrate as the ultimate proof of our Faith. But he hadn't got them, had nowhere to get them, and had to go slinking along byways, fear in his heart. You and I ate our fill and slept softly, but this man slept hard and was hungry. Look! If we were true Christians we dare not sleep a sound wink, and food should be dust in our mouths, if we knew that there was a hungry man or a hungry woman or a child whimpering with the hunger within the four seas of Ireland. It is a beneficent small island and not crowded, generous in its soil and in its race, and in it no one need go hungry — no one at all — with a little considerate thought and less planning. Men work and eat, men are idle and look to a charity that is often cold and sometimes kind, and not infrequently thoughtless — like yours and mine. Men are idle, indeed, and many of them, including a certain one, need not be so — wastrels, drifters, incompetents. But let us not judge them. God knows why they will not work, what wicked curse is on them, what terrible dreaming drives them. All that we need know is that no one should go hungry in this Christian land . . . But what is the use of talking? You know all that I would say, Mr. Pagan. I will not give an opinion in equity. I will be the judge that you wanted. You have your writing-pad on your knee. Take your pen and write this:

" 'Dear Mr. Mullarkey — law-abiding in mere honesty — don't put that in. Dear Mr. Mullarkey, the bearer of this note has my authority to pawn the pair of fishing-waders, my property, left with you on Holy Thursday evening. If necessary Detective-Sergeant Joseph O'Dowd will confirm.' Sign it. Put the address on top."

"At last I am sure," I said, "that you will never be more than the poorest curate of the poorest parish in the diocese. There's your outrageous note!"

He took it, folded it without looking, and reached it to Thomasheen James.

"Take that, you astonishing scoundrel! Bring back the ticket to our brother here. He will do the redeeming."

Without another word the priest rose to his feet and strode to the garden gate. He left his pipe behind him.

"The waders will be here tomorrow," I called after him. "I'll send them down to you, and if they don't fill with you in a deepish place I'll lose faith in cursing."

He looked back over his shoulder and smiled a little sadly.

"While you're at it, send along that thick pair of socks too."

"Miracles'll never cease," said Thomasheen James. "That man 'ud make a Christian out of you if you lived to be a hundred."

Joe O'Dowd rose to his feet too and paced solidly to the gate.

"I am going. I'm going now. I do not want to be a witness to the assault and battery that is about to take place close to here in about ten seconds flat. Wait!" He beckoned me. "Come round the corner a minute and I'll instruct you how to root a man in two places without leaving incriminating evidence. I believe in strict justice, myself."

When I got back there was no Thomasheen James, and Joe O'Dowd had known there would not be.

He took full advantage of the judgment in his favour. He pawned my waders for fifteen shillings, and I had to pay an additional ten per cent to redeem them.

This misadventure befell him and me some time ago, and Thomasheen James has his tentacles in me still. As I sit writing these last words he is coming up the garden path trundling his barrow that contains only his sweeping-brush and two half-dead leaves.

"We'll be real busy in a day or two," he says cheerfully. "The leaves is beginnin' to fall."

"I am busy now. Get to — !"

"Did you see what Pinkyvitch said in the *Moscow News* last week?"

"Who the devil — ?"

"Pinkyvitch! A big professor in Moscow beyont — up above Stamboul where I belted a Turk during the Big War. He says the culture o' the West is only for pink-eyed rabbits. He says if any prooletarian gint wants to get the straight tip on culture let him come an' study it where 'tis bound to the wheel of advancement. I wonder, now, what a ticket to Moscow would run a man in for?"

"Make it a single one," I tell him, "and you can pawn my new waders."

"May the divil dam' the mimory some people is cursed be," says Thomasheen James warmly.

8. HEADLINES AND DEADLINES

8. HEADLINES AND DEADLINES

> *"Bestow on us, thy servants, a little more of thy critical spirit, and a little less on our readers."*
>
> — From the "Newspaperman's Prayer to St. Francis"

As a member of the newspaper profession, I should like to put my best font forward and print a few words in defense of the alleged un-gentle men of the press.

You've often heard of the "average newspaper reader." But who ever heard of the "average newspaperman"? There is no such creature. I honestly believe that the modern newspaperman can neither type — a minor fault — nor be typed, a major virtue.

Your newspaperman is frequently mild, witty and scholarly like John Kieran. Mr. Kieran wrote of birds or "birdies" and scored a hit with his *New York Times* readers for twenty years by sliding Homer, the poet, into many a discussion of homer, the baseball, before he left the typewriter for the radio microphone.

Sometimes the newspaperman is gruff, salty and robust, like Westbrook Pegler, another former sportswriter. There are people who don't like the way this umpire "calls them," but few will deny that he calls them in a lusty voice, and with sweeping gestures that leave no doubt in the minds of bleacher fans. To some he is an exhilarating astringent, and to others too much pepper up the nose. In writing his syndicated column Mr. Pegler apparently believes with the fabulous Mr. Dooley that "Politics ain't bean bags; 'tis a man's game an' women, childher an' pro-hyb-itionists 'd do well to keep out'n it."

Sometimes the newspaperman pops off, but not as violently as Mr. Pegler. Red Smith, for example — and his wide audience suggests "Well-read" Smith as a better name — effervesces like champagne in his sports column "Views of Sport." This Smith a mighty man is he, with a large and sinewy vocabulary. He strikes off metaphors and similes from his typewriter which are as delightful to watch as the sparks from a small-town smithy's anvil.

Then you have a fellow like H. I. Phillips, New England's Will Rogers. Readers of the *New York Sun* have been setting their good-time-pieces by his "Sun Dial" column for a quarter of a century, along with other readers throughout the country. Though he writes for big city papers he still sees the world from the vantage point of a (Milford) Connecticut Yankee. The air must be mighty crisp and cool up Connecticut way, for it imparts some of its tangy freshness to his writings. His humor doesn't suffer from the odor of smoke-filled night clubs and tinkling glasses. All he needs is a whittling stick and a cracker barrel, and he'd fit the perfect picture of a jovial Down Easter commenting on world affairs, big and small.

Some newspapermen are very cosmopolitan, wear seven-league boots, carry seven-league expense accounts, and travel from Cambodia to Midway, from London to Libya meeting "Such Interesting People," as Robert J. Casey did, and did so well. The selection in this section, taken from his book, *Such Interesting People*, gives authentic pictures of newspapermen at work.

Opposite the cosmopolitan newspaperman is the metropolitan newspaperman. He requires no seven-league boots, just boots sufficient to permit him the pleasure of wading through puddles at fires. His expense account doesn't include "Stratoliner to Cairo to talk with King of Egypt" but might include "I.R.T. subway to Bronx to talk with Mr. Radokovsky about missing Airedale."

Many times the newspaperman is the product of a small town, like Ed Wallace who still takes a yearning look now and then back to the Midwest from which he came, as he does so entertainingly in the sketch reprinted here from his novel *Barington*. Sometimes the newspaperman is the product of a big small town, like Brooklyn. That brings me to me — and *that* is that.

I'd like to close by reprinting a prayer for the long-suffering tribe of scribes. The prayer, unearthed by the vicar of a parish not far from the Shropshire borders in England, is addressed to St. Francis de Sales, patron saint of newspapermen. It was printed in the *Journal of the British Institute of Journalists*:

"St. Francis, dear patron of a harrowed tribe, grant us thy protection. Bestow on us, thy servants, a little more of thy critical spirit, and a little less on our readers; confer on our subscribers the grace of condescension in overlooking our faults, the grace of light in acknowledging our merits; and the grace of promptitude in paying our bills.

"Make them less partial to compliments, more callous to rebuke, less critical of misprints. Give us beautiful thoughts, brave thoughts, so that we, thy children, may have the courage to write as we think and our readers the docility to think as we write.

"Then shall we, thy faithful servants, resting on thy protection, fight thy battles with joyful hearts, drive the wolf from the door, the devil from the fold, and meet thee in everlasting peace. Amen."

ROBERT J. CASEY

Multiple Managing Editors *

The lads had a downright affection for Mr. Sam Makaroff who was by turns office boy, assistant city editor and "roving city editor." Mr. Makaroff's education was sketchy and his acquaintance with the English language was purely platonic. To the best of his ability he maintained a dignified front and he seemed conscious of his position. But he made a nice foil for the stuffed shirts and so came to enjoy lasting popularity.

* This excerpt outlines some interesting people Mr. Casey met on the *Chicago Herald-Examiner*.

He became something of a legend around Chicago when he tried to board a special train bearing a lot of society notables on an errand which the world, unfortunately, has forgotten. A calm and dignified gentleman tried to shoo him off the observation platform.

"I'm Charles Harkness Harkness-Clifford," said the gentleman sternly.

"You're a son of a bitch-bitch," returned Mr. Makaroff.

His gifted repartee naturally made him famous overnight. But it was really his sense of phrase in the routine exercise of a desk job that got him his lasting place in the sun.

A weeping woman had appeared at a coroner's inquest into the death of her husband, and Mr. Makaroff wanted to make sure that the rewrite man understood the story's pathos.

"Soften it up," he directed. "Get in something about her widow's tweeds."

And once there was the matter of a story that had suddenly blown up.

"Not much on this," he ordered. "Give me half a paragraph."

One of the itinerant managing editors appeared one night with acidosis and an abiding scorn for the talents of his staff. "The trouble with this paper," he informed Mr. Makaroff, "is that nobody dares to be original. Every story in the proofs tonight is filled with old expressions — platitudes."

So Mr. Makaroff went out and shot the adrenalin into his loyal workers.

"The boss says we got too many old platitudes," he told them. "You gotta snap out of it and get a lotta new platitudes."

He uttered other aphorisms:

"The convention is waterlogged."

"We want pictures of the Big Figureheads of the American Legion."

"You don't have to write this if you don't want to. It's purely mandatory."

"Get something in about the doctors' oath of hypocrisy."

And so ad infinitum while the rewrite men patiently recorded all the bright things he had said, all that he might have said, and many, probably, that he never said at all.

Delos Avery, a quiet-mannered man of varied talents and a bitter wit, was a rewrite man who watched the procession of executives pass in and out of the office for many years. As dean of the office he acquired skill and privilege as a sniper and he was a constant source of worry to Mr. Makaroff. That was because of his willingness to stick into every story little comments intended for Mr. Makaroff's eyes alone. He was carefully watched by editors and copyreaders standing behind Mr. Makaroff but that did not prevent the appearance of some of his gems in type.

Once the pundits decided that no story in the *Examiner* should begin with A, An, or The. And shortly after the promulgation of the rule Mr. Avery was called upon to write a piece about the finding of the body of an unidentified woman in the river. That did not bother Mr. Avery.

"Hello everybody," he wrote. "Take a look at this! The body of an unidentified woman . . . etc." That got into type and the rule was changed the next day.

Then there was the occasion when William Powell, the actor, was very ill. Somebody in the front office thought it might be a good thing to cash in on the sentiment with which this star was so generally regarded.

"Here," said the city editor to Mr. Avery. "Stick in a suggestion that this guy's fans write him cheering notes in care of the *Herald and Examiner.*"

"Okay," said the imperturbable Mr. Avery. And his carefully worded account of Mr. Powell's illness came to this end:

"Mr. Powell's associates have informed the *Herald and Examiner* that messages of cheer from his numerous friends in Chicago would undoubtedly hasten his recovery. This newspaper will forward immediately all letters addressed to him.

"Write to Mr. Powell in care of the *Herald and Examiner.* Or say a little prayer."

That one got printed in a nice position next to pure reading matter and a few hours later the phone on the city desk began to ring.

"I was deeply touched by your story of Mr. Powell's illness," said a woman's voice. "And I notice that you recommend prayer. Just what sort of prayer would you suggest?"

The city editor hastily looked up Mr. Avery's work and for the first time noticed the last sentence. He went into conference with the great minds about him, then returned to the telephone.

"As for the prayer," he said with the intonation of an undertaker, "the *Examiner* approves no set formula. Just say whatever is in your heart."

Si Clare, biographer of Policeman Spiegelbuehler, came to the *Examiner* with other wreckage of the old *Inter-Ocean* and rose to great prominence. He no longer went to Dubuque when he got drunk, or rather he went there only once. On that occasion he went through his routine of telegraphing for help to Jim Crown, City Editor, the *Inter-Ocean*, Chicago. But there was no *Inter-Ocean* and there wasn't any Jim Crown in Chicago. He had gone away to New Orleans months previously. So Mr. Clare arrived at sobriety in a police station and was two days convincing anybody that he ought to be brought home. From then on, Dubuque seems to have lost its glamor.

Mr. Clare's life in the ensuing years was considerably more temperate than it had ever been before. He announced publicly that he would welcome a stomach ulcer to insure a permanent change in his habits. Once he almost became a teetotaler.

The desk next to Mr. Clare's was occupied by Mr. Earl Ackroyd, another of those geniuses who drift unsung through the newspaper business. Mr. Ackroyd in some previous existence had learned how to take a typewriter apart and put it together again and his mechanical skill had remained with him when he became a rewrite man for the *Examiner*.

One afternoon with time hanging heavy on his hands he noticed the sad state of Mr. Clare's typewriter and was seized by a generous impulse to fix it up. He sent a boy across the street for a ten-cent screwdriver and went to work. When he had finished the typewriter was mechanically as good as before but it was different. The ingenious Mr. Ackroyd had changed the position of quite a lot of the type bars without disturbing the keys. He put away his screwdriver and sat back expectantly. He had the feeling that Mr. Clare, fresh from the inspiration of a cooling saloon, would have a lot of fun with his typewriter.

Mr. Clare came in at five o'clock as expected and in the cheery state that Mr. Ackroyd had foreseen. He sat down and wrote:

By Si Clare

Gang guns blazed again today on Chicago's West Side and in the thinning smoke of black powder the police discovered the bodies of Tony ("The Flea") Raspucci and John ("Bowlegs") Iskovitch . . .

Or at least that is what he thought he was writing. When he looked at his copy he read:

Qn Lo Eswkt

Uwfu uxfl qswmtr wuwof zgrwn gf Eioewug'l Vtlz Lort wfr of zit zioffofu ldgat gy qswea hgvrtk zit hgsoet rolegcktr zit qgrotl gy Zgfn ("Zit Ystw") Kwlhxeeo wfr Pgif ("Qgvstul") Olagcozei . . .

Mr. Clare showed alarm. He tore the copy paper out of the typewriter and handed it to Mr. Ackroyd.

"Look at that," he urged. "Does that make sense?"

"Certainly," said Mr. Ackroyd, who knew in advance what assignment Mr. Clare had been covering. "It's about Raspucci and Iskovitch. They got shot."

Mr. Clare tried it again with no better result, arose in sudden panic and started out of the office.

"The hooch has got me," he announced hollowly. "I can think swell but I can't write anything that I can read. I'm going on the wagon right now." But he didn't. Instead he got a new typewriter.

Mr. Clare, despite his failings, came in time to rate as a Hearst ace. He was shrewd, volatile and filled with a fine sense of the dramatic. He never saw things exactly as less imaginative reporters saw them but his visions were always interesting and looked well in print. No wonder, then, that he figured largely in all the policy stories, solved all the mysteries, conducted all the relief trains.

One of his expeditions became a classic among students of the Vigorous Method.

Down in middle Illinois one day a banker came back to his bank after lunch and noticed that his clerk ("teller" by brevet rating) was missing. The door of the teller's cage stood open. Some $2000 in cash was gone. But that wasn't the worst of it. The big vault was closed and in front of it lay the clerk's handkerchief.

The banker sent out an immediate call for help.

"My bank has been robbed," he reported. "I don't know what the loss may total. The robbers must have overpowered Jimmy and shoved him into the vault. The door can't be opened until tomorrow morning because of the time lock. It's an airtight modern vault and he'll die there. He'll die!"

The wire services brought this sad news to the *Examiner* office and Mr. Clare was assigned to see what he could do about it. He rushed into the office of the current managing editor, got full authority to proceed and thereupon launched a campaign which for speed, vision and daring surpassed even the *Examiner's* own past performances.

Mr. Clare began as usual by calling a railroad president. The railroad president, as usual, donated the use of a special train. It consisted of one locomotive and one coach but that was enough.

Then Mr. Clare called the warden of Joliet penitentiary.

"I want to borrow a safe-cracker for a few hours," he explained lucidly.

"A what?" demanded the warden.

"A safe-cracker," repeated Mr. Clare. "This is the Chicago *Herald and Examiner* and we need a safe-cracker to save a boy who's dying in a vault. You can send guards along with him if you want to but we've got to have him. It's a matter of life and death."

"You ought to have a court order," mentioned the warden. "This is all very irregular."

But one never got anywhere talking about irregularities with Mr. Clare.

"I've got a special train waiting for me now," he said finally. "You have your yegg down at the railroad station in an hour and we'll pick him up. And you'd better find us a good one because this is a tough vault."

Within an hour after he had received the assignment Mr. Clare was on his way. Messages of good cheer were sent by the *Examiner* to the banker, the boy's worried parents and the local constable. The safe-cracker, well pleased with his prospect for a holiday, was waiting at the Joliet station with a kit of tools taken from the penitentiary museum.

Two hours later the train rolled into the banker's town. The stationmaster came out to point the way to a convenient siding. But there was no other reception committee. That annoyed Mr. Clare who had pictured himself leaping with his photographer and a safe-blower into the arms of an anxious populace. But the station agent told him how to get to the bank and he went.

There he discovered what had become of the citizenry. But he no longer cared. A garage mechanic was trundling out an oxyacetylene welding outfit. The air was filled with the reek of something burning. The vault door stood open.

"I'm sorry," said the mechanic apologetically. "But we didn't think you'd get here in time. So I cut out the lock with a torch. The kid wasn't there. He took it on the lam somewheres with about twenty thousand bucks."

———————

JOHN KIERAN

Chung Cheng-liu

One person famous in track and field annals was the lone representative of 400,000,000 Chinese in the Olympic Games of 1932 at Los Angeles, California. Visiting hordes came from other countries; runners by brigades, boxers by battalions, swimmers in great shoals, sprinters by platoons, weight-throwers by the ton. The vast nation of China sent one man. This was the way of it:

> In the month of white blossoms
> Did Chung Cheng-liu
> Leave the flowery garden
> By the little gate
> Where at twilight the Dragon sleeps,
> By moonlight the nightingale sings,

And at dawn the silkworm
Feeds on the mulberry leaves.
He went by the yellow river
Where the gray cormorant
With the silver collar
Catches the foolish fish;
Out to the great sea
Went Chung Cheng-liu,
To a strange land far away,
To California called the Golden,
To the Games called Olympic,
For the glory of China.
Now we must wait.
There is bird's-nest soup
For supper.

Back in China the children were gathered in the garden, and Chang Fu, the Schoolmaster of the Bamboo Grove, read to them the verse about the Pear Tree from the book of Odes, very old. Su Tung, the Philosopher, sat under the red cedar by the little brook, thinking.

"Tell us the story of Chung Cheng-liu, the great athlete," said the children. So the Schoolmaster began:

"Willingly do I tell you the story of Chung Cheng-liu and the Games called Olympic in the far-off land of California where the sun also shines and the rain falls only in golden showers at sunset when the roses are thirsty and in silver showers at night when the orange blossoms ask softly for water. Now, Chung Cheng-liu was a great runner in China and his fame spread from the snows of the North to the yellow sands of the South and even beyond. He was faster than the little fish that dart in the lake under the willows, faster than the deer on the mountain and the swallow above the plains."

"Li Tai Po, the great poet, always walked very slowly," said Su Tung the Philosopher, as if to himself. "I will have a cup of honorable tea. There is no hurry."

The Schoolmaster bowed deeply at the mention of Li Tai Po and continued:

"There came on the breath of the wind the tale that the great runners of the world were to strive in the land of California, and Chung Cheng-liu said, 'I will go and win for the honor of China,' and he set forth. At his parting we gathered and wished him well, and there was music from a guitar, inlaid, an ebony flute, and thirteen drums. The drums were very good. When he had departed, we went to the tomb of his honorable ancestors and strewed thereon rose petals that Chung Cheng-liu might prosper."

"Our honorable ancestors are very wise," observed Su Tung the Philosopher. "They do not run; they sleep."

The Schoolmaster bowed again and went on:

"Chung Cheng-liu traveled for days and weeks by land and sea and at last arrived in the far-off country called California, and there he found that the nations of the world had sent many strong youths to strive for the prizes — more than the leaves on the great mulberry tree, more than the blades of grass on this lawn. And Chung Cheng-liu was all alone. I will have a cup of honorable tea myself."

The Schoolmaster sipped the honorable tea while the children waited silently. Then he went on:

"Chung Cheng-liu prepared for the first race, which was called 100 meters or about the distance from where we are sitting to the tall pine yonder that listens to the ripple of the little brook. He ate of the white of chicken and rice cakes twice-baked and the thin stalks of celery to give him strength and speed for the contest. He ran in the great arena with countless thousands of strange persons looking on. But others ran faster than he did; and the judges said to Chung Cheng-liu, 'You did not win,' and he was pained."

"Pain is the beginning of knowledge," said Su Tung the Philosopher.

"It is so," said the Schoolmaster, bowing again. "But Chung Cheng-liu would again strive for the honor of China; and he put on his slippers with the little nails in the soles, and it was a race they called 200 meters, which is from here to the turret of the little summer-house that looks over the top of the plum tree."

"Did he win that race?" queried the smallest child softly.

"There were tall men from many nations," said the Schoolmaster. "There were men from the mountains and the seashore and the land between, and a great crowd again was gathered; and Chung Cheng-

liu ran, and again they said to him, 'You did not win,' and he began
to reflect."

"Reflection is the beginning of wisdom," said Su Tung the
Philosopher, who was then on his third cup of honorable tea.

"There was another race," continued the Schoolmaster, "and
Chung Cheng-liu put on his slippers with the little nails in the soles;
and then he said to himself, 'I cannot win the Olympic Games all by
myself against the runners of all the world,' and he took his shoes
with the little nails in the soles and stood aside, which was wise.
Nations were arrayed against him, and he was one man, alone. So
he came back from far-away California and was greeted in this very
garden with music from a guitar, inlaid, an ebony flute, and thirteen
drums. The drums were very good. Chung Cheng-liu had done his
best for China and his honorable ancestors. He was content."

"Contentment is the end of philosophy," said Su Tung the Philosopher. "If you will go away, I will sleep."

So the Schoolmaster quietly led the children out of the garden,
and Su Tung the Philosopher fell into an honorable sleep. Here
endeth the tale of Chung Cheng-liu, the one-man team from China
at the Olympic Games of 1932 in Los Angeles, U.S.A.

WESTBROOK PEGLER

My Day

Yesterday morning I took a train to New York and sat beside a
gentleman who was reading the 1937 Report of the International
Recording Secretary of the World Home Economics and Children's
Aptitude and Recreation Foundation of which my very good friend,
Dr. Mary McTwaddell, formerly of Vassar, is the American dele-
gate. This aroused my interest and I ventured to remark that I had

once had the pleasure of entertaining a group of young people who were deeply concerned with the neglected problem of the Unmarried Father. It turned out that the gentleman himself was an unmarried father so we had a very interesting chat until he got off at Metuchen.

In the afternoon a group of young people came in for tea and we had a discussion of the effect of early environment on the efficiency of workers. I am afraid environment is more important than many of us think and I have asked the Department of Agriculture to make a survey. Of course some people have more than others but then, I am afraid, very often the reverse is true and that is something that one cannot dismiss lightly these days.

Later in the day we took a train up the river where a group of young people were waiting to have a discussion of the psychology of youth in the postwar world. It is very stimulating to observe the eager interest of such young people, some of them not more than thirty-five, in the serious problems of the world. They seem to me to face problems much more candidly than some of us seem to think they do and it is very encouraging to see this, for I believe they will have a great influence for good in the future.

I left them after a time and went over to the Big House and had a discussion with my very good friend, Dr. Fusty, formerly of Smith College. He had written an article for the World Mothers' Planning Council of which he is the Honorary International Research Adviser, Emeritus, and one paragraph in particular seemed to me so profound that I obtained his permission to quote it for my readers. It says:

"Students will not fail to value the institutions and privileges of the tradition they inherit if they resist the temptation not to keep vividly aware that their duty to society is perennial, in the larger, rather than the narrower, sense of the word."

This seemed particularly thought-provoking to me. I shall think about it one day soon.

Returning to the Little House I mounted my bicycle and rode twelve miles up and down the path to save gasoline. I have figured that if I ride ten or twelve miles up and down the path every day that will be at least sixty miles a week and I shall save about four gallons a week.

Another group of young people had arrived at the Little House and we plunged at once into a very interesting discussion of the duty of the citizen not only toward his country but toward himself and his fellow man in relation to the past and the critical days ahead. One gentleman had rather strong ideas on the subject of nail biting and while, of course, I realize that there are two sides of the question, I am afraid capital punishment for nail biters is rather severe. I prefer what seems to me the more democratic way and proposed to approach it as a world problem, as nail biting is not a matter of race or creed. After a very spirited discussion we formed an organization which we are calling the Provisional World Extension Nail Biting Congress or P.W.E.N.B.C. Six of the young people pledged themselves to establish local committees immediately in their home cities. After all the eradication of this deplorable vice is in the hands of the future mothers of the world.

After dinner several old retainers came over to the Big House and together with Dr. Fusty and the young people we had a very enjoyable game of squat-tag on the lawn. This was followed by a brisk round of spin the plate and after bobbing for apples we retired at 9:45.

In bed I read Ludwig Donnervetter's *All Is Everything*. It is very beautiful and brings out powerfully the struggle of the young people to organize their world through student collaboration and discussion. I sometimes think we seem to miss many opportunities for better understanding because peoples are set apart by difference in language.

———————

PAUL J. PHELAN

Gorg Bernad (U No) Has a Spel

From pres reports it is lernd that Gorg Bernad Shaw, the man of many words, wants to shorten som of them. He fels al unecesary leters, such as thos not pronouncd, shuld be dropd from words, thus saving reding and riting tim and efort.

He declars he scribld the word "bomb" only eiten tims in a minut wheras he rot the word "bom" twenty-for tims, a saving of twenty-fiv per cent. This is cald simplifid speling. He dosn't say anything in refrence to fonetic speling, lik speling dos "duz" but merly asks elimination, lik speling "letter" with on "t" insted of to.

To se wether Shaw was rit is the reson for this endevor. I'll prov wether a method of simplifid speling savs reding and riting tim (unles the printer gets sor and drops the hol busness rit her).

Shaw usd to lik words, gobs of them, and tim was wen tim aperd as nothing to him except a vacum to be fild by Shavian witicisms. In the yer 1931 (u cant shorten numbers), he rot a pla, *Bak to Methusala*, wich the Thetre Gild just did manag to sqeze into fiv nits, probably by stoping the clok an our ech nit the wa Congres somtims dos.

Twenty yers ago he refusd to cut a lin from his pla, *Jon of Arc*, teling the Thetre Gild it shuld get the tran schedul changd if comuters wer mising the last expres for New Rochel.

In 1935 this internationly-non gurmet of words complaind that "we hav to makshift with an alfabet wich is about a dozen leters short of our crudest reqirements."

Of cors wat mit be behind al his present intrest in short words is the fact that Shaw is geting on in yers and its becom a cas of shorter words or fewer words. Ho culd dout wher his choic wuld li?

Al along ther has ben only on short word Shaw ever likd. That is the word "I." Only onc in his recorded lif was he at a los for words. In 1914 a dispatch to the *New York Herald* said that Shaw sat on the platform (wel, not rely on the platform, tho u wuldnt put it past him) during a debat on miracls in wich fiften famus controversalists tok part. And Shaw sat thru the hol batle with "the silenc of a carven statu." "If that wasn't a miracl, nothing ever was," the corespondent comented.

Incidently G. K. Chesterton, ho tok part in that debat, wuld undoutedly be plesd that Shaw's simplified speling wuld find it imposible to witle down the nam Chesterton. G. K. wuld ascrib this to the mystical, metaphysical conection betwen the world of mind and the world of flesh.

Maybe Shaw wants brefer words to rit his plas in becaus he has a gilty conscienc about that ocurenc in London in 1921. J. B. Fagan producd the Irish plarits *Hartbrak Hous* and wen he was reqested to cal on Shaw for a spech at the pla's end, he anouncd that Shaw was aslep in his box.

Wel, it was pland to mak this story livly and wity, but it was to much work so the hek with it. The tim it tok to rit this simplifid speling story semd as long as thos six ours at the Army induction center. If Shaw dosnt men wat it is thot he mens by simplifid speling, why dosnt he rit an articl to sho how? It wuld serv him rit.

By the wa, for the reders benefit tim out her so that u can chek ur reding tim (and ur bran to, at this point).

———————

H. I. PHILLIPS

The Better Mousetrap

(A Business Romance)

1. — A man decides to build a better mousetrap.

2. — He tries to interest somebody with capital. The first prospect listens with interest up to a point where he is convinced he would double his money. This scares him out.

3. — The inventor sees another capitalist. He almost gets him with the argument that if they are careful they can avoid quantity production and keep out of the uppermost brackets.

4. — Spurned again, he contacts a group of financiers who have been very successful at losing money. They think the mousetrap will be a flop and decide to back it.

5. — They ask him how much money he needs. He says about $100,000. They refuse to go in unless he will take a million. He reluctantly accepts.

6. — He asks if his backers would like to see the detailed drawings of the Better Mousetrap. They say no. (They are afraid the trap might look good. — Ed. note.)

7. — He needs only wood, wire, and a few holes. Owing to a wood shortage, he is asked to use plastics. He nearly gets some wire, but priorities set in and he is told to use soybeans.

8. — He can still use holes for holes, he thinks. But he is now stymied by a Washington decision to ration holes. He can only get three to a trap.

9. — He phones his backers that there are so many obstacles confronting him that they will all lose money, and he suggests dropping the project. They bring suit to make him go ahead.

10. — He turns out his first trap. It costs $8.50. As it has to sell for thirty cents retail, it looks bad. He notifies his backers. They are

quite pleased, but suggest that he turn out traps at a cost of $10 each and sell them two for a quarter.

11. — The Better Mousetrap Man asks for a factory in Elmira that can be bought for about $40,000. His backers buy him four in Detroit at a cost of $1,500,000 (with Government aid).

12. — He gets into production, but has to suspend work for six months to answer Federal questionnaires, and fill out new tax forms.

13. — After a long struggle he resumes operations. The Mouse-trap Makers Union calls a strike, demanding fewer holes in mouse-traps. He offers to cut the holes to one. The NLRB is called in and rules that one hole is too many under the Wagner Act.

14. — He asks the board how mice can get into a trap with no holes. It says: "They can't get in under the Democrats; let 'em wait until the Republicans get in."

15. — After long negotiations he is allowed to put one hole into each trap. (Except on Saturdays and Sundays. — Ed. note.)

16. — Ultimately he is all set for business except for a radio theme song. He listens to 400 goofy jingles. He chooses one sufficiently silly.

17. — Just when he seems out of the woods Washington rations cheese. It suggests that traps be baited with pigtails, sows' ears, and chitterlings.

18. — The Mousetrap Workers Union now walks out in sympathy with a strike of Rat Poison Mixers. There is also a jurisdictional strike. The Labor Board tells him unless he gives in inside of ten days the Government will seize his Better Mousetrap plant.

19. — He now goes nuts and insists he never designed a mouse-trap or was in business for himself. He swears he is a college professor.

20. — This lands him a job in Washington as a counsel to business men.

RED SMITH

Victory Spelled Backwards

LONDON, *Aug.* 10, 1948 — And now the Royal Air Force band must return to the desolate, forsaken field of Wembley Stadium and unplay "God Save the King." Blighty's only track victory in the Olympics, which was presented to Britain last Saturday under the Marshall plan, fell under the terms of reverse lend-lease today and was restored to the United States, the original copyright holders.

It was the most sensational reversal since Serutan.

At 4 p.m. on Saturday, the American team of Barney Ewell, Lorenzo Wright, Harrison Dillard and Mel Patton — identified locally as three cups of coffee with the cream on top — fled home first in the 400-meter relay by seven or eight yards.

Five minutes later a vigilante committee of judges ruled that Ewell, after running the first hundred meters, had bootlegged the baton to Wright in a sinister black-market deal consummated outside the legal zone. The United States was disqualified; England was declared the winner; the Union Jack flapped from the victor's flagpole; the British Lion looked up from his lunch of cold mutton and cheese and roared his triumph to the skies.

But they had reckoned without J. Arthur Rank and his magic lantern. Today Mr. Rank brought out his stereopticon machine and pictures of the race were shown to the American, the Frenchman, the Finn, the Dutchman, the Czech and the two Britons composing an International Jury of Appeal. The slides proved, beyond possible cavil, that the baton-snatch had been engineered in strict obedience to the laws of God and man.

The jury thereupon declared the Americans undisqualified. The decision came shortly after 12:30 p.m. Thus the United States triumph was accomplished in 68 hours 37 minutes 40.6 seconds. This is not an Olympic record.

Gold, silver and bronze medals for first, second and third place were, of course, awarded last Saturday to Great Britain, Italy and Hungary, whose runners now are required to disgorge, yield up, surrender and relinquish the hardware. Chances are that before these twelve gimcracks reach their rightful owners, Scotland Yard will have to comb every hock shop in London.

Thus history was made today, both in international athletics and ·in the film industry. It was not only the first reversal of a decision involving victory in any Olympic competition. It was also one of the few times within living memory that the movies definitely settled a disputed point in any sport. In the past, it has almost invariably turned out that the cameraman was ogling a blonde when the deed was done.

Before these pictures were shown to the jury, they were viewed by Castleton Knight, producer of Mr. Rank's sweaty epic. He gave it as his inexpert opinion that the camera had caught the Americans redhanded and the disqualification would stand. The London press quoted Mr. Knight to this effect, unaware that he didn't happen to know what he was talking about.

This was, nevertheless, a great day for the flicker industry. All through the games, there have been approximately as many camera men as athletes on the field, creating the impression that this struggle for world supremacy was mere window-dressing for a J. Arthur Rank production. That impression has been gloriously confirmed. Eighty-two thousand cash customers saw a race last Saturday. Now they've got to go to a theater to see the official contest.

Half an hour after the jury's decision, the films were run off for the press. Agreement was unanimous that Ewell and Wright had swapped the stick well over on the alkaline side of the white stripe marking the limit of the legal zone. The only argument concerned their margin of safety.

"Three feet," said Mr. Knight.

The assembled experts jeered.

Twelve feet, they insisted. Ten, anyway. Two full strides, some one estimated. Another counted three. Somebody else guessed four.

"Aw," said somebody, "give 'em three steps."

"Coo," said a small voice, " 'aven't we given 'em enough already?"

As if things weren't tough enough for the bandsmen, having to learn the anthems of fifty-nine nations, including Liechtenstein, now they've got to play "The Star-Spangled Banner" backward.

"O, Yas Nac Uoy Ees . . . ?"

EDWARD TATUM WALLACE

Storytellers

The store in Barington was a place where a million old yarns were respun by hundreds of men with a thousand techniques. There were men who never told the same story twice, who kept abreast of the times and adapted their stories to interests of the day. There were men with a sense of time who talked endlessly of things in the present; and there were men who contained a program of old stories, accounts dealing with men long dead and things past, never-changing stories which were known by everyone, yet capable of arousing new interest each time they were told. Then there was Judge Samuel Easton, and his story of the horse that blew first.

When Judge Easton was younger he won a violin for being the ugliest man in Seba County, and with that start he entered the ministry and served the Lord in his way for many years, accounting for many souls added to the Baptist Church. After this fruitful sojourn in the vineyard, he took up the practice of law and later was elected county judge. Throughout his campaign the judge had three stories with which he spiced his plea for election. They were old stories, known by everyone, but the judge told them so often that they became his own, and when people heard them told by others they would say, "That there is Judge Easton's tale," and begin to laugh. They came to identify these stories by the names of the percolator, the nightshirt, and the horse blowed first! It was the

last of these which became almost a symbol of the judge, and anyone repeating it felt bound to give credit to Judge Easton, as one
might respect the ownership of real property. Then, too, to mention
the judge assured the storyteller of additional laughter.

The things at which people laughed followed a set pattern, and
stories without wit or humor were carried along for generations because they had been given the label of being funny. Yet the fun was
in the telling, and the listeners followed along, anticipating the
end when they could release their bound laughter in a whooping
chorus. Judge Easton enjoyed the full measure of this and had more
fun than anybody, often enjoying his joke so much that his voice
would fail, causing him to stomp around and shake his frail legs, his
face tortured with mirth until he could control himself again and
continue his old story.

Bart would often pull him into the store and get him to go through
his trilogy of anecdotes for the men who sat around the store. As
was his due, the judge was given complete attention, some of the
men squaring around and arising to offer their seats, although it was
known that the judge always stood to address his audience.

"Bart, here, reminded me of a story I sometimes tell," the judge
would begin. "A feller named Johnny went to see his girl, and
about ten o'clock it began to rain. The night was so dark, and the
storm was so furious that Nellie, she was the girl, told the boy that
he couldn't go home so she'd make him a pallet in the front room.

"Well, Nellie went to fix down the pallet, but when she come
back Johnny was gone. She thought, well, he's a shy feller and didn't
want to stay — but a half hour later Johnny come back, staggered
through the door soaking wet. The poor fellow was just about
drowned.

" 'W'y, Johnny, where have you been?' the girl asked.

" 'Where have I been?' Johnny said. 'I've been home to get my
nightshirt!' "

When the judge reached the climax of his story he was so filled
with laughter, his face so twisted to contain himself, that the last
word, "nightshirt," came out in an unnatural whoop which added
to the merriment of the men. They all knew, however, that this was

but the beginning and that the judge would tell one more story before he came to the anecdote of the horse that blew first.

"I think I've got time to tell you about a feller I met when I was a young preacher," the judge began again, half solemnly. "I've always been a big coffee drinker and I met a fellow once who invited me into his house to set awhile. He introduced me to his wife, and she, knowing about me liking coffee so well, said, 'Well, you men make yourselves comfortable and I'll go put on my percolator.' The fellow looked up at his wife, a pretty little thing, and said, 'You'll do nothing of the kind, Mary. You look well enough in what you've got on.' "

The men laughed again and settled themselves for the story which was coming. It would be the judge's best, and each man primed himself for the approaching enjoyment, the story racing ahead in their minds. The judge laughed a moment before he began, and the men twitched with anticipation and made stiff cracking noises as they twisted their hands.

Pleased with their attention, and carried along with the old excitement of standing and speaking before men, the judge adjusted his spectacles and made smiling grimaces to restore quiet.

"I'll tell you one more story, and then I must go," he said. Judge Easton then began the anecdote which he had been working toward, and the tale the men were waiting for. Like all prime storytellers, he had woven himself into the story.

"When I was a candidate for judge I met a fellow down at Auburn who was leading a sick horse," the judge said. "Well, we talked of this and that for a while, and I asked him what was the matter with his horse. He said the horse had been poorly for several days and he might have to shoot him, but he looked like a pretty good animal so I examined him. I'm sort of a jack-leg veterinarian, and it looked to me like the horse could be cured."

By then the story was taking shape in their minds, and the men nodded at one another, then turned rapt attention to the judge.

" 'I'll tell you what to do, John,' I told the fellow. 'You take some Epsom salts and sulphur and mix it with copperas, and you sprinkle in some antimony and a dust of soda and some ordinary chimney soot. Mix it all together good, and I think it will cure that horse right up.' "

The judge became so amused with reciting this noxious mess that he held his breath over the last words, speaking them hollow and weak. The men guffawed and thought of the end of the story. They waited for the judge to reach it and release their laughter.

" 'Now when you get that made,' I said, 'get a piece of dry cane and put the mixture in the cane. Put the cane in the horse's mouth, and you take the other end in your mouth and blow.' " Here the judge broke down, his face contorted with painful pleasure, and the men laughed quickly, loosened their crotches, and stroked their stubble beards.

"Well, a few days later I saw this feller again," the judge continued. "But he didn't look like the same man. I hardly recognized him. His face was all drawn like he had been sick a month, and he'd lost about fifteen pounds. Well, I didn't want to mention his appearance so I asked him about the horse.

" 'Did you treat that horse like I told you, George?' I asked.

" 'Yes,' he said, 'I done what you said.'

"Well, I asked him how it turned out, and he said it wasn't any good. I could tell he was mad about something, so I asked him what happened.

" 'Did you mix up the soda and antimony like I said, and did you sprinkle in some copperas and chimney soot?'

" 'Yes, I done all them things,' the feller said.

" 'And did you put it in a cane and stick it in the horse's mouth?'

" 'I done that,' the feller said, getting madder.

" 'Then what happened, George?' I asked.

" 'I put the other end in my mouth, but the damn horse blowed first.' "

Judge Easton's face turned to splotches of red and blue, and he bent double with a spasm of laughter. He stomped about on his thin legs, shook them and tottered backward, helpless and retching with mirth. The men about him, tantalized so long with the telling, stooped off their seats and moved about, whooping with joy. When the judge had regained his speech, he repeated the phrase again, "but the damn horse blowed first," sending himself into another seizure of laughter.

From behind his high desk, where he had gone when the judge began talking, Bart watched the men subside again to their chairs. He was pleased to have occasioned such a spectacle in the weary winter afternoon. He smiled and was half amused.

9. ACROSS THE FOOTLIGHTS

9. ACROSS THE FOOTLIGHTS

"Then to the well-trod stage anon."

— From "L'Allegro"
by John Milton

This section opens with a few "cherce" words from Jimmy Durante, the marvelous hybrid of the show world created by crossing Mrs. Malaprop's tongue with Cyrano's nose. Jimmy sets the mood of summery cheerfulness to be found in the other selections, though his article on acting as an art is a bit more "balmy" than the others. Frank Fay is the man who proved that horses and greyhounds weren't the only animals who could be parlayed into a fortune. He rode a six-foot invisible rabbit named "Harvey" to the heights of fame. He has written of his long struggle to avoid being rich, in a book called *How to Be Poor.* In the chapter reprinted, Mr. Fay outlines a method of entertaining which he used preceding his role of Elmer Dowd in the play *Harvey*; a method which helped him to attain the prominence necessary for association with invisible rabbits. The chapter is supposed to show readers what not to do if they want to be unsuccessful.

Along with these stalwart actors are three stalwart playwrights. Emmet Lavery's play, *The Magnificent Yankee,* with Louis Calhern in the title role of Justice Oliver Wendell Holmes, made a magnificent showing on Broadway. Reproduced here is Act I, Scene II, which depicts Justice Holmes the day after his dissenting opinion in a Marshall anti-trust law case. The scene highlights the public life of the Justice, who, just recently arrived in Washington, makes himself "at Holmes," ready to cross swords, or big sticks, with President Theodore Roosevelt. The scene sidelights the life-long romance of the Justice and his wife.

All who saw Micheal MacLiammoir's play *Where Stars Walk* felt as if they were walking with the stars. It was an enchanting and inspiring bit of fantasy, put on so well by the Dublin Gate Theatre players that it received several mentions for the best foreign play on Broadway in the 1947–48 season. It's the story of a group of Irish actors rehearsing a Celtic "twilight legend" play to be put on for the benefit of retired cab horses in Dublin. In a typically Irish mixture of mystic soul, realistic mind and sensitive funnybone, the house in which the rehearsals take place becomes the scene of the coming-to-life of the very legend being enacted, as a maid and a hired man realize they are the shadowy Midhir and Etain, strayed from the far-off Land of the Young. Into such ethereal surroundings comes a plodding English newspaperman to interview the star of the play. His attempt to capture the Irish spirit resembles an ox chasing a butterfly, as is indicated in the scene reproduced here.

Gerard Murray's *Career Angel* which started its career at the Blackfriars' Theatre in 57th Street, New York, and later winged its way down to Broadway, was at its best when the delightful title character was on the stage. The main plot of the play concerned Brother Seraphim and his guardian angel. Brother Seraphim was the founder of a Catholic orphan's home on the coast of Georgia. The institution's funds were sinking and were about going down for the last time, when the guardian angel assumed a physical form and told Brother Seraphim that there was a valuable historic document hidden in the barn. In the scene reprinted here the guardian angel makes his first visit to Brother Seraphim, who later has trouble persuading his colleagues that an angel they couldn't see was the seer to steer them out of their difficulties.

The heckling side remarks from the gallery in this section are made by John P. Mulgrew, known throughout the Midwest as "Jazbo of Old Dubuque." His column appears in *The Witness* at Dubuque and his contributions frequently brighten Arch Ward's column in the *Chicago Tribune*.

JIMMY DURANTE

My Deproach to Art

Art? What is dis art?

Some guys tink dat nuttin but Shakespeare is art, or a paintin by Caribaldy or Michaels St. Angelo.

But I claim dat everyting is art. Pickin up a newspaper is art. Lightin a cigar is art.

Actin is an art. A difficult art. It ain't as spontanulous as it may appear. Yeh, it's difficult. It requires months of what we call studyin, learnin your lines. Dere are two ways of learnin your lines — da wrong way and da artistic way. De artistic way is to get into bed. . . . Wait, I'm getting ahead of myself.

Foist, you go home wid da script — an object of supernal beauty, a ting of joy, typed up wid a blue cover. You put on your night lounge, or whatever you decides to call it, your dressin garment. Yeh, your dressin garment. A bright color is pertinent to our purposes — vermilion or charteuse or cashmere. It lends a mood.

Anodder ting. Anodder ting about da proper costume for concentratin on your part. Never wear garters. Never. Day inhabit da circulation.

Now you're in bed wid da script. You have a box of cigars and plenty of matches and maybe a bottle of Lewis XIV brandy to excourage thought. You prop yourself up wid lots of pillows. If you ain't got enough pillows you take some cushions out of da chase long. You commence.

You work foist on two or tree lines, for several hours. You correct da structure and make necessary previsions to suit your style. You experiment wid various diflections.

So it goes, come ci come sa. Now you have learned a few lines and you are ready to get out of bed and put in da actions. So when you gets up on your feet and puts in da actions, what happens? Yeh, what happens? You forgets da lines. You find you is compelled to go back to bed.

So you fixes the pillows again and lights a cigar and excetria and excetria.

Someday I'd like a part where I didn't have to worry about da actions. Where I could just lapse in bed like Elizabeth Bartlett Browning. Or Cyril de Bergerac. Wouldn't I be a natural for Cyril? All dose odder guys dat have played Cyril have had to make up da schnoz. Not me. I don't need no makeup. I don't need nuttin. Just Jimmy. And maybe we could work out an amalgulation. Cyril played in bed. Someday I'll give dat script what you'd call extensive study and see if it couldn't be deranged.

Now, let us say, you have learned your lines. You have studied hard for maybe two, maybe tree weeks. You have been zealious, almost overzealious. You are ready to go out on da stage and rehoise. So you find da theatre where da stage is.

Den, before you goes on you must create a mood. You tink of someting. "I hear Stagehand lost in da fifth at Hialeah," you says to yourself. Dat creates a mood. Now you are ready to go out on da stage and do your lines full justice. You goes out. And what happens? You forget your lines. All you can remember is da odder guy's lines. It's a wow. A couple of bankers sittin in da back of da theatre bust up laughin. Dat stays in, da director says, so it stays in. Art, I claim, *real* art, incontrovertible art.

In dis connection, I am often asked, what about da Stanikolsky system. And what I says is, it's common gossip. Yeh, it's common gossip. I have nuttin to add.

Dere are some more tings I'd like to take up at dis point. Such as concernin how to bow, da full-bow, da half-bow, da tree-quarters bow, how to handle a valet, and so-and-so and so-and-so and so-and-so. . . .

But time flies. Time collapses.

However, I'd like to compress one ting on you. Da importance of always bein yourself, no matter how hard it is. Nuttin compares wid bein casual and uninflected.

I trust I have made myself explitious.

FRANK FAY

An Armful of Cabbage

This chapter is a bit about me and some reasons why I made an armful of cabbage.

But don't be alarmed, it's mostly about the "reasons," the "how," and the "why" I was forced, really, into acquiring a chunk of gold.

Now I don't know how many of you nice folks have ever listened to me on the radio. But if you have, you know how I have tried to improve the lyrics in the songs they write today and, as a matter of record, have written in the past.

Anyway, in case you haven't heard, here's a chorus of an "oldie" I've done many times, to give you an idea of this picking apart of songs:

You see, I would first sing the original lyric * as it is:

> Picture you,
> Upon my knee.
> Just tea for two,
> And two for tea.

Then my comment spoken:

Ain't that rich! Here's a guy that had enough tea for two. So, he's going to have two for tea. Notice — he doesn't say a word about sugar!

(Sung):

> Just me for you,
> And you for me alone.

(Spoken):

Alone. I know the old one about "look at my etchings," but "come on up and take a peek at my tea leaves," that's a new one!

* "Tea for Two" used by permission of the copyright owner Harms, Inc., N.Y.C.

(Sung):

> Nobody near us,
> To see or hear us.

(Spoken):

Who wants to hear two people drinking tea?

(Sung):

> No friends or relations
> On week-end vacations.
> We won't have it known, dear,
> That we own a telephone, dear.

(Spoken):

All he's got is a broken-down cup of tea and a telephone he won't let you use.

(Sung):

> Day will break
> And you'll awake
> And start to bake
> A sugar cake.

(Spoken):

Day will break-and you'll awake — and start to bake a sugar cake? The poor woman! What a future. She gets out of bed, washes her teeth, and bang — right to the oven. Nobody up but her. Feeling around in the dark for flour. He probably calls her up too — to remind her. Says: "Hello, honey, it's almost light out. What's cookin'?"

(Sung):

> For me to take
> For all the boys to see.

(Spoken):

Can you imagine this guy going down to the pool room? He walks in. Says: "Gather around me, fellows. Guess what I've got?" And all the one-ball players throw down their cues and say: "What? A new set of tires?" and he says, "No, fellows, look," and he whips out his cake. Chocolate fudge with a marshmallow center. And all the boys jump up and down and say, "Yummee, yum." And they pick up the cake and hit him right in the . . .

(Sung):

> We will raise a family,
> A boy for you,
> A girl for me.

(Spoken):
Well, that's all right. If you can — er — I mean — er —
There's no comment.
(Sung):

> Oh can't you see
> How happy we would be?

Forgive me, students, but things like this did earn me many a
buck.

EMMET LAVERY

Justice Holmes Greets Washington *

[*Over the scene we hear a cheerful whistle from the hall.*
HOLMES *throws open the door up center with a flourish. He
is wearing a smart dark suit, with a white vest, and he's
feeling very gay. In his lapel is a little fresh crocus which he
picked on the way home.*]

HOLMES [*saluting his wife*]: Captain Holmes reporting, Madame.
[*To* SECRETARY *fussing at desk.*] Haven't you gone yet,
Mason?

SECRETARY: No, sir. I wanted to ask — shall I get you a cab for a
little before eight, sir? If you're dining at the White House
tonight —

HOLMES [*jovially*]: My boy, what do you mean "if"? Of course

* Condensed.

we're dining at the White House tonight. Company is bound to be a bore but the food is sure to be good.

FANNY: But, Wendell, what about Mr. Roosevelt?

HOLMES [*blandly*]: Well, what about him?

FANNY: I mean — suppose he makes good his threat to throw you out of the White House. Suppose —

HOLMES [*patting her playfully on the arm*]: Woman, what's got into you today? Isn't that another new dress?

FANNY: Yes, milord. Do you like it?

HOLMES: Hm. Devilishly pretty. But not half so pretty as the woman wearing it.

FANNY: Oh, thank you, milord.

HOLMES [*with a grin*]: Or so devilish either!

FANNY: You're a horrid old man and I hope Mr. Roosevelt beats you with the biggest stick he has. [FANNY *starts to march out, with head up. Then she remembers a letter in her hand. She comes back down to him.*] Oh, I almost forgot. This came for you in the afternoon mail. It was marked personal — so I thought you might like to open it yourself!

[FANNY *gives the Judge the letter and starts out again.* HOLMES *moves over near the window to open and read the letter.* FANNY *holds her position at door and watches the Judge as he scans the letter with increasing pleasure: it's a voice from the past and it intrigues him. He gives his mustache a twist while he reads the letter and shifts his position with a nice swagger. He is oblivious of the fact that* FANNY *has not left the room.*]

FANNY: Well, Wendell — who is she? [HOLMES *does not seem to hear her at first.*] Is she pretty?

HOLMES [*softly*]: Yes. She's pretty. [*Suddenly* HOLMES *looks up and realizes it's* FANNY *he's talking to — not himself.*] Eh? What's that? Oh now, don't misunderstand me. It's nothing — nothing at all. [HOLMES *moves over toward* FANNY.] For just a moment I was back at Antietam . . . on the road to Hagerstown with a bullet in my neck . . . and no one to care for me until the Kennedys took me in . . . and a girl named Ellen Jones nursed me back to health.

. . . I never saw her again but she's in town now and . . .

FANNY [*briskly*]: Well, let's have her out to dinner by all means.

HOLMES [*embarrassed*]: Yes, that would be very nice but . . . [*Gives her the letter.*] she wants to know if I'll have dinner with her at the Shoreham some night.

FANNY: The Shoreham?

HOLMES: That's where she's stopping. Of course it's all a little silly. I don't want to go at all but —

FANNY [*looking up from letter*]: Don't be absurd, Wendell. Of course you want to go!

HOLMES: You don't think I should though — do you?

FANNY: My dear, what possible difference could it make to me? It's only that —

HOLMES: Only what?

FANNY: Some people do change, you know . . . in forty-two years . . . even if you don't.

HOLMES [*spontaneously*]: Oh, not Ellen Jones. She was the prettiest thing that ever came out of Philadelphia. She — [*Then catching himself.*] I mean — well, it can't be forty-two years, Fanny. It can't be. Why, it was only yesterday. I can still hear the pound of cannon in the hills. I can still smell the powder burning. I can —

FANNY: Can you still smell the perfume she used? Or has she changed the brand by now, perhaps?

[*This brings the Judge to with a start — but there's a rather pleasant gleam in his eye.*]

HOLMES: Fanny — you're not jealous — not at this late date?

FANNY: What do you mean by "this late date?" Was there a time when it would have been quite in order for me to be jealous of Miss Jones?

HOLMES: Now, Fanny —

FANNY: I always knew that half the girls in Boston had lost their hearts to you . . . but I had never given a thought to Philadelphia. [FANNY *is starting out, just as the door up center opens and the* HOUSEKEEPER *comes in.*]

HOUSEKEEPER: I beg your pardon, sir. Mr. Owen Wister to see Mrs. Holmes.

HOLMES [*delighted*]: What? Wister here? — well, show him up — show him up right away.

FANNY [*quickly*]: My dear, if I heard Mary correctly — [HOUSE-KEEPER *goes out, leaving the door open behind her.*] It's on me that Owen is calling — not you.

HOLMES: Eh? Well, we'll see about that —

[OWEN WISTER *comes in and moves down gaily to greet* FANNY *and* HOLMES. *He's all of 44 now and* The Virginian *is two years behind him.*]

WISTER [*to* FANNY]: You will forgive me for breaking in on you like this — [*He kisses her hand, then draws back for a good look at her.*] *Cara mia* — I don't understand it. Each year you're just a little more enchanting. It isn't fair, you know. The rest of us grow older and older and you keep getting younger and younger.

HOLMES [*imitating Southern drawl*]: I must remind you, sir, that the lady you are calling on is my wife . . . and while I am not of a jealous disposition . . .

FANNY [*sweetly*]: You may leave us now, Wendell.

HOLMES: Very well, my love. [*Then turns to* WISTER.] But I warn you, sir —

WISTER [*laughing*]: Sit down, both of you, I am a bearer of strange tidings. I shall have to have a few moments with you.

FANNY [*taking a chair*]: Well, you do make it all sound most mysterious.

HOLMES [*also sitting down*]: What's on your mind?

[WISTER *looks* HOLMES *over carefully. Obviously he expects an explosion or two.*]

WISTER: I'm really here this afternoon as . . . as an unofficial ambassador.

HOLMES [*drily*]: Hmm. Well, we're honored, Your Excellency. Proceed —

WISTER: An ambassador — from President Roosevelt.

HOLMES [*starting to rise from chair*]: Well, you can tell him for me —

FANNY: Wendell, be still.

HOLMES [*subsiding*]: Very well. But not for long.

FANNY: Go on, Owen.

WISTER: It's really very simple. As far as I can gather, the President would like to refuse the Judge admission to the White House at any and all times —

HOLMES [*to* FANNY]: May I say something now?

WISTER: But, as regards Mrs. Holmes — I am permitted to express the hope — oh, most unofficially, you understand — that at dinner this evening Mrs. Holmes will do the President the honor of sitting at his right.

HOLMES [*flabbergasted*]: Well, I'll be damned!

FANNY [*rising quickly*]: Mr. Roosevelt is most kind, Mr. Ambassador. But it will not be possible for Mrs. Holmes to accept — because Mrs. Holmes isn't going to the White House dinner tonight.

HOLMES: Eh? What's that?

WISTER: But, my dear, you don't understand. No one can decline an invitation from the White House. It just isn't done.

FANNY: Oh, isn't it? Well, we'll see about that.

HOLMES [*explosively*]: Damn it, Fanny — what's this all about anyway? Of course we're going. I don't give two straws for Teddy Roosevelt but wild horses wouldn't keep me away from the White House tonight. I'm going to look him straight in the eye and —

FANNY: Very well, Mr. Holmes. Look him in the eye if you want to — but you can look alone. [*Then more softly.*] Good heavens, Wendell. Where's your Yankee pride? Did you leave it behind you in Boston? Sit to the right of him, will I? — [*Turns to* WISTER.] You can tell the President for me, Mr. Ambassador, that he could carve a better dinner companion out of a banana! [FANNY *starts out up center — pauses at door with a notice to* MR. WISTER *that the* HOLMESES *would be deeply honored if he would stay for tea.* FANNY *goes out, leaving an admiring* WISTER *and a baffled* HOLMES *behind her.*]

HOLMES [*softly*]: You know, my boy — I'm married to a wonderful woman. She has made life poetry for me — [*Then fingering perfumed letter and putting it away.*] But there are times when I know I can never be equal to her. Right now I'm not sure whether it's I or Mr. Roosevelt she is punishing.

WISTER: But what am I going to tell the President?

HOLMES [*with enjoyment*]: My boy, I haven't the least idea! But enough of this fellow Roosevelt — [HOLMES *waves* WISTER *toward a chair.*] Sit down and let me have a good look at you.

WISTER [*smiling*]: How do you like Washington?

HOLMES [*expansively*]: Not bad, Whiskers — not bad. Of course the New Willard isn't the Parker House — and I miss those three-alarm fires that you and I and Fanny used to race to in Boston. [*Moves over to windows down right.*] But Boston was looking backwards . . . and Washington is looking ahead.

[HOLMES *is looking out the window at the fading spring sunshine.*]

WISTER: I say, Judge, isn't there any way you and T.R. could bury the hatchet?

HOLMES [*turning back to* WISTER *amiably*]: You mean he realizes that he's talked like a fool — and this is his way of saying he's sorry?

WISTER: T.R.? Good lord, no — he'd never admit a mistake. But he's a wonderful person, once you get to know him. And I do know him. I've hunted with him, fished with him, camped with him, and I tell you, Judge —

HOLMES [*sitting down*]: All right, Whiskers. All right. If he's a great man to you, why he's a great man to you. I guess there's room enough for us both in the country.

WISTER: But what's it all about — what's the real trouble deep down underneath?

HOLMES [*looking up owlishly*]: Who wants to know — you or the President?

WISTER: Right now, I do.

HOLMES: Well, my boy, mostly it's just that we're two different men doing two different jobs. I'm even willing to admit that my job is a little simpler than his — because, well, you see, my problems began to straighten out quite a lot when I woke up one fine day and decided that I was not God Almighty!

WISTER: Now you're joking.

HOLMES: Oh no, my boy. Never more serious in my life. The magic moment is the moment when you decide that there are other people in the universe, and that it isn't your high destiny to be the one and only boss of the cosmos. Well, once I found out that I wasn't God Almighty, things shook themselves down quite a bit. But you take your friend Theodore Roosevelt now — he hasn't discovered yet that he's not God Almighty and that complicates matters for him.

[HOUSEKEEPER *comes on left, with a tray full of tea things, which she puts down on a little table near the fireplace.*]

HOUSEKEEPER [*to* HOLMES]: Excuse me, sir. Mrs. Holmes said you would like to have tea in here.

HOLMES: Thank you, Mary.

WISTER: But you can't get away from one thing, Judge. The people all love Roosevelt.

HOLMES [*drily*]: Yes — but as one of the boys over in the Senate said the other day, what the folks really like about T.R. is that — he doesn't care a damn for the law.

WISTER: Well. I'll leave it to Mary. Mary, what do you think of Mr. Roosevelt.

[HOUSEKEEPER *looks over to* HOLMES, *a little puzzled.*]

HOLMES [*with a chuckle*]: It's all right, Mary. Nothing you say here will be held against you.

HOUSEKEEPER [*to* WISTER]: Well, sir — as Mr. Dooley says, I guess he is a great hand for getting things done.

[HOUSEKEEPER *nods brightly and goes out left.*]

WISTER [*to* HOLMES]: There, you see?

HOLMES: Yes, he gets things done all right. Only trouble is he doesn't care how. Oh, I'll admit some of them are steps in the right direction. That "square deal" he's always talking about . . . some of it is pretty good stuff. But he ought to remember once in a while that this is the United States of

America . . . not the United States of Theodore Roosevelt.

WISTER: Come, Judge. He's not that swell-headed.

HOLMES: Oh no? I met a fellow the other day who read the proofs on the President's book about the Spanish War. Tells me they made T.R. cut out the line which read — "The bravest man I ever knew followed me up San Juan Hill" — !

WISTER: All right. Maybe T.R. is a bit obstinate — but I suppose he couldn't help hoping that you might see things his way when the Northern Securities case came up for decision. After all, you were his first appointee to the Court.

HOLMES: Of course. When he named me to the bench, he thought I was a labor judge because I happened to go labor's way in some cases back in Massachusetts. [*Then challengingly.*] But he's all wrong. A good judge isn't anybody's judge in particular. And most of all, he isn't something that a President carries around in his vest pocket.

WISTER [*rising*]: Very well, sir. If that's the way you feel about it, I guess there isn't anything anybody can do to bring you and the President together.

HOLMES: Hold on, you fire eater — this isn't going to make any difference as between you and me, is it?

WISTER: I don't know, sir. That all depends on you. [*WISTER starts out up center. He steps back in surprise as* FANNY *comes in, radiant in a beautiful new white evening dress.*] Why, *cara mia* —

HOLMES [*admiringly*]: Well, I'll be damned. [*There's no doubt about it:* FANNY *is enchanting. She turns around archly, so that the men can admire the gown from every angle.*]

FANNY: Do you think Mr. Roosevelt will like it. [*Even at 62,* FANNY *doesn't look a day over 40 — and the evening dress of the Gibson girl period sets her off perfectly. Her waist is as slim as a girl's: the bare shoulders are a thing of grace and beauty — but above all there is the fire which is so completely captivating. Little wonder that T.R. wanted her to sit next him at dinner. She had become one of the most charming women in Washington.*]

HOLMES: But, my dear, what made you change your mind?

FANNY [*blithely*]: That's hard to say. Maybe it was the dress — [*Wheeling down to tea table at fireplace.*] Or maybe it was poor dear Mr. Roosevelt. After all, men are so easily misunderstood — [*To* HOLMES.] Aren't they, darling?

HOLMES [*with a grin*]: I give up, woman. If Teddy Roosevelt wants you to sit next to him, it serves him right. You are the devil of devils — and lovely to boot. Just tell me what you want to do with my life . . . it's yours to command.

FANNY [*purring*]: Why, darling — how sweet of you.
[*From off scene comes the sound of a fire alarm: the galloping of horses and the clanging of bells.*]

WISTER: Would it be permissible for an innocent by-stander to ask just what this is all about?

FANNY: Why, Mr. Ambassador, it's just life — that's what it is. Some of us suddenly acquire a great passion for dining with Mr. Roosevelt . . . others for dining with old flames from Philadelphia. But it's a free country, thank God, and —

HOLMES: Damn it, woman — I've had enough. Why, being married to you is like being married to a — [HOLMES *looks up keenly. Bells stronger over scene now. To* WISTER.] I say — that sounds like a big one. [*Rushes over to window, followed by* WISTER. *They look out for a second, as the fire engine goes by.*] Come on, boy — let's go. [*The two men start out together.* FANNY *rushes after them.*]

FANNY: Oh, no, you don't. If you can still go racing to fires, so can I —

WISTER: But what about your new dress?

HOLMES: And what about the man you're wearing it for tonight — that man in the White House?

FANNY [*picking up the skirt of her dress*]: What's the man in the White House compared to a fire — Come on.
[FANNY *runs out quickly up center, followed by* WISTER *and* HOLMES. *The sound of bells continues faintly over scene.*]

———

MICHEAL MacLIAMMOIR

Mr. Brunton Views Ireland

EILEEN [*entering with a card*]: There's a gentleman at the door to see madam.

TOMMY [*taking the card*]: Oh heavens, it's that Brunton fellow from the *Prattler*. You'd better tell him Mrs. Sheridan is not in, I suppose, Eileen — I don't know what to do. I'm distracted.

MARY: Wait now, Mr. Tommy, and I'll brave her. I'll brave her in her room and I'll tell her there's a stranger gentleman to see her, that'll get her out of bed.

TOMMY: Oh do, for goodness sake! Let's know something definite anyhow.

EILEEN: What'll I tell the gentleman, sir?

TOMMY: Oh, tell him what you like.

BRUNTON [*appearing at the door*]: May I come in? [*He enters the room.*]

TOMMY: Oh — of course.

MARY: Holy Smoke, let me out of this. Excuse me, sir. [*She makes to exit above Brunton.*]

BRUNTON: Of course, but, of course, I'll excuse you. I'm partly Irish myself, you know.

[BRUNTON *is marvellous. It doesn't matter whether he is tall or short, he gives an impression of bigness because he is so blonde and clean and pink-cheeked and happy. He is nicely dressed, too, with that curious easiness of an Englishman's clothes, that does a good deal to tone down the alarmingly uneasy good health and spirits that send him jerking and spinning around the room to greet people and slap their backs until they're dizzy. An endless enthusiasm emanates from him; one feels that the unspeakable journey from*

Euston to Westland Row hasn't taken a feather out of him. Only Mr. Wodehouse could have really understood him, but actually he's terribly fond of reading, especially of Anglo-Irish literature, and thinks W. B. Yeats jolly fine.]

MARY: Oh yes, sir. [*She gets out of the room somehow.*]

BRUNTON: Do forgive my butting in, won't you?

TOMMY: Of course — won't you sit down.

BRUNTON: Thanks.

EILEEN: Will I go away now, sir?

TOMMY: Yes, I suppose so.

EILEEN: Thank you, sir. [*She exits.*]

BRUNTON: Are you Mr. Sheridan?

TOMMY: Oh dear me, no. My name is Millington.

BRUNTON: How do you do?

TOMMY: How do you do?

BRUNTON: What a lovely day, isn't it?

TOMMY [*miserably*]: No.

BRUNTON: No? Oh I think it's quite peerless. Do you often have days like this in Ireland?

TOMMY: Frequently. [*His mind is miles away.*] Nearly all the time.

BRUNTON: I've fallen in love with Ireland. I arrived yesterday.

TOMMY: I'm so glad.

BRUNTON: Yes, I think Ireland's quite perfect. Of course you must be prepared to rough it, but if you are, Ireland is quite, quite perfect.

TOMMY: Yes, isn't it marvellous?

BRUNTON: Oh, you've all such an understanding of living, over here. Look at the way I came into this room. Priceless, you know. I'd never dream of doing such a thing in England. English people are so stuffy, they simply wouldn't understand.

TOMMY: No.

BRUNTON: No. Do you know, old boy, England is just too dreary for words. Oh yes. All so different here. Of course you know what's wrong with London, don't you?

TOMMY: What's wrong with it?

BRUNTON: Oh, surely you know.

TOMMY: But I don't.

BRUNTON: Well, it's gone all tatty. Simply tatty. There's only one word for it. It's tatty.

TOMMY: Oh dear.

BRUNTON: Where's Mrs. Sheridan?

TOMMY [*turns to Brunton*]: That's just what I can't tell you.

BRUNTON: But how weird.

TOMMY: Yes, I know.

BRUNTON: I mean — you don't know where she is?

TOMMY: No.

BRUNTON: Why?

TOMMY: Why what?

BRUNTON: Why don't you know where she is?

TOMMY: Well I — I just can't tell you where she is.

BRUNTON: Too weird for words.

TOMMY: She may be in bed.

BRUNTON: In bed? Do you mean in bed?

TOMMY: Yes.

BRUNTON: I say! What fun!

TOMMY: Fun?

BRUNTON: I mean it's so Irish.

TOMMY: Oh, is it?

BRUNTON [*after a pause*]: Do you know, I don't believe you're Irish at all.

TOMMY: Well, I'm not very.

BRUNTON: Ah! I knew it. Great big jolly chaps with black curly hair and blue eyes put in with a sooty finger — you know — not a bit like you.

TOMMY: I'm very Anglo, I'm afraid.

BRUNTON: Anglo?

TOMMY: You know, Protestant.

BRUNTON [*blankly*]: Oh. . . . sort of Oxford Groupish. *Where* is Mrs. Sheridan?

TOMMY: Really, I don't know.

BRUNTON: She must be somewhere.

TOMMY: I know, I know. As a matter of fact I'm rather anxious about her.

BRUNTON: SO am I . . . I've got to interview her about her little show in support of the comic cab horses and it's simply got to go by to-night.

TOMMY: I see.

BRUNTON [*after a pause*] : I represent the *Prattler,* you know. They're so frightfully thrilled about the horses and then Mrs. Sheridan was *such* a lovely artist. All we first-nighters wept like kids when she left the stage. What made her do it?

TOMMY: Oh — I think she'll tell you that herself better than I could.

BRUNTON: I haven't seen her since she played Hecuba. Very jolly she looked, sort of draped in sort of curtains.

TOMMY: Oh!

BRUNTON: I'm so looking forward to meeting her in the flesh. Is she still a vegetarian?

TOMMY: I don't think so.

BRUNTON: What a pity. Of course her acting *is* pretty staggering, but she did look a teeny weeny bit pudgey as Hecuba. Do you know, old boy, I had a spot of tummy trouble last year and I lived on brussels-sprouts for three months and I lost two pounds. Do you talk Erse?

TOMMY: Erse? Oh no, not much.

BRUNTON: I saw such lots of it written up in the Post Office this morning. Looks a bit of a mess, actually. Still I think it's fun to have one's own language, don't you?

TOMMY: I don't know, really!

BRUNTON: Oh, but you must have your language back. Of course you must. I mean why shouldn't you? It seems so cruel.

TOMMY: What seems so cruel?

BRUNTON: Well, it seems cruel to me. I mean, after all, the English have been pretty brutal to you over here, haven't they? Putting up your rents and forbidding you to keep a pig or two. Oh, it makes my blood boil. Of course I'm the most sentimental chap ever born. That's my Irish blood, I daresay. Where is Mrs. Sheridan?

[MARY DEMPSEY *enters in complete disarray.*]

MARY: Mr. Tommy! Mr. Tommy!

TOMMY: Yes, what is it?

MARY: Madam — she's —

TOMMY: Where is she — what's happened?

MARY: She's not — she's not — oh, my God!

TOMMY: Mrs. Dempsey, what's wrong?

MARY: She's not in her room, sir. She's not anywhere in the house, sir. Oh, my God, supposing anything happened to her? Oh, what'll I do? What'll I do?

TOMMY: Don't lose your head, Mrs. Dempsey.

MARY: I went into the room and there was her empty bed and the blind half up and her clothes all this way and that and she clean gone, O, Miss Sophie, Miss Sophie!

TOMMY: Was her bed slept in?

MARY: Oh, 'twas, sir.

TOMMY: Well, what are we going to do? Wait a minute — Where's that Lydon fellow?

MARY: He'll be in the kitchen, sir.

TOMMY: Go and bring him here. Quickly!

MARY: Oh, do you think would he know anything, sir?

TOMMY: I don't know.

MARY: I wouldn't put anything past that fellow.

TOMMY: Go and bring him here.

MARY: I will, sir; I will — oh, my God, if anything happened to poor Miss Sophie —

SOPHIE: [*enters, strolling in at the window*]: If anything what, darling?

TOMMY [*seizing both Sophie's hands*]: Sophie!

BRUNTON [*rising*]: Mrs. Sheridan!

MARY: Oh Miss. Oh Miss Sophie, Oh, Miss, oh, thank God.

SOPHIE: My dears. You make me feel like Grace Darling. What's wrong?

TOMMY: Sophie, what have you been doing?

MARY: Oh, where were you, Miss Sophie, where were you? Oh, thanks be to the blessed saints, you're safe.

BRUNTON: Oh, priceless!

TOMMY: I thought you'd been murdered. Oh, forgive me — this is Mr. Grunton.

BRUNTON: Brunton, old man, Brunton, do you mind? How do you do?

SOPHIE: How do you do? Go on, Tommy, what's all the fuss about? Oh, God, what a lovely morning I've had. Wait till I extract this hat, dear. [*She goes to the mirror.*] Oh, what a wind-blown wench! Well, tell me all about it, Tommy. [*To Mary*]: Mary Dempsey, darling, don't look so woebegone.

MARY: Oh, Miss Sophie.

BRUNTON: Now, Mary, don't start keening again, will you?

SOPHIE [*turning slowly round to have a good look at Brunton*]: Do sit down, Mr. Dunstan; cheer up, Mary, and get me some breakfast. I'm starving.

MARY: I will, Miss. I will. Is it rashers, Miss?

SOPHIE: Oh, any old thing.

TOMMY: You haven't had any breakfast?

SOPHIE: I never do . . . but I'll have some now.

TOMMY: But it's nearly lunch time.

SOPHIE: Is it?

BRUNTON: Brunch. You must have brunch. Breakfast is such a tatty meal for a woman like you.

SOPHIE: How right you are. Go away, Mary Dempsey, and get me food and call it what you like. [*To* BRUNTON]: Who *are* you, Mr. Huntingdon?

BRUNTON [*with a beaming smile*]: Brunton, do you mind awfully?

SOPHIE: Mr. Brunton, who are you?

BRUNTON: Well, I'm —

SOPHIE: Tell me the truth. Are you a journalist?

BRUNTON: Well, yes, I am. Sort of, you know. Aha!

SOPHIE: H'm! Have you come to interview me?

BRUNTON: Yes, for the *Prattler*, you know.

SOPHIE: Oh I know, but what can the *Prattler* want with me? I don't act any longer and I don't play golf? I don't use Pond's. I don't go to London first nights and I don't sit on shooting sticks.

EILEEN [*entering*]: Cook told me to tell you your breakfast was ready, Miss.

SOPHIE: Oh dear me, is it? Do you know, I think I'll have it in here. You'll have some, won't you, Mr. Pringle? After you've had some sherry. [*She starts relentlessly to pour out the sherry.*]

BRUNTON: Oh, no thank you. No, I'm lunching at the Shelbourne with the editor of the *Irish Mirror*. Very decent chap. Met him at Sir Thomas Foulkes'. Damned entertaining about his peasant bead-making. Oh, I say, what an endless glass of sherry. Really, I don't think I —

SOPHIE: Nonsense! You must drink it to the dregs. And you certainly must have something to eat. Never lunch with a newspaper man on an empty stomach, Mr. Brunton, it might go to your head.

BRUNTON: Really? Of course it's so kind and sweet of you but really —

SOPHIE: Well, we shall see. Bring in the brunch, Eileen.

EILEEN: The which, Miss?

SOPHIE: The rashers, you unsophisticated thing, the rashers.

EILEEN: I will, to be sure, Miss. [EILEEN *exits.*]

BRUNTON: Oh, that delicious Dublin brogue. Isn't it wizard?

SOPHIE [*with an admirable imitation of* BRUNTON]: Oh! too wizard for words. Now then, drink up, Mr. Brunton. My eye is upon you. I'm taking this little drop to keep you company.

BRUNTON: *Slanter.*

SOPHIE [*half-choking*]: I beg your pardon.

BRUNTON: Aha, I learnt that on the Mail boat coming over. *Slanter!* [*They drink.*]

SOPHIE: Oh yes, of course. Horray, Mr. Brunton.

BRUNTON: Horray. [*He drinks and gives a polite and slightly shuddering smile.*]

SOPHIE: Now to the play. Midhir and Etain are lovers in the Land of the Young — that's a sort of fairyland, you see.

BRUNTON: Enchanting. [*He drinks another sip.*] Delicious. [*He pushes the glass from him with admirably controlled nausea.*]

SOPHIE: Etain is banished from fairyland and is born on the earth as a mortal woman. Got that?

BRUNTON: Yes, yes, I'm waiting.

SOPHIE: She marries the King of Ireland and lives at Tara.

BRUNTON: I know, "The harp that once," Grand, grand.

SOPHIE: She has forgotten that she was ever an immortal when one night — it is May Day eve and all the hawthorn is in flower — one night a stranger comes to Tara.

BRUNTON: Her fairy lover.

SOPHIE: That's it. It's Midhir. And he begs her to go back with him to the Land of the Young. [MARTIN *and* EILEEN *enter, each carrying a tray of dishes, plates, a coffee pot, etc.*] And for a long time Etain doesn't recognize her lover. She can remember nothing at all — got that?

BRUNTON: Yes. [*He is writing feverishly.*]

MARTIN: Excuse me, madam.

SOPHIE: Oh, there you are. Yes, what is it?

MARTIN: Where will we put the dishes, madam?

SOPHIE: Oh, anywhere handy.

[MARTIN *and* EILEEN *begin to arrange the trays.*]

BRUNTON [*as he writes*]: Etain, — can — remember — nothing — at — all — of — her — former — life. Is that right?

SOPHIE: You know, what fascinates me so much is that non-recognition, that loss of memory. In the end, of course, the story grows more and more fantastic — Etain returns to Midhir and they go away together as two swans flying upwards among the stars. . . .

[MARTIN *who is bending over the tray slowly straightens up and looks at* EILEEN *who is busy settling the cups and plates.*]

BRUNTON: Two swans. Oh, but how charming. Pavlova!

JOHN P. MULGREW

And Life Goes On

HORSE OF ANOTHER COLOR

Jim Waring, back from the wars, is rehearsing the leading role in *Richard the Third,* shortly to be acted at Loras. Casting about for pointers on the role, Jim said to me, "What do you know about the play and what stars have you ever seen in the role?"

So I told him about the amateur night years ago at the old Bijou (now the Orpheum) when a local gentleman with thespian ambitions appeared in selections from this same play. When he came to the climax of his big scene and dramatically shouted: "A horse! A horse! My kingdom for a horse!" a voice from the gallery yelled: "Wouldn't a jackass do?" When the tumult had died down, the gentleman on the stage looked up to the gallery and replied with quiet dignity, "Yes, . . . come right on down!"

HOW COME?

In their more or less celebrated series of "Road" films, how come Bing Crosby and Bob Hope haven't put out one with a European background called, say, "The Road to Rouen"?

UPSIDE DONNA

(From a Hollywood column: "Donna Reed has a quaint way of entertaining her guests. She stands on her head.")

> When Donna gives a party,
>   And things go a little bit dead,
> She simply takes center floor fancy
> And stands upon her head.
>
> Hollywood parties apparently
>   Are temperate and discreet,

Some guests at parties I've been to
Can't even stand upon their feet.

Myself I think Donna is practising up
For a day in the future not far,
When we'll ALL be standing on our heads
If things keep on as they ARE!

And thanks to the unknown and unsigned reader who recently sent me in the following double-feature sign which he noticed on the marquee of a movie theatre in Omaha, Neb.:
"THEY ALL KISSED THE BRIDE"
"IT SHOULDN'T HAPPEN TO A DOG"

Scientists claim a vast ice field is moving slowly down on us from the far north which in the course of a little matter of 200,000 years or so may envelop the earth's surface. Verily the Ice Man Cometh!

Marcia Winn reports the sign over the marquee of a Chicago loop theatre:
"BORN YESTERDAY" — AIR CONDITIONED
Isn't science wonderful?

———

GERARD MURRAY

The Angel Arrives

ANGEL GUARDIAN [*A gaunt, angular person, in a white flowing gown. He's carrying a white covered book.*]: Hello!
BRO. SERAPHIM [*looking up from his reading*]: Hello! [*Then looks again. Realizing he is addressing a most unusual-looking person — jumps out of his chair.*] Who are you?

ANGEL G. [*with preternatural serenity*]: Take it easy, Brother, take it easy. [*Bro. S. is by this time quite appalled.*] You're not exactly finding Brother Fidelis' treatise a best seller, are you?

BRO. S.: Where did you come from? How did you get in here?

ANGEL G.: Out of nowhere. That answers the first question. Now in answer to the second: I thought you'd appreciate a dramatic entrance.

BRO. S.: I demand to know who you are! Why you are here!

ANGEL G. [*very calmly*]: Oh! Seraphim, stop being melodramatic. BRO. S. *withstands* ANGEL *majestically.*] You know, I always thought you were a ham — but somehow the critics always raved. And the way you muffed lines! If it weren't for me, many a playwright would have died aborning — still everybody raved.

BRO. S. [*more curious now than fearful*]: Say, who are you anyhow?

ANGEL G. [*nonchalantly*]: Your Guardian Angel, Brother Seraphim. D'you mind?

BRO. S. [*aghast*]: Oh, dear! [*Very perplexed — doesn't know whether to kneel, sit, stand, finally decides to kneel.*]

ANGEL G. [*showing no emotion*]: Do get up, Seraphim, old boy. We'll dispense with the formalities. [BRO. S. *gets up.*]

BRO. S.: It's all very distressing.

ANGEL G.: Really? Being with your Guardian Angel?

BRO. S.: Yes, I'm very honored and all — but — I'm — I'm — well, you realize, I've never entertained a Guardian Angel before.

ANGEL G.: Well, don't let that worry you. Angel Guardians get quite used to not being entertained — though in all fairness to you, Seraphim, I've always found you jolly company —

BRO. S. [*delighted*]: Well, I'm awfully glad you liked me.

ANGEL G.: Well, don't let my last remark induce any further relaxation, because I can tell you right here and now — you and I have a big job on our hands.

BRO. S.: You've been listening to Brother Fidelis.

ANGEL G.: Brother Fidelis has been listening to me. I tried to move that superior of yours, but I could just as easily move a sphinx. Of course the Lord says we should live like the lilies of the field and the birds of the air, but heavens above! The lilies at least grow and the birds fly from North to South — and from South to North.

BRO. S.: But the Lord has provided. He's been good. So very good —

ANGEL G.: Yes, but do you think He has nothing else to do these weary years but take care of this preposterous ranch of yours? Personally, I've worn the wings off myself flying back and forth, trying to provide for the whole lot of you.

BRO. S. [*nervously*]: Then you are displeased. Maybe after all these years I've lost my soul?

ANGEL G.: Lost his soul! [*Laughs.*] Oh dear! lost his soul. Listen to him — No, you haven't lost your soul. To my knowledge, you haven't even had an interesting temptation in years.

BRO. S.: But, Angel — I'm beset by temptation.

ANGEL G.: Sure, and what happens! You and the Lord get together and before I can get a word in edgewise, the whole scrap is over.

BRO. S.: Well, if there's anything I can do —

ANGEL G.: You can at least make my job interesting.

BRO. S.: Well, I'll do my best.

ANGEL G.: Landsakes! It's about time I had a career.

BRO. S.: A career?

ANGEL G.: Yes, a career — Seraphim, you're raised now. According to the record, you're practically saved.

BRO. S.: Very small, isn't it?

ANGEL G.: Smaller the better, Seraphim. It's a book of discredits. The latest volume. You should see the earlier ones. I mean the ones in your youth when you were "throwing roses, roses riotously with the throng." Boy, are they interesting! You've quieted down so since then. You're quite dull now.

BRO. S.: Well, you don't want me to take measures to lose my soul, do you?

ANGEL G.: No, but do something to keep this Uncle Tom's Cabin from falling around your ears.

BRO. S.: But it isn't falling around my ears.

ANGEL G.: It will if you don't do something to put it on the map.

Look at Father Flanagan. His Angel Guardian doesn't go flying around on cosmic errands, to provide them with the bare necessities. His Angel Guardian has all kinds of careers. Even got to Hollywood.

BRO. S. [*kindly*] : Well, you can go to Hollywood — if you like.

ANGEL G.: Oh, Seraphim, I don't know! You're an awful nice guy, but — so impractical.

BRO. S.: Of course I've got quite old. I feel it lately. Pains in my back, pains in my legs.

ANGEL G.: Well, by gum! I haven't.

BRO. S.: No, you're looking very well! I meant to remark that sooner.

ANGEL G.: Thank you! Look here, Seraphim. I'm not weary of my work. Angels just don't get weary. But there is so much you could do to help me out — You realize, of course, you're dead broke.

BRO. S.: Yes, dead broke. Terrifying, isn't it?

ANGEL G.: It most certainly is.

BRO. S.: Do you have any good suggestions? Something simple. I get awfully sleepy reading Brother Fidelis' notes.

ANGEL G.: Yes, I have. That's why I got me a body and barged right in here this evening. Sit down there a minute.

BRO. S. [*sits*] : By the way, does the Lord mind your being here talking to me?

ANGEL G.: No, as a matter of fact I asked Him to declare a kind of holiday. I told Him —

BRO. S. [*breaking in*] : Things were falling around my ears?

ANGEL G.: By gum, I did, Seraphim.

BRO. S.: I hope He isn't too displeased with me?

ANGEL G.: No, He isn't, Seraphim. [*Sighs.*] Somehow, you and the Don Boscos, the Vincents de Paul and the Francises of Assisi have a way with Him.

BRO. S.: He has a sense of humor.

ANGEL G.: He has to have one. Well, to get back to business, I'll start off by telling you that you're sitting right in a gold mine.

WILLIE [*Enters L. whistling. Stops, surprised, to see* BRO. S. ANGEL G., *of course is invisible to all but* BRO. S., *who seems per-*

plexed by the intrusion.] : Good evening, Brother. My turn
on duty.

BRO S.: Duty?

WIL.: Yes, telephone duty. Orders from Brother Fidelis. Haven't
you heard?

BRO. S. [*with backhand motion, trying to shoo Angel out*]: Oh, yes
— telephone duty. I forgot — the telephone — of course.
Yes, but, Willie, would you be terribly disappointed if I
took over? I'll be here a while yet.

ANGEL G. [*greatly amused*]: It's O.K. He can't see me. [BRO. S. *is
relieved.*]

WIL.: Well, if you say so! I was awfully busy tonight — studying,
you know.

BRO. S.: Is that so?

ANGEL G. [*speaking so as to be heard by* WIL.]: Yeah, Superman!

WIL. [*terribly embarrassed — thinking* BRO. S. *spoke*]: Gosh,
Brother, reading a feller's mind like that —

BRO. S.: Then you were reading Superman!

WIL.: Well — well, yes — [*Then quickly.*] But that's as important
as geography, or history, or mathematics — important as
anything.

BRO. S.: Do you mean it?

WIL.: Yessiree! You know there's a war on and — [*Looking about
cautiously before speaking.* ANGEL *drapes himself over a
chair at fireplace.*] And this building is right in a spot where
there could be spies around. They could practically come
right up to our door in submarines — you know!

BRO. S.: Still I imagine the submarines would have a little difficulty
coming through our back woods.

WIL.: Well, they could land on your property somewhere — I'm
sure of that.

BRO. S. [*kidding*]: Perhaps you're right — Maybe there is a spy —
[*Winks at* ANGEL.] In this room right now.

WIL. [*pleasantly surprised at being taken up*]: Brother — do you
think there — [*Moves over to chair where* ANGEL *is draped,
is about to sit down when* BRO. S. *rushes over to him in a
panic.*]

BRO. S.: Don't — sit — on — that — chair — Willie. I mean — er — [WIL. *about to sit — jumps away.*] I mean don't sit anywhere now — you'd better go. I — er — I mean you'd better go.

WIL. [*melodramatically*]: Brother Seraphim, there's someone in the room. Where is he? You're covering someone up.

BRO. S. [*perplexed, looking from* ANGEL *who's enjoying all this, to* WIL., *who isn't*]: Willie, don't be silly. You simply must go. I'm — well, I'm very busy — [*Waving* BRO. F.'s *papers.* WIL. *just stands doubtfully.*]

ANGEL G. [*giving a big stretch and a yawn*]: Come on, Willie, amscray!

WIL. [*aghast*]: Amscray, Brother? Did you say amscray?

BRO. S. [*an indignant glance at* ANGEL]: I don't know what I'm saying. Good night, Willie. Please go. [WIL. *runs out terrified.* *To* ANGEL *when* WIL. *leaves.*] He didn't see you?

ANGEL G. [*nonchalantly*]: Didn't expect him to, did you?

BRO. S.: No, but he heard you.

ANGEL G. [*laughing*]: Well, strictly speaking, I shouldn't have done it. I'm supposed to do one job — put you on your feet around here — But I'm a pushover for kids — All angels are, I guess.

BRO. S.: But — but — you won't do that again.

ANGEL G.: No, I promise; I'll cause enough trouble around here yet.

BRO. S.: Well, I don't mind your being here, but —

ANGEL G.: Well, that's big of you, Seraphim.

BRO. S.: Well, I mean — no use carrying on like a gremlin. [ANGEL *roars.*]

ANGEL G.: Well, let's get back to business. Where were we?

BRO. S. [*showing great interest*]: In a gold mine.

ANGEL G.: Oh, yes — Seraphim, you're the proud owner of a magnificent document worth no less than fifty thousand dollars in cold cash, possibly a great deal more.

BRO. S.: Fifty thousand dollars? What a lot of baseballs that will buy! And what a pony! When do we —

ANGEL G.: Yep! fifty thousand dollars — not to mention, of course, the pay-off in publicity — magazines will eat this stuff up, you know.

BRO. S.: But the document — where is it? What is it?

ANGEL G.: It's in the barn — in an old box, hidden away under a lot of junk.

BRO. S.: It's funny Fidelis never saw it.

ANGEL G.: Yes. But this is a mildewed box — [*Then imitating Fidelis.*] "I am allergic to mildew" — [BRO. S. *doubles over, laughing;* ANGEL *chides him gently.*] — just the same, you'd have been renting in Tobacco Road if it weren't for him.

BRO. S. [*restraining himself*]: That's God's truth — that is — But tell me — Tell me more.

ANGEL G.: Well, in that box there's a manuscript — a very early draft — of the Declaration of Independence, all in Thomas Jefferson's own hand —

BRO. S.: Wonderful! but whatever is it doing in our barn?

ANGEL G.: Oh, it's been there since the house was built. The original owner got it at an auction —

BRO. S. [*less enthusiastic now; becoming scrupulous*]: Do you notice, that man didn't sell it, Angel?

ANGEL G.: That man wasn't an ecclesiastical Santa Claus either — [*Sensing a change in* BRO. S.] Say, let me get this right, you're not going to get scrupulous on me, are you? [*No answer from* BRO. S.] Well, I like that — and me — flying the wings off myself —

BRO. S.: Yes, I know. I know — but — but, Angel, I couldn't accept the document — that's a sacred thing. Why it's the birth certificate of our country — that couldn't belong to me — that couldn't belong to any one person. It belongs to the whole world. To every human being, living or dead, whoever dreamed of, hoped for, or died for human liberty and freedom under God. It doesn't belong to me. It belongs to the world. We should give it to our government.

ANGEL G.: Now look here. It most certainly does belong to you — and stop being difficult. To whom does it belong, then?

BRO. S.: It belongs to — Oh, I suppose you're right. I have as much right to it as anyone else, but —

ANGEL G.: Seraphim, please do as I say, will you? If this document is going to make money — and it definitely is — God knows you can use some.

BRO. S.: Well, if you say so — you ought to know.

ANGEL G.: Now get Brother — Brother — Oh, you know who I mean — Brother Historian —

BRO. S.: Brother Ubaldus?

ANGEL G.: Horrible name. Whoops! Horrible pun! Where do religious get those names. Supposing he ever loses his hair — Well, let's get him anyhow — and then we're in the oneyma.

BRO. S.: I beg your pardon?

ANGEL G.: Pig-Latin for money. You wouldn't understand, Seraphim. [*Goes to door leading to corridor, and with hand on knob of door, in mock heroic.*] Oh, if you prefer: "I am sworn, brother, to grim necessity, and he and I will keep a league till death. Hie thee to the — barn — [*Opens door quickly; WIL. who was peeping through key-hole, tumbles in.*] And now, Willie, you will please take over!

BRO. S. [*laughs, then walking toward French windows, with an expansive gesture*]: To the barn!

10. FREUD AND PHOBIAS

10. FREUD AND PHOBIAS

> *"Blest who can unconcern'dly find*
> *Hours, days, and years slide soft away*
> *In health of body, peace of mind."*
>
> — From "Solitude"
> by Alexander Pope

I'm afraid that this section may cause some unwary reader to develop neurasthenia, psychasthenia, cyclothymia, or perhaps a neuropathic condition characterized by hypermnesia, hypnagogic experiences of an endogenous nature, and non-empirical hypochondriasis. If anything like this should happen, or even milder symptoms should arise such as acute cervical pains or striation of the reader's brow, I'd never forgive myself.

The fact of the matter is that dabbling in modern psychology and psychiatry is enough to make a fellow an alcoholic non-anonymous or, as the gentlemen in the psychology trade say, is enough to inculcate a tendency toward a toxic psychosis of exogenous origin.

However, I feel pretty sure that under the guidance of experts like Father Gillis and Monsignor Knox you will make your way unharmed as a few of the foolish phobias and silly psychoses of our time are dragged, in all their fumbling futility, into the light of rational day. Father Gillis examines the behavior of the Behaviorists with a raised eyebrow and shrivels some of their big ideas down to size by the use of Christian caustics. Monsignor Knox's notes, undoubtedly pilfered by a spy from the "top secret" drawer of a psychoanalyst's filing cabinet, present a half-dozen children who, if laid end to end, would make everybody happy. They make the Dead-End Kids look like prize winners in a Sunday School class.

Robert Farren, of course, has a very legitimate phobia, fear of the common cold. I'd be the last to turn the cold shoulder to such an excellent lyricist's plea for a pill, lotion or gargle to halt the cold germs' airborne invasion of his bronchial territory. In fact, I've gone and found a modern Joan of Arc, Mary Windeatt, who rides to Mr. Farren's rescue, waving a bottle of vitamin capsules which she got through the courtesy of the "cunning cod."

Norbert Engels shows how "crosswords" in a puzzle very often lead to cross words in a home, a psychological problem of immense importance in the United States where, even after all these years, acrostigrams are still an intellectual mucilage, glueing eyes to a printed page for hour on hour. The only way to cure this phobia is to throw a nice cold wet rag on it, as he shows.

The hustling Bishop Huss presented here by Herbert Kenny, is not at all an exemplary criterion of Catholic Action. His larcenous act in stealing a bus merely proves that overwrought zeal can some-times make the best of us drive in the right direction on the wrong side of the street. Huss is by no means typical of Catholic bishops, I want you to know, as a very good friend of mine who knows at least six bishops told me that not one of them had ever stolen a bus.

Sister Mary Bertrand's quatrains are offered to show how easy it is to confuse people's minds by the clever use of words. She told me, incidentally, that she wrote her quatrains after having heard a noted cleric tell how a Mrs. Gurney "fell off a tram and broke her journey."

ROY CAMPBELL

The Death of Polybius Jubb

He died in attempting to swallow,
Which proves that, though fat, he was hollow —
For in gasping for space
He swallowed his face,
And hadn't the courage to follow.

NORBERT A. ENGELS

Crossword Puzzles

Who knows a sixteen letter word meaning something that has got a deep hold on the public mind and really taken root? Something that has outgrown all other sprouts of popular fad except Amos and Andy and the funnies? Tree sitters, marathon dancers, dime chain-letters, and the Republican party have come and gone but Crossword Puzzles seem to go on forever.

Dr. Johnson's definition of a network as "anything reticulated or decussated at equal distances with interstices between the intersections" would be a cinch for a crossword expert. After mastering the code peculiar to the crossword lexicographers he can take a page of Dr. Johnson, pollinate it with a sprinkling of the *Encyclopedia Britannica* and turn out as pretty a block of hybrid acrostigrams as ever gave Noah Webster the heeby-jeebies at 4:30 in the morning.

It is nothing for him to toss off the rivers of Siberia — their names, not contents — give the biological terms for mergansers and Capuchin monkeys, tell you that a kraken is a sea monster and that thoracolumbar means "pertaining to the body." He is as familiar with the paleontological nomenclature and the hierarchy of all ancient mythologies. Paradoxically, his extensive knowledge is very limited, for to him a poem is only and always an ode, never a triolet; a snake, serpent, or reptile can only be an asp, never a fer-de-lance, bushmaster, or rattler; a beverage is always tea; and a song must be an aria, not a serenade, ballad, aubade, elegy, or epithalamium.

I suppose that after working out crossword puzzles for years people begin to think in terms of their definitions and language. Therefore I have worked out a brief dialogue to help imagine what their conversation would sound like. The reader may regard it as a puzzle in a new form, or in reverse form. All he has to do is get out a dictionary, whet up his imagination, chase the kids out of the house for a couple of days, work out what he can, invent the rest, then throw the whole thing into the fire. We will title it "The Crossword Puzzlers at Home." Cast of characters: a man and his wife who are expecting company for dinner.

She: Listen, Leo. I have a megrim. Move to the selling place and get me a type of fruit, will you?

He: Okay or okeh. How about the pulla?

She: I'm possessing the viand.

He: Who's coming?

She: The Murphys.

He: Alala!

She: Tush, and observe if he owns some pease and species of citrus. I yearn them laved and oorie.

He: Rt.

She: Before you depart, I awe if you would discover my etui.

He: What the ebblis!

She: Have you any extra Leva?

He: Scant. Pourquoi?

She: I'd admire an indefinite number of carbonadoed shanks.

He: Rt. Approximately a livre?

She: Affirmative as consuetudinarily. Now shoo!

(He leaves, returns in half an hour with bundles).

He: I glimpsed Mrs. Olsen on the iter.

She: She's positively lard, isn't she?

(She sorts the bundles).

He: I raised some golf devices in the sartorial salon.

She: Such oblivion! Where are the products of distillation!

He: You lost to aver that you craved me to barter an indefinite number. Don't be so soricine and spumescent.

She: Next time use a writing tool so you'll be abler to reminisce.

He: I'd need a vade mecum. Say, peer at the matter on your face.

She: Ou?

He: Orad. It's all striated. And hatchel your hair. It's negatively cumly.

She: I'll adjust it apres. Here, aid with this offal. Is that potage os in the container?

He: Rt. What else can I make for you?

She: None. I'm averse to effecting plus.

He: Never wit, why not quit?

She: Oh, a rimer?

He: Affirmative, Mrs. 'Twas an ode.

She: Cathode?

He: A lowest form of humor.

She (very tired and fidgety): Listen, Leo, when you sculptor the
    fowl this nocturne . . . oh baloney! The heck with this
    lingo. Cut it out before I go batty.

He: Pourquoi, my Asa? You exist at present level plus eloquent.
    You . . . hey . . . lay off . . .

(She clouts him with the dish cloth.)

    . . . cut it . . . you half wit . . . hey . . . nix . . .
    nix . . .

(He wrests the cloth from her.)

    . . . don't get so danged funny or I'm liable to hang one
    on you, see?

She: Leo! You're talking human again. I've saved you. Darling!

(She throws her arms around him.)

            CURTAIN.

ROBERT FARREN

The Common Cold

Haven't you a trick in the bag, Medicos?
Pills? A lotion? Or a gargle vinted
by djinn-like druggists behind screens? A tube?
A viscid, giddy-making glass, to bind
draughts and the puddle-making rains to terms
with a man's pneumatical and bronchial plan,
finishing snuffle and sneeze and boom and blow?

Liquid I must be, largely — bile and blood
phlegm and spittle and mucus, wash and swill
of food-conveying waters. Yes. Agreed.
I must be gaseous. True. Concedo.
Bellows, balloon, and hidey-hole for winds
to pop-in and pop-out-of. Yes, I know.
Yes! every bite and breath says Yes. But why,
why must eyes run, pores sweat, and raw red nose
gush, and then block, and gush again, like air-
locked washtaps? Why? Why must my torso heave
with whining and whooping winds like Aeolus' Cave?

Because the damps and draughts I have to have,
but must not have too much of, won't preserve
the laws of nations with my bronchial zone.
Is it supportable, that air I sieve
and free from oxygen to nurture flowers
shall fly in germ-formations through my nose?

I have been anschlussed like an unwarned foe
whose oilwells, goldmines, coalfields, cornacres lie
ready to the looter's grab! The germs
land in my tubes like paratroops! My lungs
teem with their tight Divisions! Dammit, I have
no Scorched Earth Policy, no Maginot Line,
no Spitfires, no Mosquitoes, no depthcharges
against their tanks and U-boats! I must roar,
snuffle, take aspirin, drink beef-tea and groan
and groan, and drink beef-tea, take aspirin and sneeze
then rise up cured — and take hell in again
like any helpless, hopeless neutral land.

Doctors, look here! Earthquake, landslide and flood
terrify men and tumble back red blood
onto the pumping heart: but this COLD plague
gives up my carcase as a dwelling den

to earthquake and to flood. I gush and shake
like the poor monster with the swallowed saint.
Medicos! Muster! Marshal your minds and probe
and ransack earth to end the Common Cold.

JAMES M. GILLIS

Ain't Psychology Grand

I heard recently that in a certain Middle Western University experiments were made, and $75,000 were expended, to discover how
birds come to fly. And now I read that other experiments are to be
made, and $275,000 expended, to find out why babies cry. It is, of
course, rather late in the history of birds and babies to be investi-
gating these elemental truths, but when science settles these problems, mankind and birdkind will doubtless be vastly happier. There
may be those who think that $275,000 might be spent to greater
advantage, in providing let us say, milk for poor babies, but these
people must be gross utilitarians. Or perhaps they are sentimentalists.
The true scientific attitude is neither utilitarian nor sentimental. It
merely wants to know, — to know everything, — why birds fly,
why babies cry, why we eat and why we drink, why we sleep, and
why we snore, — in a word, why we do what we do, and why we
are as we are.

And now — most important by far — comes a school of psychology, Behaviorism, based upon the question, "What will a man do
in given circumstances?" For example, "What will John Smith do
when he sees a snake?" You or I couldn't tell, but the trained observer knows: the man will run! We have that information from no
less an authority than John B. Watson, Ph.D., LL.D., formerly professor of Experimental and Comparative Psychology at Johns Hop-

kins University, "the outstanding American exponent of this (the Behaviorist) school of psychological thought." He is so expert that he even understands the psychology of women. After all, that is the crucial test. It may require a certain amount of learning to know that a man will run when he sees a snake. But who, I ask you, who unless the trained observer thoroughly instructed in Behaviorism, could answer this question: "What will a lot of women in a closed room do, if the professor 'turns loose ten fierce wild rats'?" There is the crucial problem: there is the *articulus stantis vel cadentis psychologiae*. William James didn't know. Sigmund Freud doesn't know. It was only with the coming of the very latest psychology that we have been able to answer that question. John B. Watson is the man who knows. He puts the question and, — what is more, — he answers it. Here are his very words: "Every woman in this closed room will scream, stand on a chair, or pull her skirts tightly around her, if I turn loose ten fierce wild rats." . . .

Thank heaven, we have Dr. Watson, and under his guidance I can see that we are going to learn a lot. For example, he says, "Suppose I were a stranger scientist just down from some distant planet. I know nothing of human beings as they exist on this earth. Suppose, further, that I am in a balloon so situated over the center of New York that I can watch the city and the surrounding territory. At eight-thirty in the morning I see millions of people hurrying into the city in trains, in automobiles, in subways, on ferries. The movements are rapid, confusing. There seems to be no more system in these movements than in the hurrying, scurrying movements of ants when their nest has been disturbed. With my eye aided by special instruments I follow groups of these individuals. I note that they enter great office buildings, department stores, restaurants. Some begin to wait on customers, some start to work on typewriting machines, others begin to cut and fit clothes and still others start sewing on power machines."

Now what conclusion would you or I, gentle reader, arrive at? Being novices in Behaviorism, or at best very imperfectly acquainted with the new science, we would probably say, "I give it up, I cannot for the life of me understand what these people are up to." But now again, let Dr. Watson be heard. He says, "I finally arrive at the conclusion that the people are going to work." He italicizes those last words. That's the only emphasis possible on paper. But just think, if we could actually hear the leading American exponent of Behaviorist psychology, how we should be thrilled with those words, coming resonant and vibrant from his own very lips, with the emotion that accompanies a great discovery: These people "are going to work"! Verily, though Sherlock is dead, Dr. Watson still lives.

We must not imagine that the new science can all be learned in a jiffy. It tackles some pretty tough problems, and for the solution of them even Dr. Watson sometimes has to call in assistants. Take, for instance, this complicated psychological puzzle. "I carry out my studies," says he, "by attaching myself to some individual, say John Smith. By observing him carefully day in and day out I find out his occupation. He is a bricklayer."

(Notice that it is only by observing "day in and day out," that the leading American exponent learns that John is a bricklayer. You or I, in our impetuous way, would have reached that conclusion at the end of one day. But that would have been unscientific haste.)

"I find that this man is married, that he has a small home in the suburbs, a Ford car bought on the installment plan, and a radio bought on the same plan. I find that he drinks a great deal, that he abuses his wife and children, spends a considerable part of his time in the poolroom, and that he is given to temper fits, that he is morose and sullen to his companions, that he is not particular in meeting his monetary obligations.

"He uses only fifteen hundred English words, — he practically never writes a letter and he reads only the Daily Tabloid. I may wish to make a still more circumscribed study of his behavior, so I invite him into my laboratory and study the rapidity with which he can form new habits. He has never learned to run a machine lathe. How quickly can he learn to do this? He doesn't know any French. How soon could I teach him to speak the French language moderately well? He has not a system of immaculate personal habits. How soon could I teach him these? And what methods should I have to use in order to teach him to put on this new behavior?"

That problem, I say, is a staggerer, even for Dr. Watson. So, he says, "I assemble all my data and take them to my colleagues." And do you suppose that the colleagues give an offhand decision? If so, you do not think scientifically. As a matter of fact, the colleagues "give it up." They say that they cannot answer without going back to John Smith's infancy. Their verdict runs: "Adult human behavior is too complicated to understand without knowing something of the infancy and the childhood period of man. We do not understand why one man is a bricklayer, another an artist, another a gambler. We cannot understand why some men are carefree and sober, make good husbands, and others not. We cannot understand why some men never leave home, never get married, and never are seen in women's society. We shall have to have man's early behavior investigated to see if it throws light on later behavior."

So there you are. You end where you began, — with an agnostic attitude towards the problem of why men drink, and beat their wives and children, and why they won't leave home. But Dr. Watson, a true scientist, is not easily discouraged. He starts all over again. But this time he commences, not with a full-fledged bricklayer, but with newborn infants. Now you see where the $275,000 goes . . .

HERBERT A. KENNY

Lines on a Modern Menace

A mad Catholic bishop named Huss
Stirred up a hell of a fuss
When he started to mate
The Church and the State
And drove off with a public-school bus.

RONALD KNOX

Jottings from a Psycho-analyst's Note-book *

(*From the German of Dr. Freud-Struwwelpeter*)

Peter ———, aged six, called "Shock-headed Peter" by his friends. He refuses obstinately to cut either his hair or his nails, which have consequently grown to a prodigious extent. His parents, instead of applauding his decision or trying to help him in any way, lose no opportunity of evincing a morbid disgust at his appearance. My first impression was, of course, that he wished he was a girl; but his obstinacy in the matter of the nails seems to discount this theory. I have put him down provisionally as a case of shell shock, which may be compensating itself in this way: the nails, of course, suggesting shells and his hair the shock. On the other hand, there is no positive evidence that he has ever been under fire. It is possible that he is merely a fanatic on the subject of growth — there is such a thing as vegetative hypertrophy. I have told the parents that his wishes in the matter must be rigorously respected; it is the only chance for him.

Frederick ———, aged six. From his earliest years he gave signs of what was thought to be "cruelty," catching flies with considerable agility and then tearing off their wings. He then proceeded to killing birds, and — a less unamiable but perhaps not less significant trait — breaking the chairs. It was when he threw the kitten downstairs that his parents began to fear there was something amiss; it was most unfortunate that they did not call in a psychological expert

* Reprinted from *Essays in Satire*, published by E. P. Dutton and Co., Inc.

there and then. For, up to that point, the perversion was a simple one: it was simply a gravitation complex. Only a year or two before he was born, an aunt of his narrowly escaped witnessing an aviation accident, and the whole idea of flying is therefore repellent to the boy's subconsciousness. The flies must be deprived of their wings; the birds, less easily mutilated, must be killed outright. His passion even vents itself upon chairs, because these, too, are designed to prevent human beings from falling on to the ground. A morbid curiosity on his part insists that the kitten shall make experiments in aviation. After this, however, a sudden transference seems to have turned him in the direction of flagellomania. He first beat his nurse, Mary ——— , who broke down and cried — the worst thing she could have done in the circumstances. His next victim was a dog called Tray — or rather, there was victimisation on both sides, for the dog resented the treatment and bit him, an injury which may have grave results. It is worth observing that the two names "Mary" and "Tray" both contain the letters "ary," which are calculated to suggest the idea of aviation to the subconsciousness. I have directed the discontinuance of the medicine prescribed by the family doctor, since the patient finds it unpalatable.

Conrad ——— , a pathetic instance of self-mutilation under strong subconscious suggestion. Originally it was an ordinary case of cannibalism, which had taken an autophagous direction. Conrad was a pronounced but not an irretrievable thumb-sucker. His mother, with the fatal tendency of well-meaning but uninstructed parents, adopted a deterrent policy. Nursery mythology, the juggernaut of the human species, had told her of a "great tall tailor" who always came to little boys who suck their thumbs. The bogey is represented, I need hardly say, as cutting off the thumbs with scissors. The myth in question is probably traceable to Mithras worship; but it may be obscurely derived from the classical conception of the Fates cutting the threads of the doomed person's life. The result might have been foreseen. Conrad is left alone; in an instant the supposedly succulent thumb finds its billet in his mouth. So far the action is merely instinctive, and could have led, at the worst, to nothing more serious than starvation-mania. But almost immediately "conscience," that fatal heritage of a fetishistic ancestry, gets to work; the intervention of the "great tall tailor" is momentarily expected, and under the urge of this impulse, the unhappy boy rushes to the work-basket, and performs on his own person an operation from which a qualified surgeon might have shrunk. The thumbs have gone, and this, perhaps, not the worst part of the business: Conrad resolutely refuses to have new clothes made for him, although the orange pinafore he wears is no longer suitable to his time of life. When will parents learn?

Philip ———, aged five, a victim of seismic collapse. The parents describe him as incapable of sitting still at table; an inveterate chair-tilter, he has been known to clutch convulsively at the table-cloth as if in search of support. (There are no signs of locomotor ataxia, and the family physician has been able to make nothing of the case.) The original source of the trouble is very hard to locate; he may have been born at sea; or it may be a suppression, e.g., was his mother or grandmother an artist's model? (Mem. — Make further enquiries.) The tendency has certainly been aggravated by the attitude of the parents, who have been in the habit of saying, "Let us see if Philip can be a little gentleman; let me see if he is able to sit still for once at table." This combination of irony with an appeal to class-consciousness has had the most devastating effects. I have made a start by pointing out that the habit of tying a napkin round the chin must immediately be discontinued; subconsciously, the boy is no doubt gasping for breath all through his meal-times.

Robert ———, aged seven. The parents in this case were in great distress, because Robert insisted on going out in all weathers; and there is a certain morbid love of rain which is unpleasantly suggestive of hypaethromania. But the boy is young, and it is doubtful whether we have to reckon on anything worse than claustrophobia at present. He seems to feel that his parents are unlawfully detaining him at home; and his choice of a red umbrella probably indicates that he is in a state of revolt. I have told the parents that his wishes in the matter must on no account be thwarted: "Your son," I told them, "will be developing into a great aviator one of these days."

SISTER MARY BERTRAND

Kin to Mrs. Gurney

Post Toast

A toast to the prowess
 Of Wilhelmina West
Who cleaned up the attic
 And threw out her chest.

Fact, Not Fiction

Hear, too, the story
 Of Helena Huss
Who bought a mousetrap
 Then caught a bus.

Feat 4

Then there's the achievement
 Of Gregory McGrane
Who tore up the platform
 And made a train.

MARY F. WINDEATT

Isolationist

(Or a Tribute to Scientific Advancement)

All praise to little fish that flee
Beneath the frigid Arctic sea.
Without them I would surely be

A prey to coughs and sneezes;
Lift up the laurel once — yes, twice,
For cunning cod beneath the ice
Whose livers leave me lean, and thrice
Immune to chilly breezes!

For rubbers on my feet or not,
I have not got what some have got
When Spring comes in, first cold, then hot,
Phlegmatic, also fickle;
I have a share of germs within
But also of each Vitamin,
And every year we seem to win
Against the throaty tickle.

Alas! Some folks, deep in their rut,
Profess no faith in halibut;
They flee from piscatory gut
And cry: "Pish, tush and piffle!"
But I say: "Capsules, one a day,
With Vitamins, D, C, B, A,
Then let the colds come where they may.
I shall not sneeze or sniffle."

11. FOOD FOR THOUGHT

11. FOOD FOR THOUGHT

"A man seldom thinks with more earnestness of anything than he does of his dinner."

— Samuel Johnson

"Est quiddam gestus edendi," the Romans used to say. Translated freely, this meant "Eating is an art." Finesse at the table was important in those days since a person spent a good portion of his life face to face with a roast fowl. There were so many feasts every day and so many tables at every feast and so many people at every table! In a way the great Roman civilization ate and drank itself under the table and passed out of the pages of history. The Lucullan spectacles, which probably used ten-pound chickens for hors d'oeuvres, no doubt gave the early Christians plenty of food for serious thought and resulted in some of them going in for herb and berry-eating out on the desert. But one of the most un-Christian tendencies imaginable is the tendency to call a liking for a flitch of bacon or a decanter of wine un-Christian. Until Eve ordered the wrong item, she and her husband never had menu trouble. Paradise was theirs with "all manner of trees, fair to behold, and pleasant to eat of." And the Book of Ecclesiasticus says that "the lips of many shall bless him that is liberal of his bread." But what do you suppose happens to him who sets a poor table? "Against him that is niggardly of his bread, the city will murmur." Your discontented heretic most times is a lean and hungry Cassius, I'll bet, fit for treasons and stratagems. Your happy Christian, as St. Thomas More says in his *Utopia,* accepts food and drink as one of the "pleasaunte rejoysings of life."

The savory flavor of the kitchen permeates some of the pleasantest pages of literature. I liked Izaak Walton because the "Compleat

Angler" wasn't "compleat" at all unless he knew how best to dress his catch of trout or chules and eat it to the accompaniment of "the best barleywine, the good liquor that our honest forefathers did use to drink of; the drink which preserved their health, and made them live so long, and to do so many good deeds."

As the most heart-warming and soul-filling mealtime in the annals of literature I'll nominate the Christmas dinner of Bob Cratchit's family. There were the goose, the stuffing, the sage, the onion, the slow potatoes which "bubbling up, knocked loudly at the saucepan lid to be let out and peeled," the apple sauce, the plum pudding, "like a speckled cannon ball," the chestnuts, the oranges, the apples. Above all there was the harmonious fusion of good appetite and good will which inevitably led to Tiny Tim's climactic benediction, "God bless us everyone."

Charles Lamb — an excellent name for that gentle connoisseur of fine viands — has immortalized the "indefinable sweetness" and the "animal manna," of a roast pig, the blend of fat and lean leading to one "ambrosian result." I recall too that Anthony Trollope made my mouth water at Archdeacon Grantley's breakfast table at Plumstead Episcopi. The table was filled with tea, coffee, toast, muffins, crumpets, hot bread, cold bread, wheaten bread, oaten bread, eggs, bacon, fishes, devilled kidneys, a huge ham and a huge sirloin. Would someone prefer doughnuts and coffee?

I'm not holding out for a bill of fare like that of Archdeacon Grantley. And I don't especially favor turning the kitchen clock back to the seven-day celebration by 6,000 persons of the consecration of the Archbishop of York in the fifteenth century. There were served 1,000 sheep, 304 calves, 2,000 pigs, 17,000 assorted birds, 500 stags, bucks and roes, 13,000 dishes of sweets, and probably 6,000 boxes of bicarbonate.

But I think that we Americans ought to take a good long look at Bob Cratchit's table and the dining habits of a more leisurely age. It's time that we made eating a fine art the way we have made money-grabbing a fine art. Then our national churlishness, resulting largely from mental and physical dyspepsia, would be alleviated. The abomination of desolation spoken of by Daniel the prophet most certainly referred to American dining habits. In the first place our eating is usually done in surroundings of such confusion and noise that "dinning" not "dining" is the word for it. Next, we eat so fast that fleeting time, not eating time, would best describe the dining period. Most of us do not know how to enjoy our meals. The breaking of bread is no longer a happy ritual. It's a tolerated interruption in the everyday monetary treadmill, and the shorter the interruption the better.

One of the latest and most discouraging reports has it that nowadays only about thirty-five per cent of Americans eat any meals in their kitchens. How can a person have any affection for food who has never heard a kettle sing, nor a roast sizzle in the pan, who has never watched the water churning and bubbling among the waxed beans, nor the steam pushing violently at the lid of a double boiler of luscious creamed macaroni?

In this section you will meet with five writers to whom the kitchen is the throne room of the palace called home, and to whom food and drink are not only a means of survival but also a marvelous adventure.

Mr. Eagan's shocking and heretical hatred of the fishcake — he really makes no bones about it — is included to show that Catholics are not kept in culinary chains by the Pope but are free to speak their minds in matters of fish and fowl.

Maura Laverty holds a unique place among novelists. She wrote such glowing descriptions of cooking and baking in novels like *Never No More* that her readers virtually demanded that she turn out a book all about cooking, without the encumbrance of an inconsequential thing like a plot. Miss Laverty's cookbook is not in the Boston tradition. It's sprinkled through with the spice of personal anecdote.

Someone who popped up rather unexpectedly in the kitchen was Sheila Kaye-Smith. I've known her as an excellent writer. And now she can cook! By an interesting coincidence her marriage name is Fry. Her discussion of food, like Miss Laverty's, revolves around personal experiences.

D. B. Wyndham Lewis hasn't gotten around to writing his cookbook yet. But when he does it will be shot through with the fire and fervor of an evangelist. Mr. Lewis finds most cookbooks flat and dry. His will sparkle like burgundy, and have the pungent tang of the best Jamaica ginger. If you don't think so, look at his proposed way of doing the thing. Meanwhile Mr. Lewis is no doubt happy to have found that two women, Miss Laverty and Miss Kaye-Smith, though neither the matronly type, have composed cookbooks with more than a dash of the "passion" he recommends.

CYRIL B. EGAN

Ode to a Fishcake

Dietetic dud
That droppeth into my tum-tum
With dire dum-dum
Leaden thud —
O, Lud!
Who first did this dish bake?
Who in hell invented the Fishcake?

Brood of the brine
And fruit of the mud,
Unhappy wedding of cod and spud,
I sudden start —
Cold runs my blood —
I shudder when I look on Fishcake —
Waiter, away — away such dish take!

Gruel I hate;
Eels I abominate,
Herring in pickle and salted state;
I am not partial to potted snipe,
Rather eat a hall mat than a mess of tripe —

But more, even more
Than these I abhor,
O'er and o'er I execrate
More and more profanely berate
(In such a mood I would a dish break)
Fishcake!

Fishcake!
O lumpish, lukewarm, loggy fishcake —
Mealy, muggy, soggy Fishcake —
Pallid, plebeian, slummocky ration,
Lowly cause of my towering passion —
A pock
On the culinary doc'
Who first cooked up this boggy grub!
Beelzebub —
Plague take —
Him, and his Fishcake!

SHEILA KAYE-SMITH

Cookbooks

My first act was to examine my cookery books, of which I had
a number, and decide which would be of most practical use. I chose
half a dozen. The first was a primer of cookery, the name of which
I shall not give as I have very little for it but abuse. The second was
the time-honored and world-famous *Mrs. Beeton's Book of Household Management* . . .

The primer, as might be expected, was English. I had hoped
it would give me the rudiments of cookery and genuinely enlighten

my ignorance of processes and technical terms. What did one do, for instance, to "blanch" sweetbreads? How did one "fold in" the white of an egg? And how long did one cook sprouts? — five minutes? — twenty minutes? — an hour? The anonymous author did not tell me. He or she started off with an Arabian Nights' dream of what my kitchen stores should consist of, passed on to instructions as to the management of a gas cooker which I had not got, and then abruptly decided that I knew everything. He deigned to elucidate no terms — for these I had to go to the dictionary, which I found more helpful than I had expected — and the period of cookery was always "till tender," which to my ignorance might have been any period from three minutes to three hours.

The first result of my efforts to master the primer was a decision (afterwards modified into the present work) to write a cookery book of my own — a Mug's Cookery Book, which would enlighten the darkness of females like myself driven by the fortune of war into the kitchen. Not for us lighthearted chat about blanching and folding and instructions to cook till tender. Tell us exactly what to do and how to do it, with a diagram if necessary; tell us the earliest time we should hopefully prod and the latest when we must give up hope and decide mournfully that someone has blundered.

Another result was more directly fruitful. The primer led me to consult Mrs. Beeton. For among the innumerable virtues of this lady is the fact that she always tells you how long everything should take to cook. "Time — 45 minutes . . . Time 2½ hours" . . . such instructions are invaluable to the beginner who, apart from technical considerations, likes to know exactly at what time she should give up her gardening or her darning or her writing, and start preparing dinner. One is always going from one job to another, and hanging on to each until the last moment, so it is frustrating to find one has allowed an hour and a half to prepare what takes only forty minutes, or — my more common situation — to find oneself starting a two-hour job with only half an hour to go.

Mrs. Beeton is widely abused as extravagant — she is supposed never to make a cake with fewer than half a dozen eggs. Actually I have caught her using an egg less than my primer. Of course my edition has been modified, and brought up to date; it has been stripped of much of its Victorian lushness and though its quantities are undoubtedly those of peacetime, one of the first things a war-time cook must learn is how to adapt peacetime recipes. I dislike wartime recipes — they always seem to me either defeatist, making the worst of a bad job with starchy messes, or else unwarrantably optimistic as to the results, say, of substituting vinegar for brandy in mince pies.

On the whole I have found Mrs. Beeton easier to adapt than other prewar instructors. She provides, moreover, such a gorgeous variety of dishes that one has a wide choice even in wartime. In times of abundance there is no limit. Should you, for instance, wish to cook a kangaroo, there it is, to be jugged, curried, or fricasseed according to your whim — with a swan, a bandicoot, or a wallaby for special occasions.

Another of her virtues is that nothing is beneath her notice — she will tell you how to make toast with the same care and good-will as she will tell you how to make an *omelette surprise*. She even deigns to explain her own terms; if I had gone to her first, instead of the primer, I should not have had to use a dictionary.

Her main extravagance is extravagance in labor. Even my 1923 edition presupposes a vast kitchen, with a roaring coal range, and an adjoining scullery where subsidiary menials do the jobs that you and I have to do for ourselves as well as the cooking.

"The Cook," says Mrs. Beeton, "is queen of the kitchen. The duty of others is to render her ready and willing assistance . . . the cook takes charge of the soups, fish, poultry; the kitchen-maid of the vegetables, sauces and gravies. The scullery maid waits on and assists the cook." Later on, as a concession to modernity, we are told that "in small households the cook sometimes engages to do the whole work of the kitchen."

I find Mrs. Beeton fascinating literature — too fascinating, for when I lift down her weighty mass — weightier than the telephone directory, weighter than *Ulysses* — to look for a recipe, I am lost in a maze of attractive bypaths, and it may be half an hour before I am at my destination. Even the index is full of counter-attractions. You want to know, perhaps, how to deal with a peculiarly tough-looking specimen of ox-liver, which the butcher has sent in response to your cry for offal. But before you finally decide to give it to the cat you have been entertained by much enthralling information, not only about ox liver, but about every sort of liver including your own (cirrhosis of, passive congestion of, fatty degeneration of, waxy degeneration of). Lobster leads straight to Lockjaw — then Locks — and Lodgers, Melted Butter to Meningitis, Condiments to Confinements, Drop Cakes to Dropsy and Drowning, Elderberry Wine to Electricity and Emetics, Haddock to Hair-Wash, Ices to Infants (carrying, feeding, washing, and wet-nurse). The movement ends only with the alphabet.

Who could resist following up the reference to "Groper, Head and Shoulders boiled"? I could not, though having done so, I remained unenlightened. For though I knew how to cook a groper's head and shoulders, I was no nearer having any idea of what a groper was, though some clue to its appearance had been given by the instruction that "great care should be taken of the immense gelatinous lips." This suggests that, whether it be flesh, fish or fowl, the groper is not too beautiful; on the other hand, the cook is urged not to "spoil the shape of the head by boiling it too quickly" . . .

I came nearest to enlightenment when shutting up the henhouses one evening soon afterwards. It was dusk, almost dark, and as I walked up the field a pale mysterious shape floated against the background of the woods. It seemed to be head and shoulders only . . . I gazed, peered closely . . . Could this be? . . . Was I contemplating at last a groper? The idea was favored by the profile which displayed what appeared to be "immense gelatinous lips." It had a round head and humped shoulders, and it moved in a typical spectre fashion, with a slow, gliding fall through the twilight — till it suddenly came to rest on a gatepost. Then my ghost story ended familiarly with the hoot of an owl. So there is still an unanswered riddle in my life. Hang it all — what *is* a groper?

MAURA LAVERTY

Tidbits

Perch

I may claim with a certain amount of justification to be a born cook. Consider the facts. Quite literally, I was born in a kitchen. What is more, I wasn't five minutes in the world when I was responsible for a new recipe.

It seems that I made my unobstrusive entry while my mother was in the middle of cooking four fine perch which my father had just caught in the mill-pond. Possibly, she had some miscalculation concerning the date she would require the ministrations of Nurse Cassidy, but I have always preferred to think that the perch had something to do with the way I hurried into the kitchen, and that this was the first evidence of the passionate interest in cooking which has never left me.

About that recipe which I invented at birth. My mother had always cooked perch by baking them in the pot-oven with a dollop of fat on the chest of each fish. On that particular day, she had the fish all ready except for their scapulars of fat. It appears that the pot-oven wasn't yet hot enough, so she filled in the time by cutting slices of bacon from the flitch for the following morning's breakfast, a job which could not be entrusted to Moll Slevin, our servant girl, because the poor creature had a bad cast in her eye. She had cut the fifth slice when she became the mother of an eight-pound daughter. In the confusion that followed, Moll was left to deal with the cooking. It happened that on the table were a couple of bay leaves and some milk intended for a rice pudding. Moll went out of her mind and threw into the pie-dish with the fish everything she could lay her hands on — bacon, bay leaves, milk and all. The results were so satisfactory that from then on perch was never cooked in any other way in our house. By the time it was ready, mother and child were doing nicely. Indeed, I have been told the mother was doing so nicely that she called down from the bedroom demanding her share of the fish. I hope they gave it to her, for those mill-pond perch were as good as trout, particularly when cradled head to tail in a buttered pie-dish under a quilt of fat bacon slices monogrammed with a bay leaf or two.

Soups

Once, before I got sense, I fell madly in love. I was so taken up with brooding that I had neither time nor energy for such ordinary occupations as eating and sleeping. My cheeks and eyes went in and my collar bones came out. All in all, I was in a fair way to qualifying for a straight-jacket or a wooden overcoat, or both. When my case was really becoming desperate, I appealed to help from a friend who has given his life to the study of love potions and their antidotes. He advised me to drink plenty of salt water.

I tried his prescription. On my word of honour, it worked. Within a week I was able to meet the author of my misfortunes without quivering like an aspen. Better still, I was able to look with a cold and critical eye on those little peculiarities of person and habit which until then had made him so utterly adorable. Within a fortnight I was sleeping the round of the clock, and before the cure ended I had as good an appetite as could be expected of a woman whose insides have been in a pickle for the best part of a month.

You may be wondering what my unhappy love-affair has to do with the making of soup. It has everything to do with it. I proved that salt water is fatal to love. All over the world, there are women whose hearts are breaking because their husbands have grown inexplicably cold. To such women I would say in all seriousness: What are you giving him in his soup-plate? Is it really soup? Or is it just salt water?

Meats

According to Charles Laughton, Henry the Eighth thought nothing of devouring a shoulder of lamb at one sitting. He couldn't hold a candle to Head Mooney at home in our place. He belonged to people who were notorious throughout the County Kildare for their passion for pig's head. They earned plenty of money on the canal boats and on the bog, but they never had a penny to show for it. All their good earnings were squandered on pig's head. When the boy I'm talking about got married — Paddy, he was called then — his wife was full of a bride's eagerness to please. Knowing the family failing, off with her into the town when she got the first week's wages into her hand on Saturday, and she spent the best part of it on the biggest pig's head in Miss Regan's shop. "It'll last us the week," she planned. She had it nicely cooked and bolstered on white cabbage for Paddy when he came in from second Mass the next day.

Paddy sat down, blessed himself and started in. Wrapped up in it, he continued with the good work until his wife, who had a normally healthy appetite, could stand it no longer. "What about me, Paddy?" she asked diffidently. "Aren't you going to cut a little bit for me?"

Paddy looked up in shock amazement. "And do you mean to tell me girl," he demanded, "that you didn't cook e'er a one for yourself?" It was then she christened him Head, and the name never left him.

QUICK COOKING

As a member of the working class, it gives great satisfaction to see how the universe was arranged on trades union lines. Consider how the nations are divided into guilds, each busily employed on its own particular trade. In Ireland, for instance, we all belong to the Anaesthetists' Guild. Our best energies are expended on the manufacture of Celtic twilight sleep, repeated doses of which are guaranteed to keep the most restless from wakening up to realities. This is one of the fundamental differences between ourselves and the English, and may account for our bickerings. Over there, they all belong to the Guild of Knockers-Up. Let it be hinted to an Englishman that under some far-off palm-tree a naked native is dreaming the happy hours away. Our Knocker-Up will be off, like a shot out of a gun, to waken the dreamer so that he may learn to live earnestly as they do in Bayswater. The American Guild is a grand one. It is the Guild of Cooks. The French and Germans would laugh at this statement. They have a notion that they were jointly appointed to run the Cook's Guild. That is a mere Franco-Germanic illusion. Did the French give refrigerators to the world? Did the Germans discover Boston baked beans? Who blessed humanity with lemon pie, and boiled frosting and molasses cookies? Most important of all, who conferred on harassed hostesses the inestimable benefits of canned food? If I had my way, I would add another star to the American flag in gratitude for what canned food has meant to me. Messrs. Heinz and Campbell, I love you for the trail you blazed!

> When friends come unexpected, do I fuss and tear my hair,
>   Although there's only meat enough for two?
> No; I walk into my pantry with a calm, unruffled air.
> I fetch the can of bully-beef that's waiting for me there,
>   I mix it with an onion and a fervent grateful prayer,
> And for dinner we have savoury ragout.

D. P. WYNDHAM LEWIS

Lambs' Tails with Potatoes*

An oblong packet arrived by the morning post. It looked like a book. It was a book. It was a new cookery book, written by a French man of letters with all that learning, gaiety, and balanced grace of style which the French bring to this great subject. It was not a catalogue of dishes and menus: it told you the kind of family lunch or dinner to offer a Female Poet, an Influential Official Person, a Collector of Antiques, a Country Aunt up in Town, an Intellectual, a Rich Vulgar Acquaintance, a Dashing Bachelor, a trio

* Reprinted from *Welcome to All This,* by D. B. Wyndham Lewis, published by E. P. Dutton and Co., Inc.

of School Friends, the Parish Priest and other guests of greatly vary-
ing temperament and position. And after reading and meditating
on it I retired into the interior bodega or rest-house of my immortal
soul and pondered (not without sighs) the lamentable extent to
which we in England fail in this branch of literature.

The cruel dryness of the English cookery book makes it an impossible bed-companion for any man of taste. We once nearly had
one worth reading when Dr. Johnson, dining at Dilly's in the Poultry, half undertook to compose a cookery book on philosophical
principles; and re-reading Lamb's essay on Roast Pig one can
imagine what he might have done had he devoted himself to
worthier things. I do not deny that our old English cookery writers,
Gervase Markham and Mrs. Glasse, and the anonymous sixteenth-
century author of a Booke of Cookerie and the late medieval authors
of those recipes in the Royal Society Collection — I do not deny
that these exhibit an antique charm and now and again a certain
minor lyricism. For example, to Make a Dish of Snow:

> Take a Pottle of sweet thick Creame and the white of eyght Eggs, and
> beate them together with a Spoone, and then put them into your cream
> with a dish-full of Rosewater, and a dish-full of Sugar withall. . . .
> (Finally) Then take a Platter and sett an Apple in the midst of it,
> stick a thicke Bush of Rosemary in the Apple; then cast your Snow upon
> the Rosemary and fill your Platter therewith, and if you have Wafers
> cast some withall, and so serve them forthe.

That is very pretty; and there are many others. But we have
nothing at all in English to compare with Brillat-Savarin. Listen to
this, in our most graceful modern manner:

> To Truss a Rabbit for Roasting or Boiling: Empty, skin, and wash the
> rabbit thoroughly, wipe it dry, and take out the eyes. (See instructions
> in preceding paragraph in regard to Skinning a Hare.)

Compare with this a fourteenth-century recipe for serving a pea-
cock. After the initial preparation:

> Then take the pecokke and roste him, and endore him with raw yolkes
> of egs; and when he is rosted take hym and let hym cool a while, and
> sowe hym in his skynne, and gilde his combe, and so serve him forthe.

The style in either case is about as exquisite as the Great Western Railway. *"Pas de fine flamme, pas de galanterie,"* as the Marquise very reasonably objected to Paradise Lost. One may, then, say generally of English cookery writers — and the moderns above all — that they are divorced from Helicon and strangers to Parnassus. Pigs' Feet in Jelly move the moderns to no subtle rhythms. Lambs' Tails with Potatoes they set down like goods-clerks checking bales of wool. I think I can lay my finger unerringly on the reason for this terrible banality. It is this: that none of them has any interior emotional life.

I hope there will be nobody foolish enough to pretend that passion is alien to the character of a British matron, or, consecutively, that the style of any British matron about to compose a cookery book would not be the better for a dash of it. Could Mrs. Browning have written the *Sonnets from the Portuguese,* or Mrs. Wheeler Wilcox such poetry, if they had not loved Mr. Browning and Mr. Wheeler Wilcox respectively? The same would apply, I hope, to Mrs. H. J. Ribstone, author of *A Thousand Ways with Eggs.* Had some poet, half-crazed with passion, but sung:

> For there was lightning in my blood,
>   Mrs. H. J. Ribstone!
> O, there was lightning in my blood,
> Red lightning lighten'd through my blood,
>   Mrs. H. J. Ribstone!

— we might have had a book about eggs which would have set Mrs. Ribstone on the lyric peaks with Sappho and Sulpicia. . . .

But the Cookery Book remains to be written; the book which in describing even the gutting of a rabbit shall remember that celebrated sermon of Odo of Cluny in which the terrible monk, with a similar sweep of the knife, dissects and displays the vaunted charms of woman, which have destroyed so many. As for the chapters on English Game-Pie, on Cheese Soufflé, on Truffled Goose, on Partridge roasted over Vine-Branches, on Sole Dieppoise (with the mussels and the golden cream), on Aubergines, on Yorkshire Pudding — why, men should read them as in a trance and stumble about repeating their lovely cadences, like the folk of Abdera. The section on Omelets should tell the story — with figured music for lutes — of

Ramon of Aragon, who after so many years of seeking (shall I repeat it?) found Dona Alisonde at last in disguise at the Fonda of the Moon in Xaen. Have you forgotten the knight's first words as, having eaten the golden omelet she served him with her white hands, he gazed into the lovely face of her he sought so long? "I will," he said, "have another of those."

And again, the chapter on Sausage and Mash. This I would devoutly write myself. Young children should be taught its rhythms at their nurse's knee and old men should hand it down the generations.

What a book! By the Great Mock-Steak of Chandos Street, what a book!

THE END

LIFE-LINES
(Biographies)

The biographies have been put together back here in alphabetical order to make for easy reference and comparison. The highlights of each author's career have been sketched and his more important books listed. For more complete information of a biographical nature there are available such books as: *American Catholic Who's Who*, Walter Romig's *Book of Catholic Authors* (Series 1, 2, 3, 4 — autobiographical essays), *American Catholic Convert Authors, Negro Catholic Writers* and Matthew Hoehn's *Catholic Authors, Contemporary Biographical Sketches, 1930–47*. Some authors will also be found in books like *Who's Who, American Who's Who, Twentieth Century Authors* and *Current Biography*. All these sources mentioned give helpful lists of authors' works. In addition they sometimes list critical articles about the authors. Other useful bibliographies and articles will be found listed in *The Guide to Catholic Literature* and *The Catholic Periodical Index*.

BASSET, BERNARD: Jesuit; partly American, grandmother a cousin of Gen. Robert E. Lee; now curate, retreat master at Lancashire, England; born Westminster, 1909; educated Stonyhurst College and Oxford, where he took first class honors Modern History, won Stanhope Prize Essay, Lothian Prize Essay; on staff Beaumont College, Windsor, before moving to Lancashire; books include *Marjorie and Me, The Seven Deadly Virtues, The Rhyme of Edmund Campion* and several children's pantomimes.

BOYLE, HAL: Full name Harold Vincent Boyle; Pulitzer Prize winner 1944 for war correspondence; ace penman for Associated Press, since 1932, in Kansas City, St. Louis, now New York; has degree in journalism from University of Missouri; during World War II went ashore with invasion forces in North Africa, Sicily, Italy, Normandy, first to report Battle of the Bulge; a bachelor, weighs about 184 pounds, stands 5 feet 9 inches. Born Kansas City, Feb. 21, 1911.

CAMPBELL, ROY: Full name Ignatius Roy Dunnachie Campbell. At latest report was "talks producer" for British Broadcasting Company; in Spain during civil war 1930's, wrote stirring poetry about it, saved Carmelite Archives of Toledo during siege; won steer-throwing championship of Provence in 1932 and 1933; served in Imperial Army in World War II, disabled in 1944; born Oct. 2, 1901, Durban, England, doctor's son. Brilliant Popian satirist. Married, two daughters. Says poetry is his recreation. Books include *Talking Bronco, Flowering Rifle, The Georgiad, Adamastor, The Wayzgoose.*

CARROLL, PATRICK J.: One vice-president who made good use of his time; while v.p. of Notre Dame U., 1926–28, decided to write sketches of own schooldays in West Limerick, Ireland; character "Patch" caught imagination of large audience; "more or less myself" says Father Carroll of "Patch"; born August 1876, County Limerick; entered Congregation of the Holy Cross 1896, ordained 1900; a graduate of Notre Dame U.; was college professor there, elsewhere; since 1934 editor *Ave Maria,* to which he sold first story in 1897. Latest books: *Patch and Fan, Patch of Askeaton Days, Smoking Flax, Vagrant Essays.*

CASEY, ROBERT J.: Born Beresford, S. Dakota, Mar. 14, 1890; prolific author, 21 books; inveterate traveler; educated Armour Tech., Chicago, St. Mary's, Kansas; reporter with *Des Moines Register,* 1910; with *Chicago Daily News,* 1920–46; now with *Herald-American.* Travels included Cambodia and Easter Island expeditions and, as war correspondent, France, 1939–40, London during blitz, British Army in Egypt, 1941, U.S. Pacific Fleet, 1942, British Navy, 1943; artillery captain, World War I. Latest books: *More Interesting People, This Is Where I Came In, Such Interesting People, Torpedo Junction.*

COLUM, PADRAIC: A native of Longford, Ireland, Dec. 8, 1881; childhood in Ireland of countryside, small town, street-singers, story-spinners; farmer, school teacher; then to Dublin, edited *Irish Review*; became associated with Yeats, Lady Gregory, Synge, A.E., and nationalistic movement; playwright and a founder of Irish National Theatre; to U.S., 1914; started writing on Irish folk traditions, Welsh, Norse, Hawaiian legends, and branched out to rewriting stories from *Iliad, Odyssey*; distinguished poet. Latest books: *The Frenzied Prince, Legend of St. Columba, Story of Lowry Maen, Flower Pieces* (poems), *Big Tree of Bunlahy*. Now lives in N.Y.C.

DALY, MAUREEN: Youngest writer to win an O. Henry Memorial Award, for "Sixteen." At ancient age of late twenties specializes in recollections of teen-age past; associate editor, *Ladies Home Journal* and sub-deb adviser; story "Fifteen" won 4th place, 1937 *Scholastic Magazine* contest; "Sixteen" won 1st prize; author more than 100 short stories; teen-age columnist *Chicago Tribune,* while in college. Born Mar. 15, 1921, Castlecaulfield, Ireland; A.B., Rosary College, 1942. Books: *Seventeenth Summer, Smarter and Smoother.*

DURANTE, JIMMY: Born New York City, Feb. 10, 1893, son of Bartholomew, a barber, and Rosea Millino; educated in public schools; piano player on Bowery, Coney Island, Harlem; first vaudeville appearance 1927, with Lou Clayton and Eddie Jackson; then Broadway productions like *Show Girl, Strike Me Pink, Jumbo*; 1929 to Hollywood, since mostly in films, on radio; 23 pictures include *Carnival; Start Cheering; Sally, Irene and Mary; Little Miss Broadway; Two Gentlemen from Milwaukee; Two Sisters from Boston*. Relies on warm personality, large nose (insured for $100,000, it's said), shuffling walk, linguistic mayhem, for appeal.

EDEN, HELEN PARRY: Wife of Denis Eden, artist who has illustrated some of her books; they have a son and two daughters, live in County Wicklow, Ireland. Born 1885, eldest daughter of Sir Edward Parry; educated Roedean School and Manchester University where she won prizes for history and English verse; studied painting under Byam Shaw and Rex Vicat Cole for three years. Books include *Poems and Verse, Whistles of Silver, A String of Sapphires, Bread and Circuses.*

EGAN, CYRIL B.: Contributor prose, verse to *Saturday Evening Post, Women's Home Companion, Liberty*, etc.; story "Passion Play" in O'Brien collection 1928; story "Good Samaritan," O. Henry award 1932; for last 20 years lecturer, English, Latin, at Fordham U., also teacher Regis Prep; was contributor to Don Marquis' column. Born N.Y.C., 1894, educated Fordham U.; in Army World War I as "machine gunner who never fired a gun, artillery man ditto, and student of equitation who only once rode (with dubious success) a horse."

EISELE, ALBERT: Has farmed all his life, active in farm bureau work, writes for rural papers; born Pontiac, Ill., July 12, 1896; educated at parish school; was choir director of parish church for ten years. Now lives at Blue Earth, Minn., with wife, three sons. Contributes to various Catholic magazines, especially *Land and Home*.

ENGELS, NORBERT A.: Professor of English, Notre Dame U.; started career as professional musician, toured Europe, 1925–26, taught music for a year then turned from musical lyrics to poetic ones; teaching at Notre Dame, his alma mater, A.B., M.A., since 1927. Born Green Bay, Wis., Sept. 4, 1903; contributes light essays to many Catholic magazines.

FARREN, ROBERT: Bilingual poet, short story writer; "talks" officer, Radio Eireann since 1939; director Abbey Theatre; born Dublin, Apr. 24, 1909; educated St. Mary's National School, St. Patrick's Teachers College, National U. of Ireland; grew up in time of nationalism, effect of Gaelic studies seen in poems, content and metrics; taught in Dublin primary schools 1929–39. Books include *Thronging Feet*; *Fion Gan Mhoirt* (short stories in Gaelic); *Time's Wall Asunder*; *This Man Was Ireland*; *Rime, Gentlemen, Please*; *Poetry for Pleasure*; *How to Enjoy Poetry*.

FAY, FRANK: First appeared on stage as a teddy bear, at 4, in *Babes in Toyland*; climaxed career as Elwood P. Dowd, friend of a rabbit named Harvey, in play of same name; born San Francisco, Nov. 17, 1897, parents stock company troupers; started career as

ballad singer; in vaudeville team of Dyer and Fay; became mono-
logist, 1917, hit Palace 1919. In 1920's played in many Broadway
stage hits; in 1930's made several movies, many radio appearances.
Known as Spirit of Vaudeville, in its heyday.

FEENEY, THOMAS B.: Prof. English and French, Boston College;
poet, short story writer; favorite recreation writing amateur songs;
some of poems in book *When the Wind Blows* set to music; songs
mixture Irish ballad and Gregorian chant; brother Leonard Feeney;
born Lynn, Mass., educated Boston College High, then joined
Jesuits, studied at Poughkeepsie, Woodstock, Ghent, Belgium.

GALVIN, JAMES J.: A member Congregation of the Holy Re-
deemer (Redemptorists) since 1932; editor *Perpetual Help Magazine* since 1943; contributor to other Catholic magazines, poems in
several anthologies; born Apr. 22, 1911, Newton Centre, Mass.;
a graduate of St. Mary's College (Pa.), 1931; missioner in Puerto
Rico, 1939–42.

GANNON, ROBERT I.: Jesuit; president Fordham U. 1936–49;
popular after-dinner speaker; born Staten Island, Apr. 20, 1893;
A.B., Georgetown U., 1913; M.A., Woodstock College, 1919, and
Cambridge U., 1930; S.T.D., Gregorian U., 1927; honorary de-
grees from nine universities; taught at Fordham in 1920's; founded
new St. Peter's College, N.J., and was dean, 1930–36; president, As-
sociation of Universities and Colleges of State of N.Y.; trustee of
Town Hall, N.Y., and of N.Y. Zoological Society; director Pan
American Society and Netherlands American Foundation. Books:
Technique of the One-Act Play, After Black Coffee.

GILLIS, JAMES M., C.S.P.: Father Gillis is widely known as an
eloquent speaker and writer; many years on N.B.C.'s Catholic
Hour, before that on WLWL, N.Y.; retired as editor *The Catholic
World* in 1948, after 26 years. Born Boston, Nov. 12, 1876; educated
Boston Latin School, St. Charles College, St. Paul's College, Catholic U.; joined Missionary Society of St. Paul the Apostle, 1898,
ordained 1901; taught dogma at St. Paul's College, then missionary

for 12 years before editorship; column "Sursum Corda" syndicated to Catholic papers since 1929. Books include *This Our Day, False Prophets, The Catholic Church and the Home, The Paulists.*

GOGARTY, OLIVER ST. JOHN: Poet, essayist, novelist; original of "Buck Mulligan" in fellow-student James Joyce's *Ulysses*; prominent in Irish Literary Renaissance, compatriot of Yeats, A.E., George Moore; born Dublin, Aug. 17, 1878; educated Stonyhurst, Trinity; senator, Irish Free State, 1922–36; surgeon, throat specialist F.C.R.S., Ireland; now lives in N.Y.C.; in earlier years went in for flying, archery, motorcycle racing; famed as raconteur. Books include *As I Was Going Down Sackville Street, Mourning Became Mrs. Spendlove, Elbow Room, Mad Grandeur, Selected Poems.*

HENNESSY, DOYLE: A native of Brooklyn; son of a former city editor of *N.Y. Times*; is now on administrative staff of industrial designer; was an accountant for mining company; some years conducted "The Tableteer," humor column, for *The Tablet*, Brooklyn diocesan weekly. His verse, essays and reviews have appeared in *America, Ave Maria, Columbia, The Sign, Spirit, The Magnificat*, others.

HOMAN, HELEN WALKER: Born Helena, Mont.; educated Notre Dame of Maryland, Baltimore, and Pensionnat Cyrano, Lausanne; married Dominique A. Homan in 1927; edited *Pelham Sun* for two years, after getting LL.B. from N.Y.U.; 1920–22, managing editor *The Forum*; in 1924 on editorial staff *The New Republic*; later assistant editor *The Commonweal*; now on faculty Fordham U. Books include *By Post to the Apostles, Letters to St. Francis and His Friars, Little St. Agnes.*

HURLEY, DORAN: U.S. news correspondent for Radio Dublin; born Fall River, Mass., Oct. 12, 1906; educated Fall River High, Providence College, Brown U.; dulcet voiced announcer for N.B.C.'s WJZ, 1926–27; managed WLTH, WBBC Brooklyn, 1928–31; busied self rest of 1930's with famous parish life stories; Army corporal, World War II; picture editor, *Louisville Courier-*

Journal, 1945, then copy editor *N.Y. Herald-Tribune.* Books include *The Old Parish; Herself, Mrs. Patrick Crowley; Says Mrs. Crowley, Says She.*

KAYE-SMITH, SHEILA: Mrs. Theodore Penrose Fry; she and husband, formerly an Anglo-Catholic clergyman, are converts to Catholic Church; born St. Leonard's-on-the-Sea, Hastings, Sussex, England, 1888; learned to love Sussex fields and lanes reflected in her novels; has home in Rye, Sussex now; during war, host to three mothers and four children evacuees from London; wrote first novel at 20; noted for women characters, objective style in novels; also author poems, plays. Latest books: *The Trumpet and the Drum, Tambourine, Secret Son, Ember Lane;* also *Joanna Godden,* and *Three Ways Home* (autobiog.).

KENNY, HERBERT A.: A reporter and rewrite man for *Boston Post* since 1933 where he occasionally conducts humor column; contributor to *Commonweal, The Sign, Catholic Digest, Irish Digest, London Universe;* teaches at Suffolk University, Boston; Boston College graduate; married, three children, lives at Roxbury, Mass., where he was born, 1912. Co-author, *A Catholic Quiz Book.*

KENNY, VIRGINIA: Writer, actress; born in Arlington, Mass., 1924; graduate Mt. St. Mary's College, taught dramatics as student; "hardly a week of my life that I wasn't up on some stage, large or small, to recite or act my two cents' worth"; tour of country with Clare Tree Major Children's Theatre as "Mary" in *The Secret Garden,* with Freddie Bartholomew in *Charley's Aunt,* with Arthur Treacher in *The Magistrate;* acted with the late Elissa Landi, her teacher; lately with Blackfriars' Theatre; sequel to *Convent Boarding School* in preparation.

KIERAN, JOHN: Born N.Y.C., Aug. 2, 1892; father was president of Hunter College, mother a schoolteacher; inherited parents' love for books and music; graduated *cum laude* Fordham U., 1912; taught country school several years getting opportunity for long hikes and nature study; joined *N.Y. Times,* 1915; with Army

overseas, World War I; in 1927 began column "Sports of the Times";
N.Y. Sun columnist, 1943–44; is a member radio program "Information Please." Books include *Information Please Almanac, Footnotes on Nature, Nature Books, The American Sporting Scene.*

KNOX, RONALD: A Rt. Rev. Msgr.; received into Church 1917; brother of "Evoe" of *Punch* fame; a scholar and a wit; modernizes Bible, cauterizes heathens; born Feb. 17, 1888; educated Eton, Oxford; Fellow at Trinity, 1910, chaplain 1912; Catholic chaplain, Oxford, 1926–39. Author more than 27 books: doctrinals like *The Belief of Catholics*; sermons like *The Mystery of the Kingdom, In Soft Garments, Captive Flames*; mysteries like *The Viaduct Murder*; satire like *Sanctions, Essays in Satire, Let Dons Delight*; new version Old and New Testaments.

LAHEY, THOMAS: Associate editor *Ave Maria* magazine; writes column "Bits Out of Life"; author of popular juvenile books, *God's Heroes* and *God's Wonderland*; born Michigan City, Ind., April 2, 1886; Litt.B., A.M., Ph.D., Notre Dame U.; S.T.B., Catholic U.; joined Congregation of the Holy Cross, 1915; Notre Dame U. faculty 1924–28; vice-pres. U. of Portland (Ore.), 1928–29.

LAVERTY, MAURA: Irish author, radio broadcaster; has edited woman's magazine, been president Irish Women Writers Club; married journalist, three children; some years in Spain, secretary to Princess Bibesco, foreign correspondent for a bank, newspaper woman on *El Debate*; radio work included plays, interviews, cookery talks, now weekly radio feature for women. Books include novels *Never No More*, partly autobiographical in details, *Touched by the Thorn, No More Than Human, Liffey Lane*; *Maura Laverty's Cookbook*; and a juvenile, *Gold of Glanaree.*

LAVERY, EMMET: America's No. 1 Catholic playwright; also freelance writer for screen, former president Screen Writers' Guild; started to be a lawyer in Poughkeepsie, N.Y., where he was born Nov. 8, 1902, but printer's ink was in his blood — father was an editor. At 16 sports editor of *Poughkeepsie Eagle-News*; got LL.B.

1924, year later city editor of town's *Sunday Courier*; stayed there till 1935, when he wrote hit play *The First Legion* (had started dabbling in community theatre in 1927); in 1937 helped form Catholic Theatre Conference. Other plays include *Monsignor's Hour, Second Spring, The Magnificent Yankee, Gentleman from Athens.*

LEWIS, D. B. WYNDHAM: Master of subtle, scholarly, whimsical humor; essayist, biographer, anthologist; born Wales, 1894; studying law at Oxford when World War I came; fought in France in infantry, twice shell-shocked; later got malaria in Macedonia; 1919 joined staff *London Daily Express*, wrote humor column under name "Beachcomber" four years then to *London Daily Mail*, writing weekly article; lived in Paris many years, French scholar. Books include *A London Farrago, On Straw and Other Conceits, Welcome to All This, The Nonsensibus, King Spider, Emperor of the West, The Hooded Hawk, Four Favourites.*

McCARTHY, JOSEPH: Freelance writer, contributor to *Life, Collier's, Cosmopolitan*; Legion of Merit award for work as managing editor of *Yank*, Army weekly, World War II; took time out to serve as *Yank* correspondent in Italy, ETO, Pacific; before *Yank* was private, pack artillery battalion. Born Cambridge, Mass., March 6, 1915; educated Boston College; on Boston newspaper until Army called; after war articles editor *Cosmopolitan* two years; married, three children.

MACKENZIE, COMPTON: Born West Hartlepool, England, Jan. 17, 1883; old-school eclectic English poet, dramatist, essayist, novelist, historian, satirist; first book 1907 (Poems); total now 70 volumes; distinguished military career, 2d Lieut., 1st Herts. Regt. 1900–01; Lieut., Royal Marines, 1915, Capt., 1916; wounded Dardanelles Expedition, 1915; Military Control Officer, Athens, 1916; director Aegean Intelligence Service, 1917; numerous honors, decorations; Capt., Home Guard, 1940–44; Glasgow U. rector, 1931–34; literary critic, *Daily Mail*, 1931–35. Latest books: *Whiskey Galore, Vital Flame, Dr. Benes, Mr. Roosevelt, Keep the Home Guard Turning.*

MacLiammoir, Micheal: A founder, with Hilton Edwards, of Dublin Gate Theatre, 1928; writes, acts leading parts, designs settings and costumes; born Cork, Ireland; as a boy played in Shakespeare in London with Sir Herbert Tree; turned to painting, exhibitions in many European capitals; returned to Ireland to design and paint for theatre; opened first Gaelic Theatre in Ireland. Plays include *Easter 1916, The Ford of the Hurdles, Portrait of Miriam, Dancing Shadow, Where Stars Walk,* and stage adaptations of *Jane Eyre, The Picture of Dorian Gray, A Tale of Two Cities.* He has written a volume of theatrical reminiscences, *All for Hecuba.*

MacManus, Francis: Irish novelist, biographer; general features officer of Radio Eireann; "born 1909 in ancient Norman city of Kilkenny, have done nothing so distinguished ever since," he says; his literary output belies his words, includes a dozen novels, some translated into French, Dutch, Gaelic, and widely-heralded biography of Boccaccio; educated by Christian Brothers, Kilkenny, St. Patrick's College and University College, Dublin; edited magazines, contributed to Irish newspapers and periodicals; taught school eighteen years; married, three children, lives in Dublin.

Maguire, Frances M.: Signs letters F. Margaret Maguire; wife of Australia's famed Catholic Actionist Paul Maguire, prominent herself in Catholic Action; director of studies, Catholic Guild for Social Studies at Adelaide; a founder, Central Catholic Library, Adelaide; 1939, appointed to Australian delegation to League of Nations; has traveled widely in Europe, Middle East, U.S., etc., now, in unofficial capacity, with Royal Australian Navy. Books include *The Royal Australian Navy, Handbook for Catholic Action Leaders, Twelve Tales of the Life and Adventures of St. Imaginus;* and (with husband) *The Price of Admiralty, The Australian Theatre.*

Marshall, Bruce: Full name Claude Cunningham Bruce Marshall; accountant by trade; first-rate novelist by acclamation; born June 24, 1899; educated Edinburgh Academy, Trinity College, Glenalmond, St. Andrew's and Edinburgh Universities; 2d Lieut.

Royal Irish Fusiliers, World War I; lost leg in battle, prisoner of war; chartered accountant, member Society of Accountants in Edinburgh; now spends time in places like France, Austria, Alps. Books include *Father Malachy's Miracle*; *The World, The Flesh, and Father Smith*; *Yellow Tapers for Paris*; *Vespers in Vienna*.

SISTER MARY BERTRAND, O.M.: A member of Congregation of Our Lady of Mercy since 1927; taught high school English from 1920–45; at Catholic Central High, Troy, N.Y., for 21 years. Now at Convent of Mercy, Albany, N.Y., doing research and writing; member Albany unit Catholic Poetry Society; native Olean, N.Y., Mar. 6, 1900.

MORTON, J. B.: Full name John Cameron Andrieu Bingham Michael Morton; with *London Daily Express* since 1924, writing "Beachcomber" humor column; born June 7, 1893, son of journalist and dramatist; educated Park House, Harrow, Oxford; enlisted in 1914, fought in France; turned to journalism after war; received into Catholic Church 1922. His 37 books include a series on Mr. Thake; humorous poetry like *Gorgeous Poetry, The Dancing Cabman*; biographies like *Sobieski, King of Poland, St. Martin of Tours*; humor miscellanies like *Morton's Folly, Captain Foulenough and Company*.

MULGREW, JOHN P.: Known throughout Midwest as humorist and poet, "Jazbo of Old Dubuque"; has column in *The Witness,* Dubuque Catholic paper; contributes to Arch Ward's "Wake of the News" column in *Chicago Tribune*; editor of own Yearbook, *And Life Goes On,* since 1935; in early days wrote scripts for vaudevillians at Dubuque's Grand Opera House; later wrote radio scripts, including some for "Uncle Ezra"; has directed plays at Loras College.

MURRAY, GERARD: A priest of the Brooklyn diocese, instructor in English, St. Francis College, curate of Assumption Church, Brooklyn; ordained from Huntington (L.I.) Seminary, 1937; wrote *Career Angel* for old alma mater, Cathedral College, Brooklyn, 1944, while a curate at Our Lady of Mercy, Forest Hills; play went from there to Blackfriars' and then to Broadway.

OBERMEYER, ROSEMARY: A teacher at Leyden Community High School, Franklin Park, Ill.; married, has four-year-old daughter, "much like Midge in *Golden Apples*"; born 1903, Iron Mountain, Mich.; educated St. Mary's College, Ind., and University of Michigan; taught in junior high schools "harder on the nerves but more interesting"; lives at Oak Park, Ill., with "a solitary apple tree in a grassless backyard," but has cabin near Welch Lake, Mich., "which my husband built stone by stone, alone." Book, *Golden Apples of the Sun*, won Avery Hopwood Fiction Award.

O'CONNOR, FRANK: Yeats and A.E. regarded him foremost among young Irish writers; another critic said "without doubt the most talented, versatile and prolific writer living in Ireland today"; short-story writer, poet, novelist, playwright; actual name Michael O'Donovan; born 1903, educated by Christian Brothers at Cork; director, Abbey Theatre, until 1939; books include *Guests of the Nation*, about Irish-English "troubles"; *Three Old Brothers*, poetry; *Crab Apple Jelly* and *The Common Chord*, short stories of simple Irish town and country people emphasizing realism; *Art of the Theatre, Time's Pocket*, a play.

O'FAOLAIN, SEAN: Novelist, biographer, short-story writer; took part in 1916 Irish rebellion, nationalistic spirit reflected in works; born Feb. 22, 1900; educated National U. of Ireland; M.A., Harvard, fellowships there for three years; lectured, Boston College; taught, St. Mary's College, Middlesex, England, and County Wicklow schools; now makes living by pen; lives in Dublin, wife writes children's stories; first writing Gaelic. Books include *A Nest of Simple Folk, A Purse of Coppers, The Life of Daniel O'Connell, The Life Story of De Valera, An Irish Journey*.

O'NEILL, JAMES: Traveled extensively for *Yank*, Army weekly, in India, Egypt, North Africa, Italy, France; born Philadelphia, 1916; educated St. Joseph's Academy, McSherrytown, Pa., Mt. St.

Mary's Prep, Md.; after brief career as bus boy, Hotel Warwick, Phila., thumbed way to Calif., attended U. of Southern Calif.; now with Young and Rubicam advertising agency in N.Y., "We the People" account; joined Y & R in 1940 in Hollywood, until war with such shows as Eddie Cantor, Burns and Allen, Screen Guild Theatre.

PEGLER, WESTBROOK: Columnist, *N.Y. Journal-American,* syndicated throughout country by King Features; native Minneapolis, Minn., Aug. 2, 1894; educated Lane Tech. and Loyola Academy, Chicago; United Press European correspondent, 1916–18; in U.S. Navy, 1918–19; after war went into sports side of news; sports editor, United News, six years, then Eastern sports correspondent for *Chicago Tribune;* in 1933 branched out as general columnist; pet hates were New Deal and crooked labor leaders; column in *N.Y. World-Telegram* and other Scripps-Howard papers until Sept. 1944.

PHELAN, PAUL J.: Reformed college professor; now feature writing, rewrite, general reporting, *N.Y. Sun;* honorable mention in Silurian Society competition for best editorial achievement by a N.Y.C. newspaperman in 1948; native Brooklyn, member Society Prevention Disparaging Remarks about Brooklyn; educated Brooklyn Prep, St. Peter's College, N.J. (A.B.), Fordham U. (M.A., scholarship in English), Columbia U.; English faculty, Fordham U., 1938–41; Prof. of English, Santa Clara U., 1941–44; co-author syndicated column, "Who's News Today?", *N.Y. Sun* and elsewhere, 1946–47; magazine articles, book reviews; lecturer; editor *With a Merry Heart, A Time to Laugh.*

PHILLIPS, H. I.: Full name Harry Irving Phillips; born New Haven, Conn., Nov. 26, 1887; never any doubts about career; at 25 managing editor *New Haven Register,* where he began as reporter; managing editor 1912–18; came to New York and wrote humor column for *New York Globe,* 1920–23; went to *N.Y Sun* in 1923, writing column "The Sun Dial" ever since; column syndicated; contributes to magazines; converted to Catholicism 1939; lives at Milford, Conn. Books include *Private Purkey's Private Peace, All Out Ar-*

lene, *Private Papers of Private Purkey, Private Purkey in Love and War, On White or Rye.*

QUIGLEY, MARTIN, JR.: Associate editor *Motion Picture Herald* and *Motion Picture Daily*; born Chicago, educated Loyola School, N.Y., and Georgetown U.; Dec. 1941 to Sept. 1945 on leave of absence for war-time assignments in the U.S., England, Eire and Italy. Two books result of travels: *Great Gaels* and *Roman Notes*; another is *Magic Shadows* — The Story of the Origin of Motion Pictures.

SHEHAN, THOMAS: Newspaperman with by-line since 14, he says; started on now defunct Salem, Mass., *Sunday Tribune*; on *Boston Evening Transcript,* other papers in Chicago, Miami, always sports; resigned as columnist *N.Y. Morning Telegraph* 1942 to accept post as steward at Rockingham Park, N.H., youngest in country to hold position; steward is a judge in complete control racing at track. World War II: on *Yank,* Army weekly, correspondent Africa, Italy, Alaska, Japan; freelance writer, co-author with Ben Hogan of book *Power Golf.* Born Danvers, Mass., 1911.

SMITH, RED: Actual name Walter Wellesley Smith, known far and wide as Red; native, Green Bay, Wis., graduate, Notre Dame U., 1927, edited school *Annual*; shadowed firemen a year as reporter for *Milwaukee Sentinel,* then sportswriter *St. Louis Star-Times*; 1936–45 sports columnist, *Philadelphia Record*; same capacity *N.Y. Herald Tribune* since 1945; noted for humorous slants; "a column is the soft-shoe dance in the act"; interested in personalities, "the sideshow," not sports technicalities; story of Army–Notre Dame game in *Best Sports Stories* anthology, 1944.

SULLIVAN, A. M.: Advertising manager Dun and Bradstreet, associate editor *Dun's Review*; poetry rated excellent risk by Parnassus branch, Dun and Bradstreet; born Harrison, N.J., Aug. 9, 1896; educated St. Benedict's Prep; with advertising department, Submarine Boat Corp. and ad agency before joining D & B 1934; conductor poetry hour, Mutual Network, 1932–42; director, Catholic

Poetry Society; president, Poetry Society of America, 1940–42. Poetic output includes books of ballads like *Ballad of John Castner, Ballad of Timothy Murphy, Ballad of a Man Named Smith*; poems of science, as in *Stars and Atoms Have No Size*; choral poems as in *Day in Manhattan*.

WALLACE, EDWARD TATUM: Bank clerk, telegrapher, oil field production accountant before becoming newspaper reporter; now on staff *N.Y. World-Telegram*; born Greenwood, Ark., the "Barington" of his novel of that title, Aug. 9, 1906; educated Hendrix College, University of Arkansas; while on *Oklahoma News* wrote biography of Pope Pius XI, serialized in Scripps-Howard newspapers; this led him into the Catholic Church; has since been "Catholic expert" on various newspapers; Army Air Force three years, World War II; married, two children.

WALSH, MAURICE: Distinguished novelist, short story writer; lives in Dublin, where he went at turn of century; entered British Civil Service 1901, transferred to Irish Free State Service 1922; customs job took him to various parts Ireland, Scotland, Wales, England, gave material for stories; born Ballydonohue, County Kerry, May 2, 1879; father farmer, land-leaguer, authority on blood horses; lived close to soil; educated St. Michael's College, Listowel; now retired from customs, married, three sons. Books include *The Key above the Door, Man in Brown, Spanish Lady, Thomasheen James, Sons of the Swordmaker*.

WAUGH, EVELYN: Father was literary critic, managing director Chapman and Hall, publishers; brother Alec well-known novelist too; born 1903, attended Lancing School where edited paper, wrote three-act play, won English verse prize; senior history scholar, Oxford, then studied at art school, London, one year; thereafter taught school, worked on *London Daily Express*; in World War II joined British Marines; convert to Catholicism 1930. Books include satirical novels, *Vile Bodies, Scoop, Brideshead Revisited, The Loved One*; biographies, *Edmund Campion, D. G. Rossetti*; reportage, *Waugh in Abyssinia*.

WINDEATT, MARY F.: Accomplished musician, accomplished poet, accomplished biographer; born Regina, Canada, 1910; musical accomplishments came early; piano lessons at 6, Toronto Conservatory of Music degree at 16; after A.B. at San Diego State, went to N.Y., tried advertising, wrote 99,000-word unsalable novel; finally clicked with poems and articles in Catholic magazines; saints' biographies popular such as *Lad of Lima, Saints in the Sky*; poems collected in *Sing Joyfully*.

WOODRUFF, (JOHN) DOUGLAS: Background as Lothian prizeman and 1st class honor man in modern history at Oxford shines forth brilliantly in writings; practical businessman too, Chairman Tablet Publishing Company since 1937; started career in Foreign Office, Holland, 1917–19; history lecturer, Sheffield U. 1923–24; 1926–28, staff *London Times,* then publicity work and three years with B.B.C.; born May 8, 1897. Books include *More Talking at Random, Story of British Colonial Empire, Great Tudors, Plato's Britannia.*

INDEX OF AUTHORS AND TITLES